AC. 7009

THE TECHNOLOGY
OF LOW TEMPERATURE
CARBONIZATION

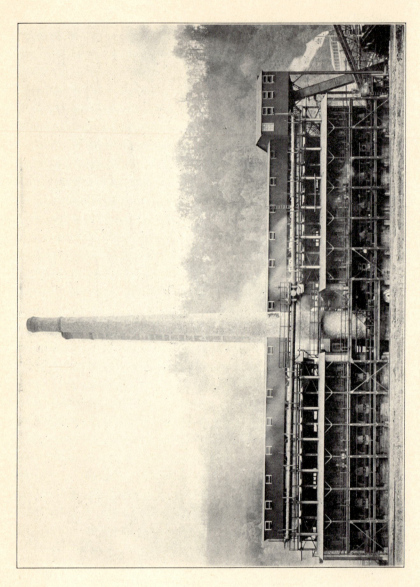

Battery of Carbocoal Primary Retorts, Clinchfield, Va.

THE TECHNOLOGY
OF LOW TEMPERATURE
CARBONIZATION

BY

FRANK M. GENTRY

BALTIMORE
THE WILLIAMS & WILKINS COMPANY
1928

Composed and Printed at the
WAVERLY PRESS
for
The Williams & Wilkins Company
Baltimore, Md., U. S. A.

To
J. M. ALLEN

"The philosopher should be a man willing to listen to every suggestion, but determined to judge for himself. He should not be biased by appearance; have no favorite hypothesis; be of no school; and in doctrine have no master."

—Michael Faraday.

PREFACE

So far as the author is aware, this is the first book in America dealing exclusively with the subject of low temperature carbonization and the first relating solely and comprehensively to its technology. A great amount of data have been made available to the industry, but, heretofore, little effort has been made to collect and correlate them so that they might be of maximum value to the art. Consequently, it is anticipated that this book will fill a vacancy in the literature relating to the carbonization industry.

More properly, perhaps, this volume should be entitled "Technology of Carbonization with Special Reference to Low Temperature Carbonization," because the principles of distillation at low temperatures are identical with the technology underlying the initial stages of carbonization at medium and at high temperatures. The technical differences between high and low temperature carbonization lie in the extent to which distillation is carried, by regulation of temperature and time, and in the procedure adopted for carrying the process to completion.

A review of the numerous patents on methods for effecting the distillation of carbonaceous materials and a study of many attempts to solve the practical difficulties lead at once to the conclusion that many otherwise creditable efforts have failed because of lack of knowledge regarding the behavior of coal and of its distillation products with respect to variations in temperature and other physical conditions. In other cases, where the behavior of coal has been well understood, failure can be attributed often to lack of knowledge of the properties of materials under severe conditions and to unforeseen operating difficulties. The justification of this book rests upon its effort to treat these subjects in such a way as to establish the art upon a scientific basis, so that, henceforth, empirical methods may be reduced to a minimum.

The economical aspect of low temperature carbonization is the one restraining feature in the advance of the industry in the United States today, but this does not apply to other countries, such as England, France, and Germany, which are not so generously endowed with petroleum and other high grade fuel resources. Because of its controversial nature at this time, the author has deemed it advisable not to treat at length the subject of economies to be derived from carbonization at low temperatures, but to adhere, as far as possible, to the technical phases of the art. In due course of events, progress in the art will demonstrate just what place low temperature carbonization will occupy in the industrial organization of each nation. When this position becomes clearly defined, the subject of economics can be treated more adequately without the necessity of discounting figures, glorified by promotion and minimized by competitive enterprises.

As a word of caution, the author takes this occasion to point out the great care necessary in reviewing the literature on low temperature carbonization. Many articles have been reprinted in the United States from English sources in which British gallons have not been converted to United States gallons. Many yields per ton of coal are quoted without specifying whether it be long tons, short tons, or metric tons. The tar yields are sometimes reported as wet tar and sometimes as dry tar, without indication of which. Calorific value of the gas is reported for either the scrubbed or unscrubbed gas, usually leaving the reader to judge by the figure which value it is. Unless otherwise specified, the figures herein given have been corrected to short tons, dry tar, and United States gallons, as far as was possible from the reports of the authorities.

The author gratefully acknowledges the assistance of all who have contributed to the preparation of this book through rendering of illustrations, translations, location of bibliographical references, stenographic work, and otherwise. Finally he expresses his thanks to The Williams & Wilkins Company for their encouragement and typographical work.

F. M. G.

March, 1928.

CONTENTS

CHAPTER I

FUNDAMENTALS

CHAPTER II

LOW TEMPERATURE COAL GAS

CHAPTER III

LOW TEMPERATURE COAL TAR

CHAPTER IV

Low Temperature Coke

CHAPTER V

Nitrogenous and Other By-Products

CHAPTER VI

Processes of Low Temperature Carbonization

CHAPTER VII

Operation, Design, and Materials of Construction

CHAPTER VIII

Economics and Conclusion

xiv

ILLUSTRATIONS

xv

CHAPTER I

FUNDAMENTALS

Historical. The low temperature carbonization of coal can lay claim to four distinct lines of descent from closely related fields of industry and research. A thorough understanding of its technology, therefore, requires a knowledge of the manufacture of coke and coal gas, of by-product recovery, and of complete gasification. Consequently, a brief review of the history and circumstances surrounding the origin and development of the various purposes for the processing of coal will be both interesting and helpful.

Even though the perpetual fires sacred among the superstitions of paganism were doubtlessly natural gases issuing from fissures in the earth in the vicinity of petroleum deposits and asphalt beds, there seems to be no published account of an investigation of the properties of combustible gases before 1658. In that year Shirley (1) communicated to the Royal Society an account of his investigation of a combustible gas issuing from a marsh in the vicinity of a coal mine near Wigan, in Lancashire. This same site was revisited by Clayton (2), Dean of Kildare, in 1739. Upon damming the water and digging beneath the creek bed, he discovered a coal deposit and, according to his account, he distilled some of the coal in a retort over an open fire, obtaining a black oil and non-condensible "spirit which catched fire at the flame of a candle." Although Van Helmont of Brussels had proposed the name of *GAS* in 1662, it is interesting to note that it had not come into general usage half a century later. Van Helmont writes in Latin, according to Richards (3), of his experiments in retorting charcoal and, referring to the gaseous distillate, he says, "This spirit . . . . I call by the name of Gas."

Hales, in his "Vegetable Staticks," published in 1726, records the first destructive distillation of coal. He states that upon distilling 158 grains of Newcastle coal, he obtained 180 cubic inches of air (gas), weighing 51 grains. Six years prior to Clayton's visit to Wigan, Lowther (4) communicated to the Royal Society that the damp air issuing from a coal mine near Whitehaven could be ignited and would burn. Bladders were filled with the gas and carried

1

away, afterwards being burned through a small pipe inserted in the bladder, according to his report.

Even though it is said by Molinari (5) that the Chinese employed petroleum vapor, distributed through wooden pipes for lighting purposes, as early as 900 A.D., it is remarkable that over half a century elapsed from 1733 until 1792 before any actual application was made

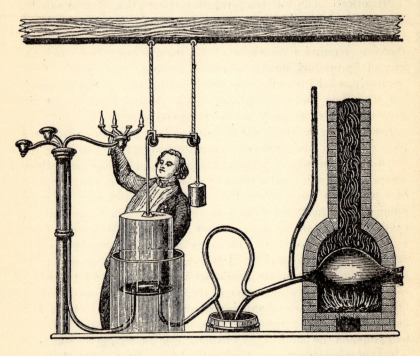

FIG. 1. THE APPROVED APPARATUS FOR DESTRUCTIVE DISTILLATION OF COAL IN 1810

(Taken from an old wood-cut in Parkes' "Chemical Catechism")

of combustible gases envolved through the destructive distillation of coal. The credit for practical application of coal gas to artificial illumination is due Murdock, according to Clegg (6). The date of his initial experiments is unknown, but in 1792 we find him manufacturing coal gas with which he illuminated his premises and offices at Redruth, in Cornwall. The first use of gas lighting as a commercial and economic substitute for lamps and candles was six years later when Murdock installed an apparatus in a factory at Soho.

An old wood-cut, taken from "Parkes' Chemical Catechism" published in 1810 and reproduced in Fig. 1, illustrates the state of the art at that time. It shows the approved experimental apparatus for the destructive distillation of coal as used in lectures to arouse popular interest. In 1807 a few street lamps were illuminated with coal gas in Pall Mall, London, but the public in general and even men of science were decidedly prejudiced against gas lighting. In fact, it is said that Davy considered the project ridiculous and inquired of one of its advocates if he proposed to take the dome of St. Paul's for a gasometer, to which the gentlemen, Clegg, replied that he hoped to see them no smaller. A century later his expectations were realized many times over.

While iron is known to have been extracted as early as 4000 B.C. and coke was an article of commerce among the Chinese before 100 B.C., the latter was not used in the metallurgy of iron until 1619, when it was introduced by Dudley. The following year in England, St. John was granted a patent for the first beehive oven. Aside from the small quantities consumed in ancient oriental trade and among certain European arts during the middle ages, the use of coke as a fuel may be said to date from the introduction of the blast furnace in the smelting of iron.

The memoirs of Becher in the end of the 17th century contain the earliest reference to coal as a source of by-products, according to Thorpe (7), and it is recorded by Wagner (8) that he received a patent in 1700 for an oven which permitted the recovery of tar in the coking of coal. He reported having found a method of treating coal, "so that it no longer smoakes nor stinks" and at the same time obtaining a tar equal to the Swedish. Stahl is said to have been the inventor of a process used at Sulzbach, near Saarbrucken, prior to 1768, where coal was coked for iron smelting with a crude by-product recovery.

Seventeen years before the introduction of illuminating gas by Murdock in 1798, the Earl of Dundonald obtained a patent for distilling coal under the heat of its own combustion, thereby obtaining the tar and oils which it contains. From the patent it is plain that Dundonald was aware of carbonization in closed retorts at that date. In 1825 Faraday discovered benzene and twenty-two years later

Mansfield (9) isolated it from coal tar. Runge (10) had isolated analine from coal tar by 1834, but the real stimulus to the by-product coke industry did not come until 1856 when Perkin (11), a lad of eighteen years, discovered the first analine dye, mauve or analine purple, while attempting the synthetic preparation of quinine. On August 26 of the same year Perkin (12) received a patent and within a year the youthful chemist had built and placed in successful commercial operation a factory for producing the new dye from coal tar, without ever having seen inside of a chemical plant of any kind.

The great chemist Lavoisier discovered in 1793 that, when steam is passed over incandescent carbon, the reaction produces carbon monoxide and hydrogen, two combustible gases. This furnished the principle by which a cheap industrial gas could be made from coke or coal. The first gas producer, constructed as such, seems to have been made by Bischof in Germany in 1839, according to Rambush (13). He was followed closely by Ebelmen in France the following year. From an industrial standpoint, the development of gas producers dates from the patent granted the brothers Siemens in 1861 for a combined producer and regenerative furnace. Mond showed twenty-eight years later that the by-products of producer plants could be recovered and made to render valuable service to the chemical and agricultural industries. This gave a decided stimulus to the producer gas industry.

Goethe in the episodes of his life "Dichtung und Wahrheit" describes his visit in 1741 to a burning hillside near Dutweiler, a village in the Palatinate, where he met Stauf, a coal philosopher, engaged in collecting the tar and oils obtained in the distillation of coal in crude ovens. How little did Goethe suspect that the black evil-smelling liquors of Stauf would some day be made to yield the richest and most vivid of colors, the sweetest of flavors, and the most fragrant of perfumes!

Solid Fuels. Solid fuels can, in general, be classified into three distinct classes, the cellulosic fuels, the sedimentary fuels, and the residuary fuels. The cellulosic fuels, of which wood is the most important member, have little value in modern industry because of their comparatively low heating quality and their cost. The sedimentary fuels consist of peat, lignite, and the two general grades of coal, bituminous and anthracite. They were, of course, originally cellulose-rich vegetation which was transformed during the geologic ages into the black, brittle, compact substance which we find in the earth's crust today. They form the most important source of power which civilization has been able to master, either in their mineral or retorted state. The residuary fuels are obtained by heating the cellulosic and sedimentary fuels out of contact with air, forming charcoal and coke, respectively. They are distinguished by their high carbon and low volatile contents.

Outside of this classification, there remain those solid materials which contribute indirectly to our fuel resources, such as the shales, which are not directly combustible, and synthetic compounds, representing the stored energy obtained from other sources of power, such as carbides. While the oil derived from shale and the acetylene obtained from carbide have local and special application, it must be stated that as a great source of energy they have not reached a position of primary importance. However, the vast deposits of shale constitute a great potential source of oil whose economic value will increase with the exhaustion of the petroleum resources.

The utilization of solid fuels follows three different methods: first, direct combustion; second, destructive distillation with simultaneous coking; and, third, complete gasification. Direct combustion is by far the simplest, oldest, and most extensively used. It consists in the burning of the raw carbonaceous material in the furnace in lump, powdered, or briquetted form. The residuum consists wholly of ash and clinker, devoid of all combustible.

When fuel, rich in hydrocarbons, is distilled in closed retorts without the introduction of air, it is separated into the solid, liquid, and gaseous phases; in other words, into coke, tar, and gas. The coking of coal resolves itself into various methods, depending upon the disposition to be made of the products. The primary object in central or municipal gasworks is to produce a good grade of gas for domestic illumination and heating. Coke is a by-product in this process. Industrial coke ovens strive for a high quality of metallurigical coke. Tar and gas are by-products of this method. The low temperature distillation of coal aims at a compromise between these two systems and seeks to obtain a coke suitable as a smokeless fuel for industrial and domestic consumption with the simultaneous production and recovery of tar, its derivatives, and of high thermal value gas. Which of the products is of paramount importance depends on the coal, the process, and the economics of the case.

As distinguished from carbonization, complete gasification intends to convert the coal entirely into gaseous and liquid combustible matter, leaving only ash as a residuum. To this end, three means are resorted to: first, gasification by air; second, gasification by water; and, third, gasification by both air and water. The air producer method is based upon the incomplete combustion of carbon to carbon monoxide, only sufficient air being admitted to maintain a temperature at which the reaction can take place. Gasification by water is an intermittent process. Air is first introduced to raise the carbonaceous material to incandescence through the heat liberated in the complete combustion of carbon. After the air is shut off, steam is introduced to disintegrate and form a mixture of carbon monoxide and hydrogen. The production of semi-water gas combines these two principles and simultaneously introduces air and steam to the combustion chamber. Recent progress has been made in the use of pure oxygen mixed with steam to effect the continuous generation of semi-water gas.

Origin of Coal. At this point a brief review of the origin and constitution of coal is pertinent as preliminary to a study of the chemical process underlying carbonization. Today it is well established that the carbonaceous deposits, ranging from peat to anthracite, represent progressive changes which have taken place in the structure of decayed vegetable matter. Unquestionable evidence is furnished by fossil remains that among the early geologic ages, millions of years ago, the dead vegetation, which was so abundant at that time, accumulated in damp lowlands and bogs. There, with the exclusion of air by the water, a slow process of disintegration took place. The vegetable tissue, consisting mainly of cellulose, decomposed with the liberation of the oxides of carbon, marsh gas, and water, to form the material known as peat. As the bottom lands sank below the surface of the water and sedimentary deposits built up, a pressure developed which rendered the peat deposits more compact and consolidated, thus forming the lignites and sub-bituminous coals. The internal forces of the earth became active at that stage and the sedimentary rocks above and below the lignite deposits were violently thrown into folds, developing additional pressure with the generation of heat. The result of this upheaval and folding was the further consolidation of the mass and its transformation into bituminous coal. The remaining metamorphosis into anthracite is said to have been brought about by further excessive pressure and by the cracking of the rock folds to permit the escape of entrapped hydrocarbons, evolved from the carbonaceous material.

The chemical representation of the resultant transformation is as follows, according to Heinrich and Ries (14):

$$5\ C_6H_{10}O_5 \rightarrow 6\ CO_2 + CO + 3\ CH_4 + 8\ H_2O + C_{20}H_{22}O_4 \qquad [1]$$

Cellulose   Lignite

$$6\ C_6H_{10}O_5 \rightarrow 8\ CO_2 + CO + 5\ CH_4 + 10\ H_2O + C_{22}H_{20}O \qquad [2]$$

Cellulose   Bituminous

$$7\ C_6H_{10}O_5 \rightarrow 8\ CO_2 + 4\ CH_4 + 19\ H_2O + C_{30}H_{16}O \qquad [3]$$

Cellulose   Semi-bituminous

Whatever the physical circumstances bringing about the vegetable transformation, or whatever the intermediate stages of the metamorphism, these equations give the initial and final stages in the transition.

The age of the coals of the United States ranges from the Carboniferous to the Tertiary epochs. In general, the Carboniferous coals occur east of the 100th meridian, the Cretaceous coals from the 100th to the 115th meridian, and the Tertiary coals between the 120th meridian and the Pacific Ocean. An exception to this geologic distribution is a large area of Tertiary lignites in the Gulf States and a small area of Trianic coals in Virginia and North Carolina.

Constitution of Coal. The constitution of coals found in the United States, determined by their proximate analyses as given by Parr (15), are shown in Table 1. These data are compiled from chemical determinations on a number of different samples and represent the average distribution of the constituents. The changes in the constitution of coal which take place with its geologic aging can be seen clearly. The moisture content of the fuel reaches its maximum in the peats and decreases to a low percentage in semi-anthracite. The volatile matter rises to a maximum in sub-bituminous coals and then varies inversely with the aging. On the other hand, the fixed carbon is almost directly proportional to the density of the coal. The ash remains about constant, but the heating value of the coal increases with the consolidation of the fuel, except for a slight decrease among the hard coals.

Table 2 gives the ultimate analyses of these fuels, showing their elementary constituents, as compiled by the author from numerous samples. The deoxygenation, occurring in the aging process, is quite apparent, but the dehydrogenation is not as rapid, although present. The percentage of nitrogen and sulphur seems to have no general relation to the antiquity of the fuel.

The ash referred to in the proximate analyses consists of a number of fused oxides, principally silica and lime. Representative analyses

TABLE 1

Proximate analyses of United States coal types

FUEL	PER CENT MOISTURE	PER CENT VOLATILE MATTER	PER CENT FIXED CARBON	PER CENT ASH	B.T.U. PER POUND
Peat.........................	78.7	11.9	5.7	3.4	1,798
Lignite......................	37.1	26.9	26.9	9.2	6,500
Sub-bituminous.............	10.2	35.2	45.1	9.5	11,603
Bituminous.................	2.9	34.3	55.6	7.4	13,630
Semi-bituminous............	2.6	18.9	72.1	6.5	14,246
Anthracite.................	4.2	4.5	79.0	12.3	12,485

TABLE 2

Ultimate analyses of United States coal types

FUEL	PER CENT CARBON	PER CENT HYDROGEN	PER CENT OXYGEN	PER CENT NITROGEN	PER CENT SULPHUR
Peat.........................	56.6	5.7	32.9	2.00	1.30
Lignite......................	62.1	5.5	26.3	1.35	2.02
Sub-bituminous.............	66.6	5.4	23.6	1.09	1.03
Bituminous.................	79.1	5.2	11.6	1.56	1.12
Semi-bituminous............	86.2	4.8	5.2	1.02	1.12
Anthracite.................	88.9	2.9	3.4	0.99	0.69

of the ash of various coals, as compiled by the author, are given in Table 3. Examination of this table discloses that the silica content increases quite regularly from peat to anthracite. The alumina increases also, but in a less orderly manner. The oxides of iron and calcium progressively decrease towards the harder coals. No generalizations can be drawn concerning the other oxides found in the ash, as they are largely dependent on the general geologic and mineralogic structure in the immediate locality of the mines. The oxides of magnesium, and of manganese, and the acid anhydrides of phosphorous and of sulphur compose the remaining part of the ash. The melting point of the ash is well above 1100°C. The usual practice of washing the coal before carbonization can, of course, be resorted to for the purpose of reducing the ash content of the coke. When coke is used as a fuel for domestic and industrial purposes, the formation of clinker on the grates should not be more of a nuisance than is ordinarily experienced with coal. If the coke is completely gasified and sold to the community for lighting and heating purposes, care must be taken to reduce the phosphorous and sulphur contents of the gas to a minimum, in order to prevent injury both to the consumers and to their property. It is not unlikely that the oxides present in the coal ash exert a catalytic effect in the decomposition of the hydrocarbons, as pointed out by Lessing (16) and as discussed later in this book.

Destructive Distillation. Four general constituents of coal can be distinguished; the carbon residuum, the humous bodies, the resinous bodies, and the hydrocarbons. The last three undergo thermal decomposition with the formation of solid, liquid, and gaseous products, according to a table prepared by Lewes (17), while the first contains principally carbon and ash.

Constituents of coal		Decomposition products	
	Solid	*Liquid*	*Gaseous*
Humous bodies ⟶	Carbon	Water	Carbon oxides
		Thin tar	Methane
Resinous bodies ⟶	Carbon	Water	Carbon oxides
	Pitch	Rich tar	Ethylene
			Unsaturated
			hydrocarbons
Hydrocarbons ⟶	Carbon	Heavy tar	Methane
	Pitch		Ethane
			Homologues

Carbon residuum ⟶ Unaffected by heat

It appears that Dundoroff (18) first extracted resin from coal by the use of chloroform and other solvents. He found that these resins have a low melting point in the vicinity of 40°C. to 80°C., and that they begin to decompose at 100°C. to 140°C. The resinous bodies, which are soft in structure and dark brown in color, appear in the coal as slender rods. Chemical analysis shows then to contain 75 per cent to 85 per cent carbon; 8 per cent to 10 per cent hydrogen; 5 per cent to 12 per cent oxygen; about 3 per cent nitrogen; and about 1.5 per cent sulphur.

Many of the volatile hydrocarbons of bituminous coal are decomposition products of the resinous and humous constituents and the characteristic cell structure of coke owes its existence to the melting and disintegration of these bodies. It will be noted from Table 4

TABLE 3

Analyses of ash of United States coal types

FUEL	SiO₂	Al₂O₃	Fe₂O₃	CaO	OTHER OXIDES
	per cent	*per cent*	*per cent*	*per cent*	*per cent*
Peat.........................	25.5	5.8	18.7	24.0	26.0
Lignite.....................	30.1	13.5	11.7	35.6	9.1
Bituminous.................	34.3	14.5	22.9	14.9	13.4
Anthracite..................	45.6	42.8	9.4	1.4	1.0

TABLE 4

Proximate analyses of resin and humus

CONSTITUENT	RESIN	HUMUS
	per cent	*per cent*
Moisture.....................................	0.68– 0.70	2.57– 2.62
Volatile matter..............................	98.00–97.94	51.68–51.74
Fixed carbon................................	0.80– 0.82	44.73–44.60
Ash..	0.52– 0.54	1.02– 1.04

that the humus differs from the resin mainly in the fixed carbon content.

In their researches on the low temperature carbonization of coal, Burgess and Wheeler (19) observed three significant facts. First, that for all coals there is a well defined point, between 700°C. and 800°C., where the evolution of hydrogen increases rapidly, thereby indicating decomposition. Second, that the evolution of paraffin hydrocarbons takes place below 700°C. and ceases above that temperature. And, third, that ethane, propane, butane, and other members of the series form a large part of the gas below 450°C. They concluded from these facts that coal was composed mainly of two substances, the first or more unstable of which yields paraffin hydrocarbons and no hydrogen, and the second of which becomes unstable at 700°C. to 800°C., yielding hydrogen as its chief decomposition product. The first of these substances has been called by Clark and Wheeler (20) the resinic and the second the cellulosic constituent of the coal.

According to many authorities, low temperature tars are easy to distill, and, therefore, require less fuel than the tars from high temperature processes. Care must be taken in the distillation procedure, however, because of the large amount of light oil present. For this reason refrigerating equipment is sometimes provided in conjunction with the cooling apparatus to insure complete condensation. Distillation must be slow on account of the large quantities of tar acids present; otherwise, frothing will be severe and subsequent separation of by-products will be rendered difficult. The cresols emulsify with the water and cause frequent trouble. Agitators have been found to decrease the time of distillation and the use of superheated steam toward the end of the process is generally recommended to secure a good yield of heavy oil. In the distillation of coal, dissociation is much more pronounced at higher temperatures. Furthermore, carbon deposited from the decomposition exerts a reducing effect on the saturated hydrocarbons of the paraffin series that are present and results in the production of higher-boiling hydrocarbons.

When highly oxygenated coals, having in the neighborhood of 15 per cent oxygen, are used, the condensed water, driven off in distillation up to 450°C., contains much more acid than that from coals of relatively low oxygen content. The hydrocarbons do not appear in highly oxygenated coals until 290°C., instead of 240°C. The acidity of the distillate is due to acetic compounds, liberated at low temperatures and originating from the ligneous or cellulosic content of high oxygen coals. Carbon dioxide is also evolved more voluminously than from the more resinous coals.

When carbonized at low temperatures, some fuels produce a char instead of a true coke. This char, however, can be converted often into coke by subsequent treatment. It is often friable, lacking in the characteristic coke cell structure and is free burning. In some cases the char is briquetted for fuel, but the pitch, ordinarily used as a binder, causes a good deal of smoke and thus defeats one of the purposes of low temperature carbonization. Further treatment by heat eliminates this difficulty.   On the other hand, some fuels, when carbonized at low temperatures in certain retorts, yield a strong dense semi-coke.   The character of the carbonaceous residuum, indeed, depends as much upon the process of carbonization as upon the raw coal.

Coal is such a heterogeneous substance and its behavior so peculiar and complicated that it is almost impossible to make generalizations. Not only are the products in each instance peculiar to the particular coal treated, but they depend upon the numerous physical and chemical circumstances surrounding the distillation.   Such diverse factors as temperature gradient, thickness of the charge, pressure, and rate of carbonization, all have a direct bearing on the quantity of gas, tar, and coke that is obtained, as well as upon their quality and constitution.

Withdrawal of the products immediately after formation is desirable from the physical as well as the chemical standpoints.   In the first case it means the saving of heat, because any excess heat absorbed by the gases is usually lost in cooling.   A low temperature of evolution throws less work on the condensing plant, thereby increasing the overall efficiency, as well as decreasing the time of carbonization.   From a chemical standpoint, it prevents cracking, which causes a deposition of carbon and an increase of gas yielded at the expense of the light oil and tar.

Low Temperature Carbonization.   One of the most discussed factors in the destructive distillation of fuels has been the temperature of carbonization.   When coal was first coked for illuminating gas over a century ago, this topic was as much in discussion as today. The early engineers recognized to some extent the value of low temperature processes, but as the production of gas was of primary importance to them, they resorted to the practice which gave the greatest yield and so adopted the high temperature method exclusively.   The knowledge which has been gained concerning distillation products, added to changing economic conditions, has given a new incentive to the carbonization of coal at low temperatures; and so again the discussion of thermal conditions has been brought forward, accompanied by its misunderstandings and its controversies.

The matter of thermal definition of the low temperature carbonization process is in considerable disagreement among the authorities. Parr and Layng (21) define it as below 750°C. to 800°C., while Bone

(22) considers it not beyond 550°C. to 600°C., and Gluud (23) fixed the range as 500°C. to 600°C. This disagreement may be understood by an examination of the coals considered and the particular type of product desired by each authority. Thus, Parr and his co-workers used Illinois coal and wished to secure a smokeless fuel for domestic use; Bone was interested in British coals; and Gluud was considering the production of primary tar, consisting chiefly of paraffins and tar acids, which would have decomposed at the higher temperatures of other experimenters. The higher the temperature, the better the grade of coke and poorer the grade of tar, if primary tar, that is, tar with a small percentage of free carbon, is desired. It may be seen, therefore, that the temperature range depends upon the quality of products desired, as well as upon the method of processing. At most, it remains a balance between a good metallurgical coke and poor tar or a good tar and poor metallurgical coke.

By way of scientific definition, low temperature carbonization, as hereafter used, is taken to mean the destructive distillation of coal at or below the cracking temperature of the hydrocarbons in primary tar. This temperature is, of course, a function of the physical conditions of retorting, thus, for example, in vacuum distillation it may not exceed 450°C., and in case of pressure distillation may run beyond 1000°C. under peculiar circumstances. It will vary in practice with the quality of the coal and with the economic balance in grade of products that is determined by local conditions. For the most part, however, under atmospheric pressure and for average coals, 750°C. may be taken as the upper limit of low temperature carbonization. Gentry (24) has advocated this definition of low temperature carbonization as the only adequate and the most scientific one that has been proposed.

From an economic standpoint, the known losses in the present method of utilization of fuel fall under two categories: smoke, arising through incomplete combustion and forming not only a civic nuisance but a real fuel waste; and loss of valuable by-products through lack of proper recovery methods. It may be said that low temperature carbonization has for its purpose the abatement of the smoke nuisance on the one hand and the increase in over-all efficiency of fuel utilization on the other hand. It does not mean conservation of natural resources, but the increased consumption of one economic good to obtain another.

The *modus operandi* is made clear when it is pointed out that certain hydrocarbons which are present in coal break down into their constituents, or crack, during the ordinary process of combustion. Elementary carbon is thus deposited in a finely divided state and carried through the stack before it has had an opportunity to burn. It is plain that if these hydrocarbons are removed from the fuel by preliminary treatment, smoke can be eliminated almost entirely. Incidental to this operation is the question of what disposition is to be made of the hydrocarbons thus removed and which in themselves represent a pecuniary value. The answer to this is found in the fractional distillation of the tar to retrieve its valuable constituents for industrial use. Some of the products can be used as petroleum substitutes, commercial solvents, and as fertilizers. The coke obtained in this primary distillation will be characterized by the absence of smoke in its combustion, it will have a reasonably low ignition temperature, and it may be handled in the raw, briquetted, pulverized, or gasified form.

Quite naturally the history of low temperature carbonization is closely associated with that of coal gas. One of the first to recognize that a maximum yield of oil is obtained at low temperatures was Perkins (25), who secured a patent in 1853 for extracting the oil from shales and other carbonaceous materials by distillation at a low temperature. The following year, Sparr (26) suggested the coking of coal for oil, rather than for gas, under the conditions of a high vacuum. In 1880 Scott-Moncrieff (27) proposed to free the atmosphere from smoke by partially coking the coal in high temperature retorts before combustion. Investigation, however, proved that only the outer layers of coal had been partially coked when removed from the retorts and the core remained as raw coal. Ten years later Parker (28), the inventor of the Coalite process, secured a patent for the production of a smokeless fuel by distillation with superheated inert gases, such as steam, water gas, or coal gas, at 600°C. to 650°C. Later, Parker (29) obtained patents for heating coal in the presence of steam below 450°C. These formed the basis upon which he developed his Coalite process, which will be discussed in Chapter VI.

In the United States, experiments had meanwhile been carried on from as early as 1902 at the University of Illinois. An announcement of the results was made in 1908 and further results were reported in

1912 by Parr (30) (31) and his various co-workers. While some of the earliest research on this subject was made in the United States, it has been extended, until recently, mostly by countries with limited or no petroleum resources and which recognized that their coal deposits could be made to yield a liquid fuel which would be of national importance. The World War gave a great impetus to research in this field, particularly in England and Germany. The British Board of Fuel Research was established in 1917 to promote fuel economy and to coördinate fuel research. To that end, it has contributed a great deal of work to the carbonization of coal. The Kaiser Wilhelm Institute has performed a similar service in Germany.

Chemistry. In addition to a relatively small proportion of pyridine bases, low temperature tar contains, in general, two types of compounds: chemically neutral hydrocarbons, forming a mixture resembling paraffin base crude petroleum; and acidic hydrocarbons, having one or more phenolic hydroxyl groups. The former consist principally of alliphatics with a certain proportion of naphthalene derivatives and aromatic compounds with extensive side chains. The proportion of acidic compounds in the primary tar depends, among other things, upon the oxygen content of the raw coal. Research at the Kaiser Wilhelm Institute für Kohlenforschung has disclosed that a coal, containing 3.0 per cent oxygen, yields a tar, containing neutral hydrocarbons five or six times in excess of the acidic hydrocarbons present, whereas a coal, containing 7.5 per cent oxygen, produces a tar composed of approximately equal proportions of neutral and acidic compounds.

The benzol ordinarily extracted from high temperature tar consists of a mixture of compounds of the aromatic hydrocarbon series, whose general formula is C_nH_{2n-6} and whose chief member is benzene, C_6H_6, although toluene, C_7H_8, and xylene, C_8H_{10}, are always present in quantities. Benzene and the other members of the cyclic hdyrocarbons are not present as such within the coal, but they are derived through decomposition of other hydrocarbons by cracking during distillation. This is demonstrated by the fact that the primary tar, obtained when coal is distilled at low temperatures, contains no benzol in the ordinary meaning of the term. The word benzol is frequently employed, however, when referring to that fraction of low temperature tar, or to the light oil extracted by scrubbing the low temperature gas, which is suitable as a motor fuel and should more properly be designated as light oil or motor spirit. On the other hand, it has been pretty well established that the alliphatic hydrocarbons, belonging to the general formula C_nH_{2n+2} are present as such within the coal. The formation of aromatic compounds from those of the paraffin series can be explained (32) by the fact that the higher paraffin hydrocarbons within the coal are broken into the lower members of the series and into olefines of the general formula C_nH_{2n}. Further heating will split the olefines into methane, CH_4, and acetylene, C_2H_2, which latter is a member of the series C_nH_{2n-2}. Acetylene, C_2H_2, is a polymer of benzene, C_6H_6, and the latter can be formed by polymerization of the acetylene molecule.

The specific mechanism of the transformation from methane to anthracene has been outlined by Bertholet as follows, according to Audibert and Raineau (33):

$$2CH_4 \rightarrow C_2H_2 + 3H_2 \qquad [4]$$

$$2C_2H_6 \rightarrow 2CH_4 + C_2H_2 + H_2 \qquad [5]$$

$$2C_2H_4 \rightarrow C_2H_6 + C_2H_2 \qquad [6]$$

which are the pyrogenic reactions entering into the first stage of the transformation. The second stage of the transformation is represented by the equations:

$$3C_2H_2 \rightarrow C_6H_6 \qquad [7]$$

$$C_6H_6 + C_2H_2 \rightarrow C_8H_8 \qquad [8]$$

$$C_6H_6 + 2C_2H_2 \rightarrow C_{10}H_8 + H_2 \qquad [9]$$

$$2C_6H_6 + C_2H_2 \rightarrow C_{14}H_{10} + 2H_2 \qquad [10]$$

which are all pure polymerising reactions.

Schültz and Buschmann (34) in an examination of products, obtained from the Fellner-Ziegler process, found nearly a hundred different chemical compounds in the low temperature light oil, whose boiling point ranged from 30°C. to 200°C.; in the pressure condensed liquids below 30°C.; and in the residual gas. Schültz and Buschmann (35) reported, in addition to water, hydrogen, and nitrogen, twenty hydrocarbons of the paraffin series; nine hydrocarbons of the olefine series, representing each of the diolefines with chain and cyclic structures; twenty aromatic hydrocarbons, comprising eight of the benzene series, four of the naphthalene series, six representatives of the indenes and hydrindenes, and two representatives of the more highly condensed aromatics. Only three compounds of the hydro-aromatic series derived from perhydronaphthalene were identified. Four series of organic oxygenated compounds, consisting of aldehydes, ketones, phenols, and cumarones, were found. Phenols were represented by eight simple aromatic phenols, one bivalent phenol and one naphthol. Among the other oxygenated compounds, only two aldehydes, four ketones, and one cumarone were determined. Five sulphur compounds were identified, while the nitrogen derivatives were represented by five pyridine bases, two quinoline bases, one aromatic primary amine, and two aliphatic nitrates, including hydrocyanic acid. From − 250°C. to 0°C. there were about twelve substances which comprised some 6

TABLE 5

Quantitative determination of low temperature tar

COMPOUND	PER CENT OF FRACTION	PER CENT OF COAL
Carbon disulphide (CS_2).....................	0.01	0.0001
Acetone (C_3H_6O)............................	0.77	0.0077
Benzene (C_6H_6)............................	4.0–5.9	0.04–0.06
Toluol and xylol............................	20–25	0.20–0.25
Phenol (C_6H_6O)............................	1–1.3	0.06–0.08
Aniline (C_6H_7N)...........................	0.043	0.0004
Pyridine bases...............................	0.9	0.009
Paraffin hydrocarbons........................	20–25	0.20–0.25
Olefine hydrocarbons........................	50–60	0.15–0.20

per cent by weight of the coal, whereas from 0°C. to 200°C. there were more than fifty chemical compounds whose total quantity was only about one-fifth of this. Table 5, after Schültz and Buschmann (35), gives a quantitative determination of certain constituents identified in the tar fraction from 0°C. to 200°C.

Fieldner (36) has examined and compared the unpurified volatile products obtained from the McIntire externally heated primary retort at Fairmont, W. Va., with the products of low temperature distillation educed from a Utah non-coking coal processed at two different temperatures in an externally heated retort and also in one heated internally with superheated steam. Table 6, after Fieldner (36), shows the make-up of the volatile products in the respective cases.

Gentry has compiled a list of chemical compounds which have been definitely identified in the volatile products of low temperature carbonization, as reported in the researches of a number of different authorities. This list in classified form is given in Table 7. Many additional compounds remain unidentified and a great deal of study will be required before their structure is definitely known. This is especially true of the high boiling constituents, which are difficult to isolate without decomposition. Many of the compounds listed in

TABLE 6

Quantitative comparison of low temperature volatile products

CONSTITUENT	UTAH COAL; INTERNAL HEATING		UTAH COAL; EXTERNAL HEATING		MCINTIRE PROCESS; PITTSBURGH COAL
	Temperature of superheated steam entering retort		Temperature of retort wall		
	500°C.	850°C.	500°C.	850°C.	
	per cent	per cent	per cent	per cent	per cent
Carbon dioxide (CO_2), (H_2S), etc........	22.3	13.1	15.7	8.6	8.8
Nitrogen (N_2)...........................	1.2	0.6	0.0	0.9	1.5
Oxygen (O_2).............................	0.2	0.2	0.0	0.0	0.0
Hydrogen (H_2)...........................	3.2	21.9	14.5	55.7	23.4
Carbon monoxide (CO).................	9.8	10.0	8.8	14.9	4.7
Methane (CH_4)...........................	35.7	38.5	45.0	15.0	46.3
Ethylene (C_2H_4).........................	2.7	1.8	1.3	1.0	1.6
Ethane (C_2H_6)...........................	10.8	6.6	7.6	1.32	6.7
Propylene (C_3H_6)........................	2.6	1.65	1.4	0.58	1.3
Propane (C_3H_8)..........................	4.5	2.6	3.2	0.46	2.0
Butylene (C_4H_8).........................	2.0	0.96	1.2	0.37	0.65
Butane (C_4H_{10}).........................	1.5	0.61	0.85	0.17	0.85

the following table do not occur in all low temperature volatile products, a great deal, of course, depending on the coal and on the process of carbonization. Some of the compounds listed, such as benzene and phenol, although occasionally present, are found only in very small quantities in true primary products.

A critical examination of Table 7 discloses the presence of a number of compounds involved in Bertholet's mechanism for the transformation from chain to cyclic hydrocarbons. That aromatic derivatives are decomposition products in coal carbonization becomes conclusive when a list of the volatile products, of high and low temperature distillation are compared.

Coal Assay. A number of attempts have been made to devise a satisfactory method of coal assay for purposes of carbonization, notably by Burgess and Wheeler (57), who experimented with a closed silica tube, containing 2 gram samples which were heated at temperatures ranging from 400°C. to 1000°C., and by Lessing (58), who advocated the insertation of a piston within the silica tube to compress the coal slightly. Gray and King (59) devised a standard apparatus for coal assay and conducted extensive experiments to determine its peculiarities and applicability in determining the yields to be expected from a given coal in full-scale operation. By correlating results obtained in the assay apparatus and those obtained in commercial retorts it has been possible to derive the necessary conversion factors for gas, tar, and coke. In cases where these factors have been determined by tests conducted by the Fuel Research Board, they will be reported hereafter under the discussion of each individual process. Other methods have been devised also by Fischer and Gluud (23), who used a small rotating cylinder, by Nielsen (61), by Layng and Hawthorne (62), and by Foxwell (63), all of whom used a method of internal heating.

Thermochemistry. In studying the thermochemistry of coal carbonization, it is necessary to bear in mind the distinction between gross and net heat values, that is, between the heat liberated, or absorbed, referred to liquid tar and water and that referred to gaseous volatile products. The net value is the only one of importance in practice.

Coal is such a complex and heterogeneous substance that it is almost impossible to make a detailed analysis of the endothermic and exothermic reactions which occur during distillation. As a matter of fact, both exothermic and endothermic reactions take place simultaneously and only the net effect can be observed.

At high temperatures, Mahler (64) found that the heat of combustion of coal was about 460 B.t.u. per pound less than that of all the products of carbonization, while Euchène (65), using a coal of the same analysis at lower temperatures, found an evolution of heat amounting to about 115 B.t.u. per pound. Constam and Kolbe (66) studied a number of British coals and found an absorption of heat

TABLE 7

Chemical compounds identified in low temperature volatile products

CONSTITUENT	FORMULA	AUTHORITY
A. HYDROCARBONS:		
I. Paraffins:		
1. Methane	CH_4	Many observers
2. Ethane	C_2H_6	Many observers
3. Propane	C_3H_8	Many observers
4. Butane	C_4H_{10}	Many observers
5. N-Pentane	C_5H_{12}	(37) (38)
6. Methylbutane	C_5H_{12}	(38)
7. 2-Methyl-2-3-pentane	C_6H_{12}	(55)
8. N-Hexane	C_6H_{14}	(37) (38)
9. Methylpentane	C_6H_{14}	(38)
10. N-Heptane	C_7H_{16}	(37) (38)
11. N-Octane	C_8H_{18}	(38)
12. N-Nonane	C_9H_{20}	(55)
13. Decane	$C_{10}H_{22}$	(39)
14. N-Nondecane	$C_{19}H_{40}$	(39)
15. Tetrakosane	$C_{24}H_{50}$	(40) (41) (55)
16. Pentakosane	$C_{25}H_{52}$	(55)
17. Hexakosane	$C_{26}H_{54}$	(40)
18. Heptakosane	$C_{27}H_{56}$	(42)
19. Octakosane	$C_{28}H_{58}$	(40)
20. Nonakosane	$C_{29}H_{60}$	(41)
21. N-Dotricontane	$C_{32}H_{66}$	(40)
22. Tritricontane	$C_{33}H_{68}$	(40)
23. Tetratricontane	$C_{34}H_{70}$	(40)
II. Ethylenes:		
24. Ethylene	C_2H_4	(38)
25. Propylene	C_3H_6	(38)
26. $\alpha\beta$-Butylene	C_4H_8	(38)
27. $\beta\gamma$-Butylene	C_4H_8	(38)
28. $\alpha\beta$-Pentene (amylene)	C_5H_{10}	(38)
III. Diolefines:		
29. Allene (propadiene)	C_3H_4	(42) (43)
30. Divinyl (2-3-butadiene)	C_4H_6	(42) (43)
31. Piperylene (pentadiene)	C_5H_8	(42) (43)
32. Diallyl	C_6H_{10}	(42) (43)
IV. Acetylenes:		
33. Acetylene	C_2H_2	(44)
34. Allylene (methylacetylene)	C_3H_4	(44)
35. Crotonylene	C_6H_6	(44)
V. Naphthenes:		
36. Trimethylene	C_3H_6	(42) (45)
37. Tetramethylene	C_4H_8	(42) (45)
38. Pentamethylene	C_5H_{10}	(42) (45)
39. Hexamethylene (cyclohexane)	C_6H_{12}	(42) (45)
VI. Benzene hydrocarbons:		
40. Benzene	C_6H_6	(55)
41. Toluene	C_7H_8	(42)
42. O-Xylene	C_8H_{10}	(37)
43. M-Xylene	C_8H_{10}	(37)
44. P-Xylene	C_8H_{10}	(37)
45. Mesitylene	C_9H_{12}	(37)
46. Pseudocumene	C_9H_{12}	(46)
47. Durene	$C_{10}H_{12}$	(46)
48. 1-2-Dimethyl-4-isopropylbenzene	$C_{11}H_{16}$	(55)
VII. Naphthalene hydrocarbons:		
49. Naphthalene	$C_{10}H_8$	(46) (56)
50. Decahydronaphthalene	$C_{10}H_{18}$	(46)
51. α-Methylnaphthalene	$C_{11}H_{10}$	(47)
52. β-Methylnaphthalene	$C_{11}H_{10}$	(47)
53. Acenaphthalene	$C_{12}H_8$	(55)
54. 1-6-Dimethylnaphthalene	$C_{12}H_{12}$	(46)
55. Perhydroacenaphthalene	$C_{12}H_{12}$	(46)
56. Dodecahydrodiphenyl	$C_{12}H_{12}$	(46)
VIII. Indenes:		
57. Indene	C_9H_8	(55)
58. Hydrindene	C_9H_{10}	(55)
59. 4-Methylindene	$C_{10}H_{10}$	(55)
60. 4-Methylhydrindene	$C_{10}H_{12}$	(55)
61. Dimethylindene	$C_{11}H_{12}$	(55)
62. Dimethylhydrindene	$C_{11}H_{14}$	(55)

TABLE 7—*Concluded*

CONSTITUENT	FORMULA	AUTHORITY
IX. Other hydrocarbons:		
63. Cyclopentadiene	C_5H_6	(38)
64. 1-2-3-Aethylxylol	$C_{10}H_{14}$	(55)
65. l-Methyldekaline	$C_{11}H_{20}$	(55)
66. Undecane	$C_{11}H_{24}$	(55)
67. 1-6-Dimethyldikaline	$C_{12}H_{22}$	(55)
68. Anthracene	$C_{14}H_{10}$	(55)
B. Oxygenated Compounds		
X. Alcohols:		
69. Phenol	C_6H_6O	(48) (49)
70. Isohydroquinoline	$C_6H_6O_2$	(52)
71. Benzecatechin	$C_6H_6O_2$	(55)
72. Hydroquincline	$C_6H_6O_2$	(52)
73. Cathechol (o-dihydroxybenzene)	$C_6H_6O_2$	(50)
74. O-Cresol	C_7H_8O	(50) (42)
75. M-Cresol	C_7H_8O	(50) (42)
76. P-Cresol	C_7H_8O	(50) (42)
77. Methylhydroquinoline	$C_7H_9O_2$	(48)
78. 1-2-4-Xylenol	$C_8H_{10}O$	(48) (50) (51)
79. 1-3-4-Xylenol	$C_8H_{10}O$	(55)
80. 1-4-2-Xylenol	$C_8H_{10}O$	(55)
81. 1-3-5-Xylenol	$C_8H_{10}O$	(55)
82. Ethylhydroquinoline	$C_8H_{10}O_2$	(48)
83. 1-Naphthol	$C_{10}H_8O$	(55)
84. Dimethylcumaron	$C_{10}H_{10}O$	(55)
85. Trimethylphenol	$C_{10}H_{12}O$	(40) (50)
86. Tetramethylphenol	$C_{10}H_{14}O$	(52)
87. Pentamethylphenol	$C_{11}H_{16}O$	(52)
XI. Aldehydes:		
88. Acetaldehyde	C_2H_4O	(55)
89. Paraldehyde	$(C_2H_4O)_3$	(43)
XII. Ketones:		
90. Acetone	C_3H_6O	(53)
91. Methylethylketone	C_4H_8O	(38)
92. P-Methylolylketone	$C_9H_{10}O$	(55)
93. Methylheptyketone	$C_9H_{18}O$	(55)
C. Sulphuretted Compounds:		
94. Hydrogen sulphide	H_2S	(44)
95. Carbon disulphide	CS_2	(38) (32)
96. Methylmercaptan	CH_4S	(38)
97. Dimethylsulphide	C_2H_6S	(38)
98. Toluolmercaptan	C_7H_8S	(55)
D. Chlorinated Compounds:		
99. Hydrochloric acid	HCl	(42)
100. Ammonium chloride	NH_4Cl	(42)
Nitrogenous Compounds:		
101. Nitrogen	N_2	Many observers
102. Ammonia	NH_3	Many observers
103. Acetonitrile	C_2H_3N	(55)
104. Pyridine	C_5H_5N	(42) (48)
105. α-Picoline	C_6H_7N	(48)
106. β-Picoline	C_6H_7N	(48)
107. γ-Picoline	C_6H_7N	(48)
108. Aniline	C_6H_7N	(55)
109. α-Ethylpyridine	C_7H_9N	(48)
110. β-Ethylpyridine	C_7H_9N	(48)
111. γ-Ethylpyridine	C_7H_9N	(48)
112. O-Toluidine	C_7H_9N	(52)
113. M-Toluidine	C_7H_9N	(52)
114. P-Toluidine	C_7H_9N	(52)
115. 1-3-5-Trimethylpyridine (collidine)	$C_8H_{11}N$	(54)
116. Chinoline	C_9H_7N	(55)
117. Chinaldine	$C_{10}H_9N$	(55)
F. Inorganic Compounds:		
118. Hydrogen	H_2	Many observers
119. Water	H_2O	Many observers
120. Carbon monoxide	CO	Many observers
121. Carbon dioxide	CO_2	Many observers

equal to as much as 6.0 per cent of the thermal value with a Nottingham coal and as little as 2.1 per cent of the calorific value with a Welsh coal.

Hollings and Cobb (67) (68) studied the thermal reactions of Mockton coal during low temperature carbonization. They observed that endothermic reactions predominated in the decomposition region 250°C. to 410°C. Exothermic reactions predominated in the short region 410°C. to 470°C. A second endothermic period was found from 470°C. to 610°C. Above 610°C. the reactions were decidedly exothermic in character, but between 750°C. and 800°C. the reactions again became endothermic. This variation between the predominance of reactions involving the liberation and absorption of heat within various temperature limits explains sufficiently the discrepancies of earlier observations.

Strache and Fromm (69) studied the heat required for carbonizing various grades of fuel, ranging from wood to bituminous coal, at 750°C. and found that the heat liberated was a function of the percentage of oxygen present in the fuel. With oxygen contents below 15 per cent, the fuel is usually endothermic during its decomposition, while fuels containing more than this amount of oxygen are exothermic in character. Of course, when very wet fuels are treated, the amount of heat required to evaporate the moisture may be so great as to entirely obscure any heat which might be liberated. In some cases, particularly in low temperature carbonization, where close temperature control is desirable, the exothermic reactions may be of importance. Thus, Parr and Layng (70) base their process upon this phenomenon and Gentry (71) has pointed out its importance in the carbonization of pulverized coal.

More recently, Davis and Place (72) (73) have investigated the thermal reactions of carbonization at the United States Bureau of Mines. They found that the exothermic heat varies not only with the oxygen content of the fuel but also with the conditions of distillation. Under conditions of low temperature carbonization, they found that most American coals have positive heat reactions. They confirmed the research of Klason (74) on wood cellulose, obtaining a liberation of 318 B.t.u. per lb. of pine sawdust.

Davis, Place, and Edeburn (75) have made a very careful study of the heat of carbonization of various fuels by the calorimetric method devised by Davis (76). They showed that the primary decomposition of coal was exothermic in character, while the tendency of secondary reactions was endothermic. In other words, that the reactions involved in low temperature carbonization are principally those which liberate heat, whereas the reactions involved in the transition from low to high temperature carbonization products are those which absorb heat.

The difficulties of making such thermometric measurements are enhanced by the numerous variables affecting the results. Hulett and Capps (77) have shown that the pressure has considerable effect on the character and quantity of the products and, hence, upon

TABLE 8

Analyses of fuels tested for heat of carbonization

FUEL	PROXIMATE					ULTIMATE				
	H₂O	V.M.	F.C.	Ash	B.t.u.	S	H	C	N	O
	per cent	per cent	per cent	per cent	per pound	per cent	per cent	per cent	per cent	per cent
Pine sawdust................	6.3	74.4	18.8	0.5	8,560	0.0	6.6	48.6	0.1	44.2
Minnesota peat.............	9.1	55.7	27.4	7.8	8,700	0.3	6.1	49.8	2.2	33.8
Texas lignite................	10.4	41.8	36.5	11.3	9,410	0.5	5.3	55.4	0.8	26.7
Utah bituminous............	7.1	39.8	48.5	4.6	11,620	1.3	5.6	66.5	1.2	20.8
Illinois coal.................	7.3	37.5	44.4	10.8	11,170	3.5	5.3	62.5	1.1	16.8
Ohio coal...................	1.7	37.7	54.8	5.8	12,970	3.4	5.2	72.3	1.1	12.2
Freeport coal...............	1.0	28.0	61.2	9.2	13,470	1.6	4.7	75.9	1.3	6.7
Pittsburgh coal.............	1.6	36.4	55.7	6.3	13,960	1.1	5.3	77.6	1.5	8.8
Pocahontas coal............	0.6	17.0	72.3	10.1	13,730	0.9	4.2	79.7	1.4	3.7
Anthracite..................	0.6	5.5	80.4	13.5	12,820	0.8	2.8	78.3	0.8	3.8

the heat of reaction, according to the principle laid down by Thompson (78) that the heat of formation of a compound is equal to the difference between its heat of combustion and the heat of formation of its products of combustion. The rate of heating determines the proportion of secondary reactions taking place simultaneously with the primary reactions and, therefore, causes a variation in the net heat evolved. Even then, the character of the inert gaseous atmosphere is not without its influence, as might be expected from its bearing on the reaction equilibrium. Thus, Davis and his co-workers found that at 930°F. the heat evolved was about 85 per cent greater in an atmosphere of carbon dioxide than in an atmosphere of hydrogen, when using Illinois and Ohio coals. Preoxidation renders the coal less exothermic, while preheating in hydrogen up to 390°F. has no effect.

Analyses of the fuels, whose heat of carbonization was determined by Davis, Place, and Edeburn (75), are given in Table 8. These analyses are given on an air-dried basis. The heats of carbonization were determined in an atmosphere of nitrogen. The results are shown graphically for the coals in Fig. 2 and for pine sawdust and peat in Fig. 3. An examination of these illustrations discloses that all the fuels are slightly endothermic below the decomposition temperature, which is at about 600°F. for the coals and 500°F. for peat and sawdust. There is a rapid evolution of heat when primary decomposition sets in between 600°F. and 800°F. The maximum heat evolution is reached at about 900°F. with coals and at about 1000°F. with peat and sawdust. After attaining the maximum, the heat evolution curves drop off fairly rapidly and actually become endothermic again at 1050°F. for the older and more consolidated coals.

Heat Balance. Euchène (79) was one of the first to recognize the value of a heat balance in coke ovens, but, since his early experiments, a great deal of valuable research has been done. The heat applied to decompose a fuel into its final products of coke, tar, and gas can be attributed to eight factors, *viz.:* heat abstracted by moisture; heat abstracted by non-condensible gas as it leaves the retort; heat abstracted by tar oils; heat abstracted by liquor; sensible heat of the coke; sensible heat of the ash; internal heat of decomposition; and heat losses from the retort. Rambush (80) has proposed a method of estimating the heat balance of coal distillation by the use of tables, prepared to show the heat abstracted by each of the above factors as a function of the temperature of the gas outlet and yields of the various products.

Catalysis. The catalytic action of mineral matter in the coal, particularly in the ash, has long been overlooked, although attention was called to it in 1914 by Lessing (81). Experiments conducted by Lessing and Banks (82) showed wide variations in the amount of coke produced when carbonizing sugar and cellulose in the presence of different inorganic compounds. The results were confirmed by Marson and Cobb (83). In view of the vital importance of catalysis in the synthesis of liquid hydrocarbons by hydrogenation of coal, it would not be at all surprising to find that the mineral matter in coal has a far more marked effect upon the volatile products than upon the solid residuum.

Plastic Layer. The mechanism of carbonization in a retort can be described as follows: the raw coal introduced into the chamber rapidly absorbs heat in its surface layer, thereby driving off free moisture, which moves inward and condenses in the interior regions

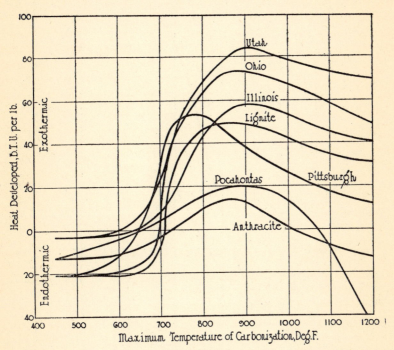

FIG. 2. HEAT LIBERATED FROM AMERICAN COALS AS A FUNCTION OF TEMPERATURE

of the cold charge; the temperature of the surface layer rises to 575°F. or 750°F., within which temperature range it becomes fused or plastic; a rapid evolution of volatile products follows the fusion stage and the coke assumes a porous structure. From each wall of the retort the plastic layers migrate slowly inward until they meet at the center of the chamber, producing a line of demarkation always found as a central crack in the charge. The plastic layer is estimated to be from 0.5 inch to 1.5 inches in width and it is characterized by a large temperature drop across the fusion zone and a great resistance to the passage of gas through the layer.   In fact, Evans (84) found that the

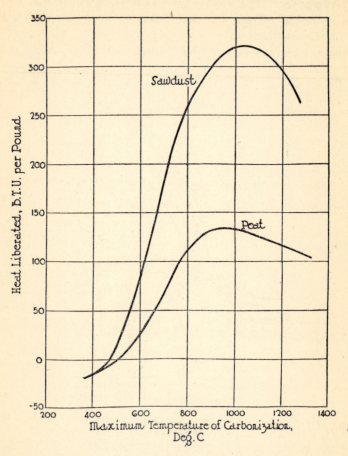

Fig. 3. Heat Liberated from Peat and Sawdust as a Function of Temperature

resistance to passage of gas offered by the plastic layer was 3000 times that offered by screened lump coal, 75 times that offered by coal dust, and 300 times that offered by 1400°F. coke.

Foxwell (63) investigated the temperature at which the plastic layer is formed and found that it lay between 752°F. and 842°F., which is slightly above what is usually considered the fusion range. A pressure as high as 480 mm. of water was required to force the passage of gas across the plastic layer, as compared with about 20 mm. before and after fusion.   Layng and Hawthorne (86) also investigated

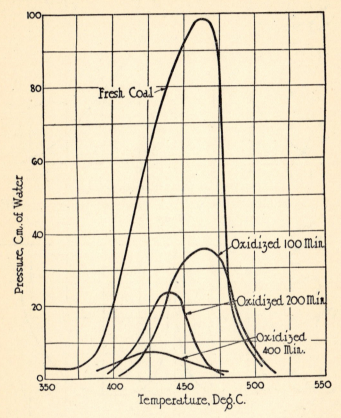

FIG. 4. RESISTANCE OF PLASTIC LAYER TO GAS FLOW AS A FUNCTION OF OXIDATION

this problem for over forty American coals and found pressures as high as 1500 mm. of water in the case of Pocahontas coal.   It is very apparent, therefore, that in coke ovens the gas evolved must develop quite a pressure to penetrate the plastic layer.   The resistance offered by the fusion zone depends greatly upon the coal, particularly upon the degree to which it has been preoxidized.   Fig. 4 shows the result of some experiments by Parr (87) to determine the effect of preoxidation on the phenomena occurring during fusion.   The reduc-

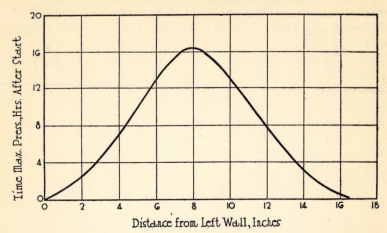

FIG. 5. PROGRESSION OF PLASTIC LAYER ACROSS COKE OVEN AS A FUNCTION OF TIME

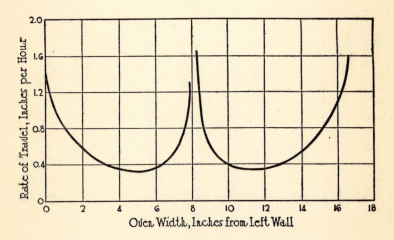

FIG. 6. RATE OF TRAVEL OF PLASTIC LAYER ACROSS COKE OVEN AS A FUNCTION OF DISTANCE

tion in resistance to gas passage, which accompanies preoxidation, evidently must be attributed to reduction in the coking power of the coal.

Ryan (88) has determined the progress of the fusion zone across a 16.5 inch Rothsburg coke oven and found that 16.3 hours were required for the two plastic layers to reach the center from each side when the flues were maintained at a temperature of about 2100°F. The progress of the plastic layer is shown clearly in Fig. 5. The rate of travel of the plastic layer can be determined quite easily by graphical differentiation of the progress curve given in Fig. 5. The result of such a differentiation, using 0.5 inch increments to calculate the slope, is shown in Fig. 6. With reference to the last illustration, it is seen that, when the raw coal is introduced into the hot retort, the surface layers in contact with the flue have a high heat transfer. Consequently, in the initial stages of coking, the plastic zone travels at the relatively high velocity of about 1.5 inches per hour. However, as the plastic layer recedes from the oven wall, it becomes more and

TABLE 9

Variation of heat transfer in retorts with thermal gradient

TEMPERATURE	THICKNESS OF COAL	HOURS TO ATTAIN TEMPERATURE	TRANSFER VELOCITY	THERMAL GRADIENT
°C.	cm.	hours	cm. per hour	°C. per cm.
1100	51	32.5	1.57	21.5
1100	41	18.0	2.28	26.9
1100	14	4.5	3.11	78.6
550	14	7.0	2.00	39.3

more difficult to transfer the heat necessary to raise the charge to plasticity and, therefore, the rate of travel rapidly falls to a minimum of about 0.3 inch per hour. During the progress of the plastic layer, additional heat has been expended immediately in front of the fusion zone to drive off the moisture, which condensed on the interior of the charge, and to raise the temperature of the center of the mass. Finally, the chilling action of the center of the charge is checked and the rate of heat transfer to the plastic zone becomes greater, thereby raising again its rate of migration.

Heat Transfer. Because of the poor heat conductivity of coal, the time of carbonization is greatly influenced by the size of the particles, porosity of the charge, method of heating, shape of the retort, and other peculiarities of the particular process under examination. In addition to the time consumed in heat transfer, there is a time interval required, while the coal is maintained at the maximum temperature, until coking is complete. Both the time of carbonization and the rate of heating depend, among other factors, upon the ratio of the mass of the charge to the surface of the charge.

The thermal conductivity of coal is so low that, even with a high temperature gradient of 1100°C. in the flues of the retort and 100°C. in the center of the carbonization chamber, the rate of heat transfer rarely exceeds 0.8 inch per hour in practice. Thickness of the

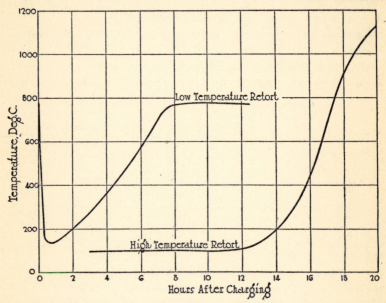

FIG. 7. TEMPERATURE OF CHARGE IN HIGH AND LOW TEMPERATURE RETORTS
AS A FUNCTION OF TIME

charge, therefore, becomes of primary importance, when carbonizing between 400°C. and 800°C. Measurements, under commercial conditions, have been made by Wellington and Cooper (89) with retorts of different thicknesses to study the rate of heat transfer and are given in Table 9. In accordance with the laws of heat transfer, we find that, for a high thermal gradient, there is a high velocity of heat transfer and a low time interval for the center of the charge to attain its maximum temperature. For a reduction of 50 per cent in the thermal gradient, however, there is a reduction of but 35.5 per cent in the velocity of heat transfer and an increase of 33.4 per cent in the time of retorting.

The slow rate of heating of the charge is seen clearly by reference to Fig. 7, where some data on the experimental determination of temperature inside of the carbonization chamber during coking are given. The measurements on the low temperature process are reported by Wellington and Cooper (89), who used a vertical fireclay

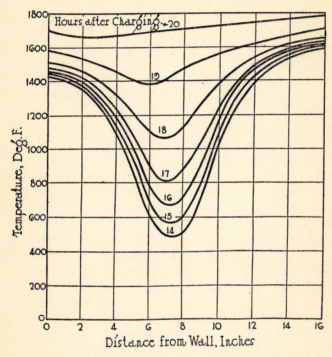

FIG. 8. ISOTHERMS OF A COKE OVEN AS A FUNCTION OF TIME

retort, 11.5 feet high and 5 inches wide. It was heated externally with producer gas and the flues were maintained at 765°C. About eight hours were required for the center of the charge to reach the initial temperature of the retort. The results presented for the high temperature process are from measurements made by McBride and Selvig (90) on standard Koppers ovens. These ovens were of the horizontal variety, 39 feet long and 18 inches wide. Over twenty hours elapsed before the interior of the charge reached its maximum, while the flues were kept at 1200°C. In the first case, the rate of heat transfer was about 0.625 inch per hour and in the second case about 0.850 inches per hour.

In Fig. 8 are shown some isochronic temperatures across a coke oven for various times after charging, as measured by Ryan (88). The measurements begin with the 14th hour after charging, or just about two hours before the plastic layer reached the center of the retort, after which it is apparent that, once the fusion stage is over, the rate of temperature increase becomes rapidly greater until, after the 20th hour, the charge attains almost a uniform temperature throughout.

According to Newton's law, the flow of heat through a body by conduction, after the steady state has been attained, is expressed by the differential equation:

$$\frac{dQ}{dt} = kA \frac{dT}{dx} \qquad [11]$$

where Q is the unit of heat; T, the temperature; x, the distance in the direction of heat flow; t, the time; A, the area perpendicular to heat flow; and k the coefficient of heat transfer. The complexities of carbonization, however, render this equation inapplicable in its simple form for two reasons. In the first place, the coefficient of heat transfer is not constant, but is a function of both the time and the distance from the retort wall and, secondly, because the rate of change of temperature with respect to distance is also a variable with respect to the time as well as the distance. The coefficient of heat transmission for coke is considerably greater than for coal, hence, the manner in which the mean coefficient might vary can be gathered from consideration of Fig. 5, recalling that coke exists between the wall of the retort and the plastic layer, while coal exists in the center of the chamber. The manner in which the temperature gradient varies as a function of time and distance can be gathered by graphical differentiation of the family of curves in Fig. 8 to determine their slope.

It will be seen from Fig. 8 that for several hours after charging, on account of the low thermal conductivity of the coal, the temperature range within the oven is very great. Different zones of the charge, therefore, undergo different carbonization transformations at the same period. Nielsen (91) has nicely illustrated this point under conditions of low temperature distillation by determining the varia-

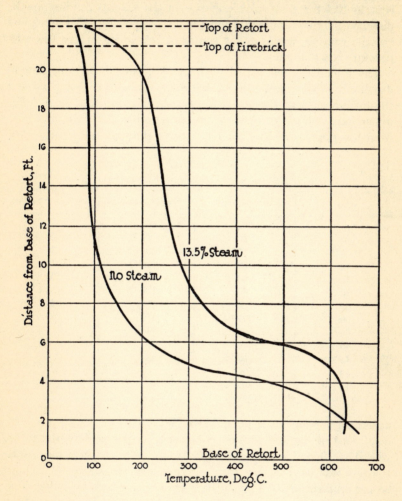

FIG. 9. EFFECT OF STEAM ADMISSION ON THE DISTRIBUTION OF TEMPERATURE IN VERTICAL RETORTS

tion of the percentage volatile matter remaining in the coke with the distance of the distillation residuum from the retort wall for a retort 6.5 inches thick. The carbonization was carried on for 6 hours at about 600°C. before the coke was examined. It was found that, even after this period of retorting, there is a range of from 10.4 per cent to 13.4 per cent volatile matter in the coke, depending on the distance of the residuum from the chamber wall. The maximum volatile content occurs in the center of the charge where the temperature is a minimum.

The Fuel Research Board (92) has determined the longitudinal distribution of temperature in vertical retorts, both with and without the introduction of steam. The results are shown in Fig. 9. The upper curve shows the change in temperature distribution, arising from the passage of 13.5 per cent steam through the retort. The

TABLE 10

Effect of coke breeze on heat transfer

TIME	RAW WELSH COAL	20 PER CENT BREEZE	30 PER CENT BREEZE
minutes	°C.	°C.	°C.
0	20	20	20
5	20	30	30
10	32	58	72
15	60	88	130
20	100	128	183
25	135	170	240
30	167	210	287
35	200	245	
40	222	278	
45	252	330	
50	275		
55	302		

experiments were made on a Glover-West retort. Under ordinary conditions of distillation, only the lower 25 per cent of the retort was above 300°C. and 50 per cent above 100°C. When steam distillation was used, 48 per cent of the retort was above 300°C. and 98 per cent above 100°C. In the zones of the retort, extending from 5 feet above the base to the top, constituting about 75 per cent of the carbonization chamber, the use of 13.5 per cent steam raised the temperature of the charge over 100 per cent. It will be pointed out later that one of the functions of steam distillation is to assist in the uniform distribution of heat throughout the charge, heat being absorbed in the lower hot portions of the retort and distributed through the upper cooler zones.

The introduction of coke breeze has a material effect in the transfer of heat. Roberts (93) examined the time required for the interior of the charge to reach 360°C., and found that 58 minutes were required, when using raw Welsh coal; 46 minutes when 20 per cent breeze was added; and 31 minutes when 30 per cent breeze was mixed with the charge. Table 10 shows the result of his investigation. Apparently, the beneficial effects of coke breeze are derived from the fact that it increases the thermal conductivity of the charge and gives a certain amount of porosity to the mass, which allows the transfer of heat by internal convection currents.

Internal and External Heating. It is easier to withdraw vapors soon after their formation in horizontal than in vertical retorts. In

TABLE 11

Comparison of rate of gas evolution in externally and internally heated low temperature retorts

HOURS	CUBIC FEET GAS PER HOUR	
	External	Internal
0	0	0
0.4	2,930	4,110
1.0	4,080	4,760
1.4	3,830	4,190
2.0	3,080	2,970
3.0	1,680	825
4.0	610	

a static horizontal retort, where the material moves progressively, eduction pipes can be placed at intervals along the top of the retort to withdraw the vapors. Thus, the mechanical design of the retort is found to play an important part in determining the yield of the desired products.

Two methods of heating have been resorted to, external and internal. In external heating, the solid, liquid, or gaseous fuel is burned in an outer chamber and the coal is placed in a gas-tight retort. When carbonization is carried on by internal heating, the sensible heat of producer gas, generated externally or in the retort itself, superheated steam, molten lead, or some other agency, is employed to effect the distillation. One of the main differences between the two methods lies in the quantity of gas evolved.   Thus, in the producer gas method of low temperature carbonization, the yield of gas is of the order 25,000 to 35,000 cubic feet per net ton of coal, as compared with 3,000 to 4,500 cubic feet obtained in external distillation.   On the other hand, the great volume of gas yielded by the producer gas method is of low heating value, such as 250 B.t.u. per cubic foot, as compared with the high calorific value of 800 to 1000 B.t.u. per cubic foot obtained in the externally heated retorts.

The uniform distribution of heat in the retort by steaming suggests the advantage of internal heating over the external method.   Nielsen (91) obtained the results in Table 11 by comparing the rate of evolution of gas from carbonization at low temperature in externally and internally heated retorts.   The rate of evolution rises to a maximum after about three-quarters of an hour of carbonization, after which it gradually falls in value.   Internally heated retorts attain an 18.5 per cent higher maximum in the same period than those heated by external methods.   The recession in the rate of evolution is also much more rapid when the heat is conducted through the charge by the internal heating process.   By integrating these curves, that is, by measuring the area beneath them, the total quantity of gas evolved over any period of distillation can be found.   Comparison of the two areas discloses that, over a period of 2.75 hours, 75 per cent to 80 per cent of all the gas evolved from the coal during low temperature carbonization in internally heated retorts has been yielded, whereas 70 per cent to 75 per cent has been given off in externally heated processes.   For the same character and yield of products in the two cases, this is equivalent to a material reduction in the time of carbonization.

High and Low Temperature Carbonization.   For the sake of concise presentation, it would be permissible, perhaps, to risk a generalized comparison.   Considering a coal containing approximately 35 per cent volatile matter, 7 per cent ash, and 58 per cent fixed carbon, it is reasonable to expect under ordinary circumstances the yields per net ton of raw fuel shown in Table 12.

The gaseous products of low temperature carbonization consist mainly of the lower saturated and unsaturated aliphatics.   Aromatic compounds are generally absent.   The gases, while produced in lesser quantities than in high temperature ovens, are rich in their thermal value.

Low temperature tar contains more members of the paraffin series and fewer aromatic compounds than high temperature or coke oven tar. One of the chief characteristics of low temperature tar is its high tar acid content. The fraction up to 170°C. and the pitch usually contain about 40 per cent tar acids, while the coke oven distillate runs as low as 15 per cent or less. Very little phenol, itself, is produced, but this varies to a great extent with the coal. Of the tar acids, more cresol and homologues of phenol are present than in high temperature tar. Naphthalene is absent, but other members of the series have been found in minor quantities. While coke oven tar has a specific gravity of about 1.17 at 15°C. and contains about 6.5 per cent free carbon, the low temperature product runs less than 1.10 specific gravity and usually contain less than one per cent

TABLE 12

General comparison of high and low temperature processes

PRODUCT	YIELD PER NET TON	
	High temperature	Low temperature
Gas (cubic feet)............................	11,000	5,100
B.t.u. per cubic foot.......................	540	825
Tar (gallons)................................	10	20
Light Oil (gallons)...........................	2.5	3
Ammonium sulphate (pounds)..............	22	14
Coke (pounds)...............................	1,500	1,500

free carbon. The presence of free carbon in tar is partly indicative of cracking, which is reduced to a mimimum at low temperatures. The presence of as much as 3 per cent free carbon in some low temperature tars, however, is due to dust and not to cracking.

The evolution of ammonia gas from coal under destructive distillation begins below 300°C. and ceases above 1200°C., so that it is to be expected that the ammonium sulphate yield of low temperature carbonization should be low. A great part of the nitrogen present remains in the coke and methods have been proposed for increasing the yield.

The two cokes are entirely different. The high temperature coke is coarser, denser, and harder to burn than low temperature coke. The latter is usually characterized by its friability, softness, fineness of texture, and high combustibility, but some semi-cokes are quite as hard and dense as the high temperature variety.

Since it is obvious that high temperature carbonization removes the hydrocarbons and resinous compounds, which cause the formation of smoke, as well as does low temperature carbonization, the question arises as to why the coke from gas ovens is not itself a suitable smokeless fuel for domestic consumption. The difference is that the former is not generally free burning. The physical condition accounting for this difference in the free burning property is said by Brownlie (94) to be in the porosity of the coke. High temperature coke is very spongy, while low temperature coke is more like charcoal. Furthermore, in the gas coke a graphitic film, deposited from the cracking of hydrocarbons, covers the walls of the pores and adds to its incombustibility.

CHAPTER II

LOW TEMPERATURE COAL GAS

Evolution of Gas. It is worth while to examine the behavior of the lower types of carbonaceous fuels under destructive distillation as a preliminary to the discussion of the gaseous products evolved from coal under the influence of temperature. Börnstein (95) carefully examined the composition of gas evolved from distillation at various temperatures of a peat and a lignite, whose ash-free analyses approximated those shown in Table 2, and a wood whose ultimate analysis showed 48.8 per cent carbon, 6.5 per cent hydrogen, 40.8 per cent oxygen, 0.63 per cent nitrogen, 3.2 per cent water, 0.10 per cent ash, and 0.08 per cent sulphur. These data have been compiled in Table 13. It should be observed that, in the case of wood, hydrogen is rapidly evolved at comparatively low temperatures and, as a matter of fact, it will be shown that the temperature of hydrogen evolution progresses with the geologic aging of the fuel. The percentage carbon dioxide increases steadily, at any given temperature, with the position of the fuel in historical reckoning.

Lewes (17) carbonized bituminous coal at temperatures ranging from 400°C. to 900°C. and measured the volume of gas liberated at the respective temperatures. He found that the volume of gas liberated increased approximately 1,200 cubic feet per gross ton of coal for each 100°C. rise in temperature throughout the range. A glance at Table 14 will show that, within the temperature interval 400°C. to 900°C., the volume of gas liberated increases over 100 per cent from the lower to the higher temperature. At the same time, the percentage composition of the gas undergoes a considerable change. The percentage of hydrogen present more than doubles, while the percentage of saturated and of unsaturated hydrocarbons each decreases about half. The amount of unsaturated hydrocarbons in the gas is small, compared to the other constituents.

American Coals. Studies of the gas obtained in the destructive distillation of coals found in the United States have been made by a number of experimenters. Particular mention should be made of the work of Porter and Ovitz (96), who used coals from Pennsylvania,

TABLE 13

Composition of gas distilled from wood, peat, and lignite

CONSTITUENT	TEMPERATURE			
	300°C.	350°C.	400°C.	450°C.
	per cent	per cent	per cent	per cent
Wood:				
CO_2.................................		53.5	55.0	28.0
CO..................................		27.7	32.6	29.0
CH_4..................................		14.9	7.9	20.6
Olefines............................		0.2	1.5	5.0
H_2..................................		3.7	3.0	17.3
Peat:				
CO_2.................................		89.2	63.8	55.4
CO..................................		10.1	7.2	12.3
CH_4..................................			25.5	25.4
Olefines............................		0.3	0.4	3.7
H_2..................................		0.3	3.1	3.1
Lignite:				
CO_2.................................	91.4	90.9	69.6	47.8
CO..................................	6.4	7.6	15.8	15.1
CH_4..................................	1.1		3.2	21.2
Olefines............................	0.3	0.5	8.8	11.9
Sulphur compounds................		0.7	0.5	0.4

TABLE 14

Gas evolved from bituminous coal at various temperatures

TEMPERATURE	GAS VOLUME PER GROSS TON	HYDROGEN	SATURATED HYDROCARBONS	UNSATURATED HYDROCARBONS
°C.	cubic feet	per cent	per cent	per cent
400	5,000	21.2	60.1	6.3
500	6,400	28.3	56.2	5.8
600	7,750	33.8	50.7	5.0
700	9,000	41.5	45.0	4.4
800	10,000	48.2	39.1	3.8
900	11,000	54.5	34.2	3.5

Illinois, West Virginia, Virginia, and Wyoming; Davis and Parry (97), who examined coal from the Pittsburgh and Upper Kittanning beds of Pennsylvania; and Taylor and Porter (98), who investigated the coals of Pennsylvania, Illinois, West Virginia, and Wyoming. Representative analyses of the coals studied are given in Table 15 and Table 16. Comparison of these data with Table 1 and Table 2 seems to classify the West Virginia and Virginia coals as semi-bituminous, the Pennsylvania coal as bituminous, and the Illinois, Utah, and Wyoming coals as sub-bituminous.

TABLE 15

Proximate analyses of coals of the United States

CONSTITUENT	PENNSYL-VANIA	ILLINOIS	WEST VIRGINIA	VIRGINIA	WYOMING	UTAH
	per cent	*per cent*	*per cent*	*per cent*	*per cent*	*per cent*
Moisture...............	1.1	7.5	0.9	0.5	2.2	4.1
Volatile matter..........	30.7	30.4	32.5	20.9	34.0	42.3
Fixed carbon............	60.4	54.5	61.2	75.5	57.4	48.1
Ash....................	7.5	7.4	3.5	3.2	6.5	5.6
B.t.u. per pound........	14,000	12,000	14,600	15,400	12,000	13,100

TABLE 16

Ultimate analyses of coals of the United States

CONSTITUENT	PENNSYL-VANIA	ILLINOIS	WEST VIRGINIA	VIRGINIA	WYOMING	UTAH
	per cent	*per cent*	*per cent*	*per cent*	*per cent*	*per cent*
Carbon..................	76.9	69.9	85.9	84.7	65.6	72.7
Hydrogen...............	5.2	5.1	4.7	5.0	5.3	5.4
Oxygen.................	7.9	15.5	4.0	6.0	20.1	10.4
Nitrogen................	1.4	1.5	1.5	1.2	1.5	1.4
Sulphur.................	1.6	0.8	0.7	0.4	1.0	0.4
Ash....................	7.1	7.3	3.2	2.5	6.5	5.6

Table 17, Table 18, and Table 19 give the quantity of gas evolved and its composition at three different temperatures of distillation for Virginia, West Virginia, and Wyoming coals, respectively. In these three tables the Virginia coal is the oldest coal, the Wyoming coal the youngest, while the West Virginia coal occupies an intervening position historically. As a matter of fact, we shall see later that the geologic age of the coal has a direct bearing on the composition of the gas yielded at a given temperature.

Porter and Ovitz made a careful determination of the gas evolved

TABLE 17

Temperature variation of gas composition from Virginia coal

CONSTITUENT	TEMPERATURE		
	500°C.	700°C.	1000°C.
Cubic feet gas per gross ton............	850	4,260	11,600
Analysis:	*per cent*	*per cent*	*per cent*
CO₂.................................	5.5	1.4	0.4
CO..................................	3.5	5.1	4.6
CₙHₘ...............................	70.6	55.2	26.8
H₂..................................	15.2	34.8	64.5
Illuminants........................	5.2	3.5	3.7

TABLE 18

Temperature variation of gas composition from West Virginia coal

CONSTITUENT	TEMPERATURE		
	600°C.	750°C.	900°C.
Cubic feet gas per gross ton............	490	3,550	7,140
Analysis:	*per cent*	*per cent*	*per cent*
CO₂.................................	12.7	4.1	2.7
CO..................................	6.2	5.8	7.6
CₙHₘ...............................	61.6	57.0	40.5
H₂..................................	9.8	25.1	41.0
Illuminants........................	9.7	8.0	8.2

TABLE 19

Temperature variation of gas composition from Wyoming coal

CONSTITUENT	TEMPERATURE		
	500°C.	700°C.	1000°C.
Cubic feet gas per gross ton............	1,860	4,670	13,710
Analysis:	*per cent*	*per cent*	*per cent*
CO₂.................................	54.3	21.7	10.4
CO..................................	19.6	21.5	22.3
CₙHₘ...............................	18.9	29.4	16.3
H₂..................................	3.5	23.9	46.5
Illuminants........................	3.7	3.5	4.5

at different temperatures with Pennsylvania and Illinois coals. The results of their determinations are shown in Fig. 10 and Fig. 11. It is plain from an examination of these diagrams that below 500°C. there is practically no decomposition of the hydrocarbons, as evidenced by the absence of hydrogen, except for insignificant quantities. After a temperature of 600°C. is reached, however, the decomposition of the hydrocarbons becomes exceedingly great.

Giles and Vilbrandt (99) made a study of the gas distilled from Farmville, N. C., coal at somewhat lower temperatures, the results

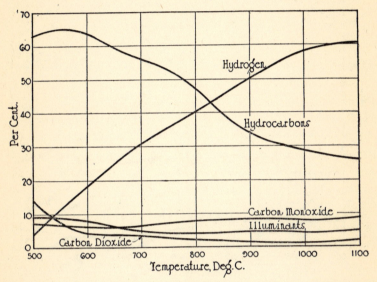

FIG. 10. COMPOSITION OF GAS FROM PENNSYLVANIA COAL AS A FUNCTION OF TEMPERATURE

of which are shown in Fig. 12. This particular coal has the reputation of producing excessive smoke and of disintegrating when exposed to the atmosphere. These characteristics give disfavor to this fuel for domestic and industrial purposes. Reference to the illustration shows the large quantities of oxygen and nitrogen driven off in the initial stages of heating which, together with the small quantity of hydrocarbons evolved, demonstrates the reason for the ease with which this coal disintegrates. From 200°C. to 650°C., the proportion of ethane formed from this coal remains about constant. The formation of heavy hydrocarbons reaches a maximum at the very low temperature of 300°C., after which their formation gradually decreases to a second critical point just below 600°C., thereafter only a fraction of one per cent being produced.   It is an interesting fact that no hydrogen was formed up to 660°C., which shows that the volatile products were educed in their primary condition.   It is to be expected, however, from the drop in the hydrocarbon curve at

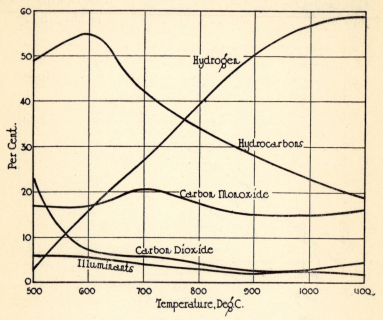

Fig. 11. Composition of Gas from Illinois Coal as a Function of Temperature

600°C., that from that temperature onward hydrogen will be produced in quantities.   Any decomposition of the heavy hydrocarbons below 660°C. in this case evidently goes to form methane, for the percentage of this constituent of the gas has a striking inverse relationship to that of the heavy hydrocarbons.   Although not shown in the illustration, carbon monoxide to the extent of 0.40 per cent appeared at 420°C. and remained about constant throughout, while carbon dioxide to the extent of 0.65 per cent appeared at 300°C. and gradually increased in amount to 1.55 per cent at 660°C.   Ethylene and other unsaturated hydrocarbons, amounting to 0.74 per cent, were produced at 200°C., but gradually decreased to 0.12 per cent at 660°C. At 360°C. the specific gravity of the total gas referred to air was 1.167, as compared with 0.952 specific gravity at 600°C. The laboratory gas yields of Porter and Ovitz and of Giles and Vilbrandt, as a function of the carbonization temperature, have been computed to a gross tonnage basis in Table 20.

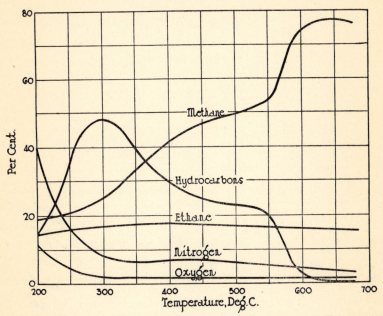

FIG. 12. COMPOSITION OF GAS FROM NORTH CAROLINA COAL AS A FUNCTION OF TEMPERATURE

Monett (100) examined seventeen Utah coals under maximum carbonization temperatures of 1000°F., twelve of which were deemed worthy of further study. The average composition of the gas from these coals was: 6.7 per cent carbon dioxide, 7.6 per cent carbon monoxide, 28.8 per cent hydrogen, 2.7 per cent nitrogen, 39.6 per cent methane, 7.1 per cent ethane, and 6.7 per cent illuminants. This agrees with the results of Parr and Layng (101), who also used Utah coals at maximum distillation temperatures of 1450°F. and obtained a gas composition of 8.3 per cent carbon dioxide, 8.9 per cent carbon monoxide, 37.6 per cent hydrogen, 3.9 per cent nitrogen, 30.7 per cent methane, 5.1 per cent ethane, and 4.8 per cent illuminants.

TABLE 20

Gas yielded by various coals at different temperatures

TEMPERATURE	CUBIC FEET OF GAS PER GROSS TON		
	Pennsylvania coal	Illinois coal	North Carolina coal
°C.			
200			97
300			525
400			1,550
500	575	710	2,360
600	2,580	925	3,640
700	4,390	3,520	
800	6,190	5,570	
900	7,480	8,400	
1,000	10,400	9,710	
1,100	12,900	11,210	

TABLE 21

Variation of low temperature gas composition with geologic age of coal

CONSTITUENT	OLDEST	← GEOLOGIC AGING			YOUNGEST
	Virginia coal	Pennsylvania coal	West Virginia coal	Illinois coal	Wyoming coal
Cubic feet gas per gross ton.....	4,300	4,400	3,600	3,500	4,700
Analysis:	*per cent*	*per cent*	*per cent*	*per cent*	*per cent*
CO_2..........................	1.4	3.2	4.1	6.4	21.7
CO............................	5.1	6.3	5.8	21.1	21.5
C_nH_m........................	55.2	55.8	57.0	41.5	29.4
H_2..........................	34.6	30.4	25.1	26.9	23.9
Illuminants....................	3.5	4.3	8.0	4.1	3.5

These data can be correlated to show the variation of the composition of low temperature gas with the age of the coal. While no definite facts are available, it has been pointed out that probably Virginia coal is the oldest and Wyoming the youngest of the five coals examined. Table 21 gives the comparative analyses of the gas obtained from the retort at 700°C. It is plainly evident that there is little change in the volume of gas evolved, that the percentage of the oxides of carbon contained in the gas greatly increases in the younger coals and that there is a corresponding decrease in the proportion of hydrocarbons and hydrogen liberated from the less consolidated fuels. The illuminants remain about constant. They consist of heavy hydrocarbons, which deposit soot at the temperature of the flame, thus providing minute incandescent particles which give illuminating properties to the flame.

British Coals. Burgess and Wheeler (57) carried on an extensive investigation of Welsh coals to determine their behavior throughout

TABLE 22

Temperature variation of volume of gas evolved from Welsh coals

TEMPERATURE	CUBIC FEET OF GAS PER GROSS TON	
	Minimum	Maximum
°C.		
500	470	1,220
600	760	3,560
700	1,580	4,850
800	4,780	7,840
900	6,940	9,760
1,000	8,270	10,960
1.100	9,780	11,970

the temperature range from 450°C. to 1100°C. The average ultimate analysis of the coals used in their experiments was as follows: 89.9 per cent carbon, 4.7 per cent hydrogen, 5.1 per cent oxygen, 1.6 per cent nitrogen, 1.4 per cent sulphur, and 5.14 per cent ash. Comparison with Table 2 shows that these coals have an ultimate analysis almost identical with that of the semi-bituminous coals of the United States.

In 2-hour distillation experiments, they observed that the percentage of total gas evolved during the first ten minutes increased rapidly with the temperature. Thus, at 600°C., 59.7 per cent of the total gas produced in two hours was educed in ten minutes; 64.6 per cent at 700°C.; 75.1 per cent at 800°C.; 88.9 per cent at 900°C.;

94.4 per cent at 1000°C.; and 94.3 per cent at 1100°C. The commercial application of low temperature carbonization is confronted with an obstacle of first importance in the shape of retorting period, due to the low thermal conductivity of coal. The difference between the maximum and the minimum yields of various coals, examined by Burgess and Wheeler (57), is as much as 300 per cent up to 700°C., after which the two values approach equality until at 1100°C. the difference is less than 20 per cent. Table 22 shows the range of yields obtained at various temperatures in the course of their experiments.

TABLE 23

Analyses of low temperature gas from Altofts Silkstone coal

CONSTITUENT	TEMPERATURE					
	450°C.	500°C.	600°C.	700°C.	750°C.	800°C.
Cubic feet gas per gross ton....	432	1,080	3,560	4,450	5,540	7,840
Per cent of coal................	9.1	18.8	28.4	32.3	34.1	36.3
Analysis:	per cent	per cent	per cent	per cent	per cent	per cent
NH_3.......................	4.7	1.4	1.4	1.6	1.0	1.0
CO_2........................	11.0	3.6	3.5	4.1	3.3	1.7
CO.........................	8.8	6.5	7.1	7.9	9.4	11.9
H_2.........................	7.0	16.6	26.6	32.7	41.7	48.6
CH_4........................	25.0	37.6	35.2	34.6	29.9	26.1
C_2H_2......................		0.4		0.4		
C_2H_4......................	0.9	1.7	1.8	1.1	0.8	0.9
C_2H_6......................	34.1	27.6	19.2	14.3	9.8	6.3
C_6H_6......................	8.6	4.9	5.2	3.4	4.2	3.7

Burgess and Wheeler (57) (102) (103) also made a careful study of the rate of gaseous evolution and of gaseous composition, as a function of the temperature of carbonization, with Altofts Silkstone coal, the results of which are shown in Table 23 and Table 24. These are very interesting data. It should be noted that there is an initial large evolution of carbon dioxide, but that this constituent decreases as the temperature rises. At the same time, the percentage of carbon monoxide increases. It will be pointed out later that this is probably caused by reduction of the dioxide to the monoxide at high temperatures in a reducing atmosphere. This same coal was distilled under reduced pressure and the gas collected *in vacuo* with the results shown in Table 24.

Carbonization *in vacuo* completely alters the character of the gas. The volume of gas evolved increases enormously above 300°C., at which temperature both the oxides of carbon reach their maximum proportions. In contrast to normal pressure distilllation, small quantities of oxygen, probably occluded, are liberated. The gas obtained *in vacuo* has about the same hydrogen content at 400°C. as normal pressure low temperature gas has at 700°C. Burgess and Wheeler (104) studied the decomposition of Lancashire coal under

TABLE 24

Gas analyses from vacuum distillation of Altofts Silkstone coal

CONSTITUENT	TEMPERATURE				
	100°C.	200°C.	300°C.	350°C.	400°C.
Cubic feet gas per gross ton	12	24	21	350	1,440
Analysis:	*per cent*	*per cent*	*per cent*	*per cent*	*per cent*
CO_2...........................	6.7	8.9	35.4	21.0	2.9
CO...........................	1.4	2.6	10.5	3.4	3.4
O_2...........................	1.7	0.7	0.6	0.2	
H_2...........................	1.9	2.8	13.4	15.4	36.9
C_nH_{2n}........................	2.1	3.8	20.0	19.8	8.5
C_nH_{2n+2}.......................	84.6	81.0	18.9	37.2	46.6
H_2S...........................				1.7	0.7

heat and vacuum. Table 25 shows that the results of their investigations on this fuel agree with the findings of Table 24.

The succession of events, as the temperature of the coal is advanced during exhaustion, can be grouped into five stages. First, occluded gases, which cannot be removed under atmospheric conditions, are driven off up to about 150°C. These gases are largely paraffin hydrocarbons, principally belonging to the higher series. Second, a a copious evolution of water appears at about 200°C. and continues up to 450°C. This is evidently water of constitution and its evolution is accompanied with the formation of a large percentage of the oxides of carbon. Third, between 200°C. and 300°C., organic sulphur compounds begin to decompose, as is manifest by the appearance of hydrogen sulphide. The hydrogen sulphide evolution begins at about 270°C. and practically ceases at 300°C. Within this stage, higher olefines begin to appear in the volatile products, but their evolution does not fall off until 350°C. is reached. Fourth, at 310°C., a reddish brown oil is driven off and thereafter liquids other than water are produced. As this evolution of oil is not accompanied by a marked evolution of gas, apparently oil is not necessarily to be considered a decomposition of the coal conglomerate. Fifth, at about 350°C., there is a rapid evolution of gas, accompanied by the formation of viscid oil, indicating a major decomposition stage, after which chemical transformations increase rapidly with the temperature rise.

TABLE 25

Gas analyses from vacuum distillation of Lancashire coal

CONSTITUENT	TEMPERATURE			
	100°C.	200°C.	300°C.	400°C.
	per cent	*per cent*	*per cent*	*per cent*
CO_2	4.0	8.4	50.1	19.2
CO	2.5	3.9	9.1	2.7
H_2	0.0	0.6	1.8	16.0
C_nH_{2n}		0.5	1.1	2.6
C_nH_{2n+2}	93.0	86.5	38.0	57.4
N_2	0.5	0.1	0.1	2.1

It has been mentioned that the composition of the gas issuing from an internally heated retort is vastly different from that obtained in closed retort operation. Carbonization is effected in the Maclaurin retort by the sensible heat of producer gas. The gas obtained from a Maclaurin retort at 700°C. by Burgess and Wheeler (105) and in an externally heated horizontal retort of the Fuel Research Board (114) at 600°C. are compared in Table 26. The samples were taken from large-scale apparatus. The vast difference in the volume and calorific value of the gas obtained in the two processes is seen at once. The nitrogen and carbon monoxide are enormously increased by partial gasification, the former coming from the atmosphere and the latter from the combustion of carbon in the manufacture of the producer gas.

The gas from low temperature coking can be passed through scrubbers and washed with certain solvents to extract the light oils, which may then be combined with the low-boiling cut from the tar fractionation to increase the yield of motor spirit. Scrubbing with creosote oil removes certain of the hydrocarbons, so that, after washing, a low temperature coal gas contains about 4.0 per cent carbon dioxide, 8.0 per cent carbon monoxide, 35.0 per cent nitrogen, 46.0 per cent methane, and 4.0 per cent other hydrocarbons. Unfortunately, no data are available on the composition of this particular gas before scrubbing, so that the conclusions drawn must be limited. By comparison, however, with the 700°C. gas in Table 23, it will be

TABLE 26

Comparison of gases from internally and externally heated retorts

CONSTITUENT	HEATED	
	Externally	Internally
Cubic feet gas per gross ton.................	3,150	27,700
B.t.u. per cubic foot.........................	1,030	247
Analysis:	*per cent*	*per cent*
CO_2, H_2S, etc.............................	7.1	6.2
CO...	5.4	16.0
O_2..	1.3	0.6
H_2..	16.0	16.1
N_2..	9.3	48.1
C_nH_m.....................................	8.6	
C_nH_{2n+2}.................................	52.4	13.0

seen that the amount of saturated and unsaturated higher hydrocarbons has been greatly reduced by the treatment.

Peat and Lignite. The Fuel Research Board (106) conducted a series of experiments on the winning of peat by carbonization in standard vertical retorts with the introduction of about 6 per cent steam. This work was carried on at moderate temperatures of about 900°C. in the heating flues, which for these retorts approximated low temperature conditions within the charge. The sample of peat tested had an ultimate analysis approximating that shown in Table 2, but it had been air-dried to a moisture content of about 20.0 per cent. The volatile matter present amounted to 49.5 per cent, with 26.8 per cent fixed carbon and 3.4 per cent ash. As charged, the peat had a heating value of about 7,675 B.t.u. per pound. The yield of products shown in Table 27 was obtained. The peat gas was very dense, owing to its high carbon dioxide content, but, despite this, it burned with a satisfactory flame of slight luminosity. It was difficult to scrub light oil from this gas, because of the large amount of carbon dioxide present.

Trenkler (107) has reported some tests by Müller on the coking of German brown coals at or below 500°C., which are reproduced in

TABLE 27

Yield of products and composition of gas obtained in carbonization of peat

CONSTITUENT	TEMPERATURE	
	980°C.	848°C.
Yield per gross ton:		
Gallons dry tar	14.7	25.6
Pounds char	592	594
Pounds ammonium sulphate	29.2	24.8
Cubic feet gas	14,900	13,760
Gas analysis:	*per cent*	*per cent*
CO_2	17.3	14.7
CO	22.0	22.0
H_2	29.5	23.8
O_2	1.0	1.0
C_nH_m	10.9	18.1
N_2	19.2	20.2
B.t.u. per cubic foot	296	310
Specific gravity (air = 1)	0.746	0.757

Table 28 to give some idea of the results to be expected from treatment of this class of fuel. A further consideration of brown coals will be given under the name of certain processes particularly designed for this purpose.

Benson and Canfield (108) investigated the possibility of winning Newcastle lignite, from the State of Washington, by low temperature distillation. This material, although of sufficient size for fuel, is generally considered too dirty to be worked. It contains about 12 per cent moisture, 37 per cent volatile matter, 41 per cent fixed

carbon, 10 per cent ash, 1.4 per cent nitrogen, and 0.34 per cent
sulphur. It has a calorific value of about 10,400 B.t.u. per pound.
The yield and composition of gas obtained from this lignite when
distilled at various temperatures is shown in Table 29. The decomposition of the lignite became marked between 300°C. and 400°C.,
as indicated by a large increase in the production of gas as well as by
an increase in the proportion of hydrogen present within this temper-
nature range.

The American lignites differ greatly from German brown coals, in
that it is impossible to form a stable and satisfactory briquet from

TABLE 28

Products yielded in carbonization of brown coal

CONSTITUENT	BROWN COAL		
	Stier	Hessian	Hessian
	per cent	per cent	per cent
Coal analysis:			
Moisture	27.7	61.8	49.5
Fixed carbon	38.5	17.7	29.5
Volatile matter	33.9	20.6	21.0
Ash	7.9	4.5	15.4
B.t.u. per pound	7,600	4,100	3,900
Yield per net ton:			
Pounds char	904	408	900
Pounds tar	90	150	48
Cubic feet gas	2,520	6,040	3,690
B.t.u. per cubic foot	372	441	387

them by the simple procedure of drying and pressing into shape under
heat and pressure. The reason for this is that the former contain
insufficient binder to consolidate and waterproof the mass. On the
other hand, lignite char, when briquetted, forms quite a satisfactory
fuel and, if by-products can be recovered from its carbonization,
the cost of its production may be materially lessened. Further
results of experience in the carbonization of lignite and other low
grade fuels will be given in connection with the discussion of the
various processes with which experiments have been conducted and
reported.

Shale. The distillation of oil shale has been carried on for many years in Scotland and in France, but the two industries are of independent origin.   James Young, according to Redwood (109), while engaged in oil refining seems to have conceived the idea that oil originated from coal by distillation, due to subterranean heat. Young (110) tested a number of low grade fuels, which resulted in the patent on his first oil shale retort.   Since that time, the industry has become well established in Scotland, although the financial status of the many companies engaged in this enterprise did not generally become satisfactory until 1900.   In 1919, however, changing economic conditions practically caused a shut-down of the Scottish shale oil plants, but some recovery has since taken place.

TABLE 29

Composition and yield of gas from lignite distillation

CONSTITUENT	TEMPERATURE			
	300°C.	400°C.	500°C.	600°C.
Cubic feet per net ton................	2,070	4,850	6,910	8,310
Analysis:	per cent	per cent	per cent	per cent
CO_2.................................	33.2	18.9	16.4	12.6
CO.................................	8.3	11.8	14.5	16.8
H_2.................................	0.9	9.8	13.0	15.9
CH_4.................................	10.7	21.2	18.4	17.2
O_2.................................	0.8	0.4	0.4	0.4
N_2.................................	42.7	32.3	32.2	31.8
Illuminants.......................	3.8	5.0	5.1	5.3

Naturally, the yield and composition of shale gas depends upon the composition of the shale and the conditions of retorting.   Gas is evolved long before the first indications of oil appear and it continues for a long time after the eduction of oil ceases.   However, the evolution of gas drops off rapidly after oil is no longer produced. According to Mills (111), Scotch shales have an average ultimate analysis of 25.3 per cent carbon, 3.7 per cent hydrogen, 5.7 per cent oxygen, 1.1 per cent nitrogen, 0.5 per cent sulphur, and 63.8 per cent ash.   Most American oil shales contain from 2 per cent to 4 per cent sulphur and the gas contains from 1.5 per cent to 6.0 per cent hydrogen sulphide, the greater part of which is evolved in the early stages of distillation.   Garvin (112) has reported the composition of shale gas from Scottish and American practice. The gases in Table 30 from the Colorado and Utah shales were obtained under conditions of dry distillation, whereas that from the Scottish shale was obtained

TABLE 30

Composition of gas from Scottish and American shales

CONSTITUENT	SHALE		
	Colorado	Utah	Scotch
Cubic feet per net ton..................	1,120	1,219	9,800
B.t.u. per cubic foot..................	1,079	765	303
Analysis:	*per cent*	*per cent*	*per cent*
CO_2...............................	13.8	11.0	20.0
CO.................................	4.4	3.9	4.3
H_2...............................	30.2	47.5	34.2
CH_4, C_2H_6, etc.....................	42.0	34.5	10.8
C_nH_{2n}..............................	11.6	3.1	3.1
O_2...............................	0.0	0.0	5.1
N_2...............................	0.0	0.0	22.6

TABLE 31

Effect of oxidation on analyses of oil shale gas

CONSTITUENT	RAW	OXIDIZED
Yield:		
Gallons oil per net ton....................	70.6	31.9
Cubic feet gas per net ton.................	1,660	1,800
Gas analysis:	*per cent*	*per cent*
CO_2................................	18.2	37.9
CO.................................	5.3	7.8
H_2................................	34.8	22.1
CH_4................................	13.5	17.9
C_2H_6...............................	13.7	7.4
N_2................................		0.2
H_2S................................	4.9	4.1
Illuminants...........................	9.6	2.6

from steaming the retorts. It will be observed later that the admission of steam during carbonization introduces several desirable complications into the process, among which is a partial formation of water gas, thereby accounting for the production of a large quantity of low thermal value gas.

Finley and Bauer (113), in distilling some American oil shales at 1000°F., found considerable effect in the analysis of the gas caused by oxidation of the shale before carbonization. It will be seen in Table 31 that preoxidation reduced the oil output 55 per cent, increased the amount of carbon dioxide in the gas 120 per cent, and decreased the amount of hydrogen 37 per cent, as well as causing an increase in the proportion of methane and a decrease in the proportion of ethane and illuminants.

Time Effect. In any industrial process, the time required for the necessary operations is of primary importance. The overhead

TABLE 32

Effect of distillation period on gas yielded by Pennsylvania coal at 350°C.

CONSTITUENT	1 HOUR	24 HOURS	54 HOURS	96 HOURS	168 HOURS	240 HOURS
Cubic feet gas per gross ton...	43	280	407	494	594	679
Composition:	*cubic feet per ton*	*cubic feet per ton*	*cubic feet per ton*	*cubic feet per ton*	*cubic feet per ton*	*cubic feet per ton*
CO_2................................	25.2	35.9	35.9	41.2	37.7	44.9
CO................................		9.0	12.6	14.3	19.8	28.8
H_2................................		16.2	27.0	34.2	45.0	52.1
H_2S................................	3.6	25.2	28.8	32.2	32.3	37.7
Saturated hydrocarbons.....		165.2	257.2	320.0	392.0	424.0
Unsaturated hydrocarbons..		16.2	45.0	52.1	66.5	68.3

charges demand the maximum output per unit of investment and this can be attained only through reduction of the time interval between raw material and finished product. In their work on the volatile products of coal carbonization, Taylor and Porter (98) made some important observations on the yield and composition of low temperature gas, as a function of the time of distillation. Table 32, Table 33, Fig. 13, and Fig. 14 have been compiled and plotted from their data, converted for convenience to units per gross ton of coal.

Table 32 admirably illustrates what a large part of the gas is composed of saturated hydrocarbons, as compared with the other constituents. The yields of the oxides of carbon, of hydrogen, and of hydrogen sulphide are not greatly increased beyond 25 hours of carbonization at 350°C. with Pennsylvania coal. The unsaturated hydrocarbons increase but little beyond the 50 hour period, but the saturated compounds continue to be evolved in large quantities, although at a constantly decreasing rate, even to beyond ten days.

The results with Wyoming coal are shown in Fig. 13. Contrasted with the harder Pennsylvania coal, we find that carbon dioxide has moved from one of the minor to the chief constituent of the gas, and that carbon monoxide, too, has become a major constituent. With Wyoming coal, heated at 350°C., over a long period, the amount of

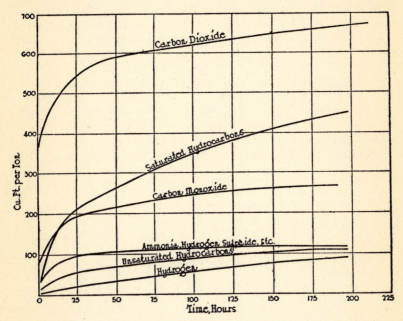

FIG. 13. COMPOSITION OF GAS FROM WYOMING COAL AS A FUNCTION OF TIME

ammonia, hydrogen sulphide, and unsaturated hydrocarbons evolved increases only slightly beyond 25 hours of retorting. Hydrogen has a steady increase, but even after ten days remains the smallest proportion of the gas.

Even after prolonged heating of 240 hours at 350°C., the entire volatile matter of coal is not removed. Subsequent treatment of the residuum at higher temperatures will yield further and even more voluminous products. The residuum from Pennsylvania coal, discussed in Table 32, was submitted to such an experiment and the composition of the gas is indicated in Table 33. By comparison of the two tables, it is seen that the yield of hydrogen becomes second in importance when the coke is subsequently heated at 450°C., after preliminary carbonization at 350°C. The saturated hydrocarbons are still the major components of the gas, while the other constituents remain of minor importance as before.

Fig. 14 shows the total gas evolved from Pennsylvania and Wyoming coals and from the residuum of Pennsylvania coal, previously heated for 240 hours at 350°C. It will be seen that almost 500 per cent more gas is evolved from the coal residuum than from the original coal, when the temperature is advanced but 100°C.

TABLE 33

Residual gas evolved from 350°C. Pennsylvania coke at 450°C.

CONSTITUENT	1 HOUR	10 HOURS	20 HOURS	40 HOURS	60 HOURS	100 HOURS	180 HOURS
Cubic feet gas per gross ton..........	316	1,550	1,830	2,090	2,230	2,410	2,630
Composition:	*cubic feet per ton*	*cubic feet per ton*	*cubic feet per ton*	*cubic feet per ton*	*cubic feet per ton*	*cubic feet per ton*	*cubic feet per ton*
CO_2.................	9.0	34.2	39.6	46.7	48.5	50.4	57.6
CO.................	9.0	62.9	72.0	77.3	90.0	107.9	113.3
H_2.................	35.9	368.8	489.1	602.8	674.5	784.0	899.5
H_2S.................	32.4	72.0	107.9	115.0	115.0	116.8	118.6
Saturated hydrocarbons......	215.8	935.0	1,043.0	1,150.0	1,205.0	1,259.0	1,341.0
Unsaturated hydrocarbons......	9.0	58.7	61.1	61.1	62.9	62.9	64.7

During the first few hours after charging, in coke ovens operating at 1000°C., the gas evolved approximates the composition of low temperature gas. The layers of coal a short distance from the retort wall do not reach the higher temperatures until the lapse of considerable time. The illustration in Fig. 15 shows the change in composition of the gas from an Otto coke oven, operating at 1000°C., as a function of the time after charging (89).

Examination of Fig. 15 makes it evident that, during the first two or three hours after charging, the gas has all the characteristics of the low temperature product, that is, high calorific value, exceeding 800 B.t.u. per cubic foot; high percentage of saturated hydrocarbons,

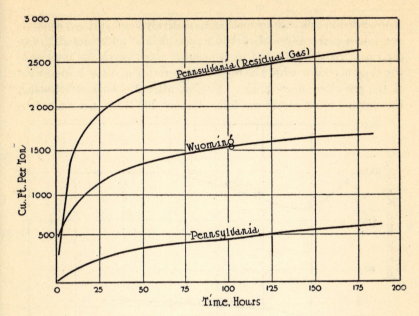

FIG. 14. TOTAL YIELD OF GAS FROM PENNSYLVANIA AND WYOMING COALS AS A FUNCTION OF TIME

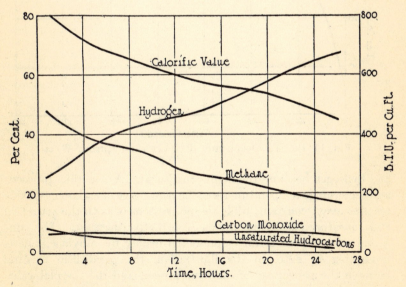

FIG. 15. COMPOSITION OF COKE OVEN GAS AS A FUNCTION OF TIME

represented in this case by methane; relatively low hydrogen content; and minor percentages of carbon monoxide and unsaturated hydrocarbons. As the period of carbonization is extended, the interior of the mass of coal reaches the higher temperature and the composition of the gas alters accordingly. Finally, after 20 hours of retorting, the thermal value of the gas falls to about 400 B.t.u. per cubic foot

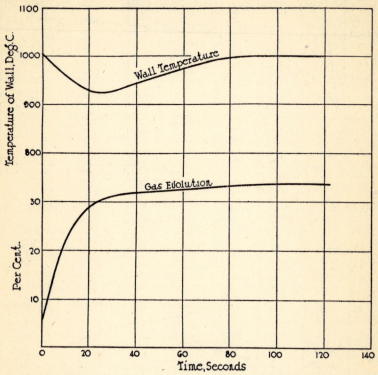

FIG. 16. INITIAL ABSORPTION OF HEAT FROM RETORT WALL

and hydrogen becomes the main constituent. As the time proceeds and the average temperature rises, the percentage of carbon monoxide remains about constant, while the proportions of both the saturated and unsaturated hydrocarbons constantly decrease. The unsaturated compounds are represented mainly by ethylene. It is interesting to note, in the illustration, the parallelism existing between the percentage of methane present and the thermal value of the gas. This is easily understood when it is recalled that the calorific value of methane at constant pressure is 1072 B.t.u. per cubic foot, while that of hydrogen is but 347 B.t.u. per cubic foot, so that the resultant heat value of the gas is largely dependent on the percentage of saturated hydrocarbons present.

No data are available on the initial gas evolution and the temperature adjustments when raw coal is introduced to a heated retort, but Taylor and Porter (98) have made experiments on small quanti-

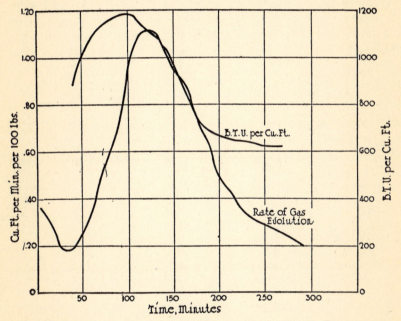

FIG. 17. RATE OF GAS EVOLUTION AND CALORIFIC VALUE AS A FUNCTION OF TIME

ties of Pennsylvania coal plunged into a tube heated to 1000°C. The curves in Fig. 16 show how the coal absorbs heat from the walls of the retort with a corresponding reduction in their temperature. As the charge absorbs heat, the wall temperature falls until at the end of about 30 seconds the layer of coal next to the wall has reached the equilibrium temperature, then the whole mass gradually absorbs heat and rises in temperature. Over 30 per cent of the volatile matter was evolved during the first 30 seconds of heating and thereafter the increase in gaseous evolution was comparatively slow.

The Fuel Research Board (114) has investigated the effect of the
time element in the low temperature carbonization of five British
coals in horizontal retorts. These experiments were conducted on a
large scale at 600°C. The average results are represented graphically
in Fig. 17. The initial evolution of gas during the first 40 minutes,
as shown in the illustration, consisted mostly of carbon dioxide and
some air expansion. After reaching a minimum, the rate of gas
evolution attained a maximum after about 2 hours of retorting.
At this point, the charge yielded gas at the rate of over 1.1 cubic
feet per minute per hundred pounds of coal. Thereafter, the rate of
evolution gradually fell to less than 0.20 cubic foot per minute per
hundred pounds after 5 hours of carbonization. The calorific value

TABLE 34

Products of vacuum distillation of United States coals at 600°C.

CONSTITUENT	PENNSYL- VANIA COAL	WEST VIRGINIA COAL	ILLINOIS COAL	WYOMING COAL
Cubic feet gas per gross ton	4,240	4,980	5,650	6,440
Analysis:	*per cent*	*per cent*	*per cent*	*per cent*
CO_2.................................	2.3	3.2	5.6	17.5
CO.................................	6.4	4.4	12.0	16.3
H_2.................................	44.7	46.8	44.9	38.3
NH_3, H_2S, etc......................	2.9	1.2	1.8	3.0
C_nH_{2n+2}.............................	40.4	41.2	33.5	23.1
Unsaturated hydrocarbons..........	3.3	3.3	2.3	2.0

of the gas had a rapid rise to a maximum of 1200 B.t.u. per cubic
foot slightly before the rate of evolution reached its highest point.
It then fell rapidly and flattened out, after 3 hours, at a thermal value
above 600 B.t.u. per cubic foot.

Taylor and Porter (98) found that the rapidity with which the coal
is heated has little effect upon the composition of the gaseous
products, when the gas evolved is immediately removed from the
carbonization chamber. When Pennsylvania coal was carbonized
at a maximum temperature of 1050°C. over a period of 270 minutes
and compared with another sample brought to the same temperature
in 6.5 minutes, it was found that the only appreciable change in the
composition of the gas was a slight increase in the percentage of

hydrocarbons present and a corresponding decrease in the proportion of hydrogen. Thus, in the first case, the hydrocarbons made up 21.3 per cent and the hydrogen 69.1 per cent of the gas, while, in the second case, they composed 26.7 per cent and 63.1 per cent, respectively. The other components of the gas remained practically unchanged in their proportions.

Vacuum Effect. The destructive distillation of United States coals *in vacuo* at temperatures ranging from 250°C. to about 1000°C., has also been investigated by Taylor and Porter (98). Due to the different periods of carbonization which they selected, no comparative data can be drawn, except for two temperatures, but these will serve to show the effect of vacuum distillation at both high and low

TABLE 35

Products of vacuum distillation of United States coals at 1050°C.

CONSTITUENT	PENNSYLVANIA COAL	WEST VIRGINIA COAL	ILLINOIS COAL	WYOMING COAL
Cubic feet gas per gross ton	10,000	12,920	10,980	11,000
Analysis:	*per cent*	*per cent*	*per cent*	*per cent*
CO_2...............................	1.5	1.4	3.3	9.7
CO................................	5.0	3.5	9.8	17.5
H_2................................	70.1	76.6	67.3	58.5
NH_3, H_2S, etc....................	1.5	0.4	0.9	0.6
C_nH_{2n+2}..........................	20.1	17.1	17.1	12.2
Unsaturated hydrocarbons..........	1.9	1.2	1.7	1.5

temperatures. The duration of carbonization was 6 hours at 600°C. and one hour at 1050°C. We have already seen in Table 24 and in Table 25 the effect of vacuum distillation on two British coals at somewhat lower temperatures.

Table 34 affords another excellent example of the effect of the consolidation of the coal on the quality of the gas yielded, as pointed out in Table 21. Like the Welsh coals, vacuum distillation of United States coals increases the hydrogen content of the gas evolved and decreases the percentage of hydrocarbons.

A critical comparison of Table 34 and Table 35 shows that increasing the temperature of distillation *in vacuo* of American coals from 600°C. to 1050°C. almost doubles the amount of hydrogen present in the gas and approximately decreases by half the proportion of saturated hydrocarbons present. Very little change in the amount of unsaturated hydrocarbons and oxides of carbon was observed.

Secondary Decomposition. We have seen that the fundamental purpose of low temperature carbonization is to obtain primary decomposition products from coal and its related solid fuels. Superimposed upon this task is the equally difficult problem of preventing secondary decomposition of the volatile products after they have been educed from the charge, thus entirely defeating the purpose for which this special branch of destructive distillation was designed. If, after liberation, the volatile matter is allowed to become superheated

TABLE 36

Secondary reactions induced by superheating low temperature gas

CONSTITUENT	NORMAL GAS AT 450°C.	SUPERHEATED TO 750°C.	SUPERHEATED TO 800°C.
	per cent	*per cent*	*per cent*
Volume increase......................	0.0	8.6	13.9
Analysis:			
CO_2..............................	11.5	10.6	10.2
CO.................................	8.4	7.9	8.4
H_2...............................	11.9	11.0	15.5
N_2...............................	1.7	2.1	1.5
C_nH_{2n+2}......................	58.1	56.7	50.3
NH_3, H_2S, etc......................	1.8	1.0	0.7
Unsaturated hydrocarbons..........	6.6	10.6	13.5

or to come in contact with incandescent surfaces, secondary reactions set in and the composition of the products is changed accordingly. In continuing their research, Taylor and Porter (98), made an investigation of this phenomenon. Table 36 gives some quantitative results obtained by superheating low temperature gas secured from the carbonization of Illinois coal at 450°C.

Superheating tends to crack the heavier saturated hydrocarbons, with the formation of hydrogen and unsaturated compounds. Similar observations were made on Pennsylvania coal gas obtained at 475°C., except that the area of heated surface to which the gas was exposed was considerably altered. In the first case, the heated area was reduced in size and increased in temperature by passing the gas over a glowing wire and, in the second case, the area was increased by the presence of a column of broken firebrick. The catalytic effect of even small incandescent surfaces is really interesting. In Table 37 we see that the saturated hydrocarbons have been dehydrogenated, as evidenced by the decrease of the percentage

TABLE 37

Secondary reactions induced by highly heated surfaces

CONSTITUENT	NORMAL GAS AT 450°C.	AFTER PASSING OVER GLOWING WIRE
Cubic feet gas per gross ton	1,260	2,560
Analysis:	per cent	per cent
CO_2..	4.4	3.0
CO..	3.9	4.9
H_2..	6.9	18.1
C_nH_{2n+2}....................................	72.3	51.4
NH_3, H_2S, etc..............................	5.8	3.8
Unsaturated hydrocarbons.................	6.8	18.9

TABLE 38

Catalytic effect of brick column on secondary reactions of gas

CONSTITUENT	NORMAL GAS AT 475°C.	SUPERHEATED TO 550°C.	SUPERHEATED TO 650°C.
Cubic feet gas per gross ton	1,410	1,490	2,650
Analysis:	per cent	per cent	per cent
CO_2................................	5.0	4.3	3.3
CO................................	4.5	2.9	4.3
H_2................................	5.3	6.4	13.1
C_nH_{2n+2}.............................	73.0	73.0	62.0
NH_3, H_2S, etc.......................	4.7	3.9	2.8
Unsaturated hydrocarbons..........	7.6	9.2	14.5

of saturated compounds present and by an increase of almost 300 per cent in the proportions of hydrogen and unsaturated hydrocarbons.

Table 38 shows that the temperature at which cracking manifests itself, in the case of Pennsylvania coal, is fully 150°C. lower than in the case of Illinois coal, discussed in Table 36. It is unlikely that this difference in cracking temperature arises from the nature of the coal carbonized, but it is probably the result of the increased catalytic surface presented by the brick column. This investigation was extended to the case of reduced pressure, both with and without the presence of broken brick. It was found that, with a pressure below 4 cm. of mercury, the cracking temperature rose from 650°C. to about 800°C. in both cases, the only effect of the brick column being to increase the total volume of gas and the percentage of hydrogen.

Gaseous Atmospheres. The effect of various atmospheres on the modification of Illinois coal by low temperature distillation has been investigated by Parr and Francis (30). They carbonized coal in atmospheres of oxygen, nitrogen, and steam, and studied the character

TABLE 39

Composition of gas evolved under atmosphere of nitrogen

CONSTITUENT	TEMPERATURE		
	340°C.	370°C.	380°C.
Cubic feet gas per gross ton	306	394	392
Analysis:	*per cent*	*per cent*	*per cent*
CO_2...............................	50.3	24.8	20.8
CO................................	19.3	11.0	11.6
CH_4...............................	5.8	46.7	46.5
H_2................................	4.6	3.5	3.5
Illuminants.........................	20.0	13.6	17.4

of the coke and gas under these conditions. Table 39 shows the result when Illinois coal was coked at various temperatures in an atmosphere of nitrogen. This table, as well as Table 40, has been computed to a nitrogen and oxygen-free basis. As may be expected, less carbon dioxide and more hydrogen was present in this case, than when an atmosphere of oxygen was used, as indicated by Table 40. The greatest effect on the composition of the gas evolved under nitrogenous atmospheres seems to be in the illuminants. The proportion of these heavy hydrocarbons was greatly increased, as may be seen by comparing Table 39 with Fig. 11.

Table 40 shows the effect of carbonizing Illinois coal for 4 hours in an atmosphere of oxygen. The most important point to be noted here is the high percentage of carbon dioxide present which, coupled with the fact that temperature variations occured which were wholly independent of the external heating, is positive evidence that oxidation of the charge has taken place. This should be compared with Fig. 11, where it is seen that, in ordinary atmospheres, the percentage carbon dioxide in the gas normally decreases with the temperature rise. No hydrogen was evolved up to 380°C.

Steaming. It has been pointed out that superheating the primary gaseous products introduces secondary reactions and that large moderately heated surfaces, as well as small incandescent surfaces, catalyze the cracking of the saturated hydrocarbons. The primary object of steam distillation in the carbonization of coal is to remove

TABLE 40

Composition of gas evolved under atmosphere of oxygen

CONSTITUENT	TEMPERATURE		
	280°C.	350°C.	380°C.
Cubic feet gas per gross ton..........	26	160	313
Analysis:	*per cent*	*per cent*	*per cent*
CO_2................................	34.6	49.0	36.4
CO................................	16.3	15.6	13.5
CH_4................................	46.1	29.0	40.0
Illuminants.........................	0.0	5.8	10.1

quickly the volatile products, so as to prevent their coming in contact with the hot retort walls. By suitably regulating the flow of fresh steam, the gases and vapors can be swept clear of the retort and the cracking effect largely reduced. Of secondary importance, and sometime of undesirable consequence, is the reaction between the steam and coal which tends to increase the gas evolved at the expense of the coke yield. The physical chemistry, determining the extent to which this action occurs, will be discussed later.

In low temperature carbonization, only a small amount of decomposition takes place when steam is introduced into the retorts and, if any reaction with the charge does occur, the dioxide, rather than the monoxide of carbon, is more likely to be formed. This will cause a decrease, rather than an increase, in the total calorific value of the gas. Therefore, any value that steaming may be found to have in low temperature methods must be of a physical rather than of a chemical nature. Thus, the steam absorbs heat in the hot bed near the bottom of the retort and distributes it through the cooler portions of the fuel bed near the top, thereby assisting in the transfer of heat throughout the charge. This function has been adequately illustrated in Fig. 9.

The Fuel Research Board (115), as a result of their experiments on the steaming of coal during coking, recommend that high temperature vertical retorts should never be used with less than 5 per cent of steam. This was found to increase greatly the heating quality of the

TABLE 41

Effect of steam distillation on high temperature gas

CONSTITUENT	5 PER CENT STEAM	10 PER CENT STEAM	15 PER CENT STEAM	20 PER CENT STEAM
Duration: hours......................	144	120	168	72
Cubic feet gas per gross ton	15,690	16,980	18,950	19,980
B.t.u. per cubic foot.................	503	492	469	457
Analysis:	*per cent*	*per cent*	*per cent*	*per cent*
CO_2................................	2.0	3.4	4.2	5.4
CO...................................	11.1	13.9	16.2	16.5
CH_4................................	25.3	22.0	19.4	18.7
C_nH_m..............................	2.0	2.1	1.9	1.9
H_2.................................	51.1	52.4	51.7	50.4
O_2.................................	0.7	0.6	0.4	0.2
N_2.................................	7.9	5.4	6.3	6.9

gas and the yield of ammonia. Steaming has not proved practical in horizontal retorts in experiments so far conducted. The effect of various percentages of steam on high temperature gas, as determined by the Fuel Research Board using Arley coal, is shown in Table 41. The carbonization was carried on at 1170°C.

As the percentage of steam increases, the volume of gas becomes greater and the thermal value decreases. It will be shown later that, in this case, the temperature is too great to favor the formation of carbon dioxide in the presence of steam, but that there should be an increase in the carbon monoxide present. That this is the case, may be seen by reference to the table. The percentage of methane slightly decreases and, doubtlessly, this in part accounts for the lower heating value of the gas. Carbon monoxide has a calorific value of only 341 B.t.u. per cubic foot as compared with 1072 B.t.u. per cubic foot for methane, so that the increase in the percentage of monoxide cannot be expected to compensate, from a calorific standpoint, for the decrease in the proportion of methane. The other constituents of the gas are not greatly influenced by the presence of steam.

Investigations, on a laboratory scale, of the effect of steam in low temperature carbonization were made by Davis and Parry (97), who

TABLE 42

Steam distillation of Pennsylvania coal at low temperatures

CONSTITUENT	WITHOUT STEAM		WITH STEAM		
	Temperature				
	550°C.	650°C.	475°C.	550°C.	650°C.
Cubic feet gas per net ton.......	3,400	7,200	1,500	4,100	7,200
B.t.u. per cubic foot.............	684	681		640	
Analysis:	*per cent*	*per cent*	*per cent*	*per cent*	*per cent*
CO_2...........................	2.2	2.7	3.7	4.1	5.6
CO.............................	4.1	5.5	3.4	4.3	7.2
H_2.............................	28.1	47.2	12.5	29.1	51.8
O_2.............................	0.8	0.3	2.6	1.4	0.7
CH_4...........................	47.1	33.7	38.7	44.2	24.0
C_nH_m.........................	10.1	8.3	22.4	8.7	8.6
N_2.............................	7.6	2.3	16.7	8.2	2.1

studied Pennsylvania coal. In the large-scale experiments of the Fuel Research Board, shown in Table 43, only up to 20 per cent steam was admitted, while in this case up to 88 per cent steam was passed through the retort to sweep the chamber clean of gas five to seven times a minute. While the greatest possible effect would be obtained by agitating the coke, stirring of the charge was avoided in order not to introduce another variable and nullify the comparative value of the data. There are so many variables in low temperature carbonization that it is best to reduce these to a minimum for simplicity of interpretation.

The effect of steam in this case is plainly evident. Comparing the distillation with and without steam at corresponding temperatures, it will be observed that the percentage of carbon dioxide just about doubles in the presence of steam, while the carbon monoxide is only slightly increased at 650°C. and remains practically unchanged at 550°C. This, together with the increase of hydrogen content, is indicative of the following reactions:

$$H_2O + C \rightleftharpoons CO + H_2 \qquad [12]$$
$$2H_2O + C \rightarrow CO_2 + 2H_2 \qquad [13]$$

The data in Table 42 show that the first reaction, represented by the foregoing chemical equation, is hardly apparent at all at 550°C.,

TABLE 43

Effect of steam distillation on low temperature gas

CONSTITUENT	0.0 PER CENT STEAM	7.3 PER CENT STEAM	13.5 PER CENT STEAM	20.0 PER CENT STEAM
Cubic feet gas per gross ton..........	7,190	6,700	7,350	7,750
B.t.u. per cubic foot.................	585	602	594	573
Analysis:	*per cent*	*per cent*	*per cent*	*per cent*
CO_2.................................	4.9	5.6	5.6	7.2
CO....................................	11.2	8.5	9.7	10.0
H_2.................................	32.2	35.5	37.6	38.0
O_2.................................	0.2	0.2	0.2	0.2
C_nH_m.............................	4.7	5.0	4.8	4.5
C_nH_{2n+2}.........................	33.0	33.4	33.0	32.5
N_2.................................	13.8	11.8	9.1	7.6

but takes place to a minor extent at 650°C. On the other hand, the second reaction occurs to a considerable degree even below 500°C.

The experiments of the Fuel Research Board (92) on the effect of steam in low temperature carbonization were carried on in Glover-West vertical retorts, using a blend of 60 per cent Mitchell Main, a coking coal, and 40 per cent Ellistown Main, a non-coking coal. The temperature of distillation ranged from 850°C., at the bottom of the retort, to 700°C. at the top. Examination of Table 43 discloses that the introduction of steam has little effect on the percentage of carbon monoxide, but that there is a slight increase in the proportions of carbon dioxide and hydrogen. It may be concluded, therefore, that there was a slight reaction between the steam and coal and that this took place in accordance with the principles deduced and in agreement with the data derived from the work of Davis and Parry.

It cannot be concluded that steam has any effect on the remaining components of the gas, but it will be observed later that, under certain conditions and in certain processes, the introduction of steam during carbonization has a beneficial effect on the removal of sulphur from the coke.

Physico-chemical Equilibrium. From the standpoint of physical chemistry, it is necessary to consider four reactions when steam is passed into a hot coal bed. Of these, two are primary reactions, represented by Equation [12] and Equation [13], previously mentioned, and two are secondary reactions, indicated as follows:

$$C + CO_2 \rightleftarrows 2CO \qquad [14]$$

$$H_2O + CO \rightarrow H_2 + CO_2 \qquad [15]$$

With reference to Equation [15], we have by the law of mass action,

$$\frac{(H_2O) \times (CO)}{(H_2) \times (CO_2)} = K \qquad [16]$$

In other words, the product of the concentrations of the reagents divided by the product of the concentrations of the products is a constant at any given temperature, regardless of the proportion of the components present at the beginning of the reaction. The constant, K, however, is a function of the temperature, as expressed by Van't Hoff's equation:

$$\frac{d \log_e K}{d T} = \frac{Q}{RT^2} \qquad [17]$$

where T is the absolute temperature; Q, the heat evolved in the reaction, and R, the universal gas constant (1.985 calories per degree). The integral,

$$\log_e K = \int \frac{Q \, dT}{RT^2} \qquad [18]$$

cannot be solved directly because, Q, is a function of, T, and this relationship must be established by experiment. Such experiments have been performed and it has been determined that the constant has the following values, according to Landolt-Börnstein (116):

Temperature................686°C.   886°C.   1005°C.   1205°C.

K.......................... 0.534   1.197   1.620   2.600

Equation [15] is a first order reaction and, in such a case, the rate of formation of the product is proportional to its own concentration and to a coefficient known as the specific reaction rate, that is,

$$\frac{d\,(CO)}{dt} = k_1\,(CO) \qquad [19]$$

As the equilibrium is a dynamic one, the reverse reaction must be considered also:

$$\frac{d\,(CO_2)}{dt} = k_2\,(CO_2) \qquad [20]$$

This, too, is a first order reaction, because in the carbonization of coal, sufficient hydrogen is liberated to cause no appreciable decrease in its concentration.   The resultant rate at which the monoxide is formed, therefore, is the difference between these two equations:

$$\left[\frac{d\,(CO)}{dt}\right]_r = \frac{d\,(CO)}{dt} - \frac{d\,(CO_2)}{dt} = k_1\,(CO) - k_2\,(CO_2) \qquad [21]$$

Now the equilibrium constant, K, is equal to the ratio of the specific reaction rates of the direct and reverse reactions, $K = k_1/k_2$, from which it will be seen that, if the value of the equilibrium constant is greater than unity, the rate of formation of the monoxide, in accordance with Equation [15] is positive and, if $K < 1$, then the rate of formation is negative.   In other words, it becomes possible at any temperature to determine the extent to which the reaction occurs. In the simultaneous occurrence of reactions [12] to [15], therefore, it may be determined, with sufficient data available, which reaction predominates.   At any given temperature, it depends merely upon the rate at which equilibrium is established.

At temperatures below 700°C., reactions [13] and [15] predominate, so that the steam reacts with the coal to produce the dioxide and any monoxide that is formed is oxidized to the higher compound.   The reaction velocity of Equation [14] is slow in any case, so that its effect is negligible.   Above 700°C. reaction [15] is very rapid, while beyond 1000°C. reaction [12] becomes of first importance.   These theoretical deductions are substantiated by the data given in Table 41 and in Table 42.

CHAPTER III

Low Temperature Coal Tar

Eduction of Primary Tar. Designation of the condensible products from low temperature carbonization, taken collectively, as a tar is most unfortunate, for they more nearly resemble oils or petroleums than they do tars. Since it has become well established by prior usage, the name tar will be retained in this volume and the term primary tar will be used synonymously with low temperature oil. This confusion in terminology has caused a great deal of misunderstanding and may persons have thereby been led to evaluate low temperature crude oil in terms of high temperature coal tar, to which it bears very little relation.

Like any industry in the early stages of its development, the products of low temperature carbonization have had no established market in the past. This applies in particular to the primary oil. The chief assured industrial uses of low temperature tar, at present, is as a crude stock for the preparation of creosote oil and as a liquid fuel. While the valuable by-products, which may be obtained by fractionation of the tar will doubtlessly find industrial favor eventually, no such outlets can at this time (1928) be guaranteed. There are but few plants operating on a large scale, and, consequently, no standard method of industrial analysis has been developed, despite the quality and quantity of work that has been done in the study of low temperature tar by numerous investigators. For the most part, these workers were interested more from the chemical than from the engineering standpoint and, therefore, planned their investigations more from the standpoint of science than of technology.

The attitude of the tar distillers, in regard to low temperature tar at the present time (1928), appears to be that its refinement will require extensive alterations in their plants, due to the manner in which primary tar differs from the high temperature tar, which they are accustomed to handle. The absence of regularly operating large scale low temperature carbonization plants of sufficient capacity to assure them of dependable quantities of raw material has thus far rendered the necessary changes impractical. This situation is

73

rapidly being remedied and will be overcome in proportion as sources of raw material increase and as markets for the refined products develop.

According to Parrish (117), whatever coal may be used in the same high temperature coke oven, the resultant tars resemble each other to a great extent. Primary tar, on the other hand, is much more closely allied to the coal from which it originated and variations in the composition and quantity of the tar yielded follow more closely variations in the character of the coal from which it was produced. It will be observed later, that, in general, the younger the coal and the greater its oxygen content, the greater is the quantity of low temperature tar yielded per unit of weight.

The influence of the conditions of carbonization can almost wholly be attributed to the action of heat upon the tar vapors. The effect of these conditions on the low temperature tar has already been alluded to in the definition of low temperature carbonization. Aside from the bearing which the chemical nature of the coal and the conditions of retorting have upon the character of the tar, there remain certain influences, resulting from the physical properties of the coal. If the coal is a readily fusing one, the formation of a plastic layer may so retard the passage of the primary tar vapor from the carbonization chamber as to cause it to remain for a comparatively long time in contact with hot surfaces. The effect of hot surfaces in catalyzing secondary decomposition has already been demonstrated.

Low temperature tars differ materially from high temperature tars. The former are brownish black, fluid at ordinary temperatures, and more viscous than crude Pennsylvania petroleum. In general, the low temperature tars consist of hydrocarbons of the aliphatic series, a few aromatics, and a high proportion of the tar acids. This tar is not greatly different from shale oil and crude petroleum, and for that reason some of the methods used in the petroleum industry may be applied to the evaluation of low temperature tar.

Table 44 gives a representative comparison of the fractions obtained from high and low temperature tars. The high temperature tar yields are the average of six coke oven tars of the United States, while the low temperature yields are the average of eight British experiments at 600°C. In the high temperature product, only about 25 per cent of the tar is volatile up to 315°C., while low temperature tar yields nearly 55 per cent of its weight in oils. High temperature pitch is almost three-quarters of the entire yield of tar and contains a high percentage of free carbon, whereas the primary tar is characterized by less than 50 per cent pitch of a low free carbon content. The decrease in the yield of oils at high temperatures is complementary to the high gas yield. It has been demonstrated that, in this case, the primary volatile products are cracked and decomposed at higher temperatures, with the formation of gas and the deposition of carbon.

TABLE 44

Comparison of fractionation of high and low temperature tars

FRACTION	HIGH TEMPERATURE	LOW TEMPERATURE
	per cent	*per cent*
Up to 170°C...............................	1.1	9.6
170° to 270°C...............................	15.9	32.0
270° to 315°C...............................	8.9	15.3
Pitch..	74.0	43.0
Free carbon in pitch........................	9.3	2.0

TABLE 45

Tar yields of United States coals

TAR	OLDEST ←———— GEOLOGIC AGING ————→ YOUNGEST				
	Virginia coal	Pennsylvania coal	Illinois coal	Wyoming coal	Utah coal
Gallons per gross ton.............	12.4	19.0	20.5	17.7	21.2
Per cent of coal..................	7.2	11.3	11.9	10.3	12.3

Experiments conducted in England, in especially constructed cast-iron retorts, on five high class Barnsley coals, whose proximate analyses were almost identical with that of Pennsylvania bituminous coal, showed that in low temperature carbonization the average yield of tar was 23.5 gallons per net ton of coal. The average of six Pennsylvania coals distilled at 550°C. by Davis and Parry (97) gave 27.8 gallons of dehydrated tar, with a specific gravity of 1.039, per net ton of coal carbonized. This is equivalent to 12.2 per cent of the coal by weight. The Fuel Research Board, in large-scale horizontal retorts, obtained a tar yield of from 17.9 gallons to 19.6

gallons per net ton. They recommend, as a result of their extensive investigations, that 19 gallons of tar per net ton of coal is the average yield to be counted upon in low temperature distillation. The present author, however, believes this figure to be unduly low for other processes and for high volatile American coals. The fuel value of this primary tar is very high, the average of eight British experiments giving 16,360 B.t.u. per pound.

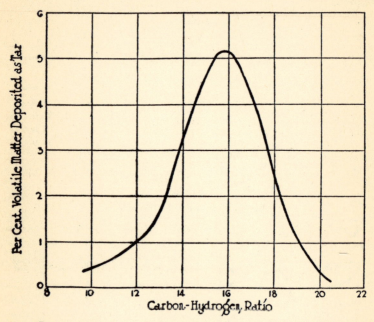

Fig. 18. Volatile Matter Deposited as Tar as a Function of Carbon-Hydrogen Ratio

Porter and Ovitz (96), in their investigation on the volatile matter of coals of the United States, obtained from 12.4 gallons to 21.2 gallons of tar per net ton of coal in small-scale experiments, depending to a great extent on the geologic age of the coal examined. The experiments were conducted over a period of one hour in a furnace adjusted so that the interior of the charge remained at 800°C. Monett (100) observed, from a study of eleven Utah coals, that the tar yield ranged from 16.1 gallons to 29.4 gallons per net ton. It is interesting to note in Table 45 the general decrease in yield of tar accompanying the consolidation of the fuel.

The results of Table 45 have been observed, also, by Berry (118), who found a distinct relation between the amount of tar distilled and the geologic formation of the coal, or more specifically the carbon-hydrogen ratio of the fuel. The curve in Fig. 18 is due to him. According to this curve, the maximum amount of thick tar is to be

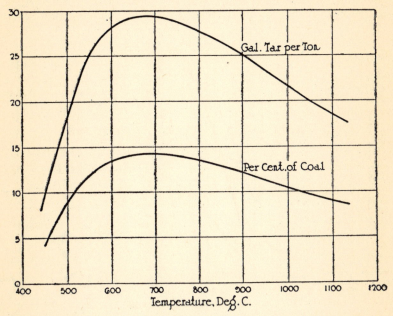

FIG. 19. YIELD OF TAR FROM WELSH COALS AS A FUNCTION OF TEMPERATURE

expected from fuels having a carbon-hydrogen ratio ranging from 13.5 to 18.0.

Berry (118) investigated the tar-forming temperatures of American coals and found that the first traces of tar appeared, in all the coals examined by him, at about 300°C. and the last traces disappeared at about 550°C., although in a few instances tar formation did not cease until over 600°C. was reached. Tar was formed in quantities in the temperature range from 375°C. to 475°C. He found no evident relation between the volatile matter in the coal and the amount of tar evolved. He also concluded that neither geologic age, carbon-hydrogen ratio, nor percentage volatile matter in the coal had any relation to the temperature of tar evolution.

Burgess and Wheeler (57), in examining Welsh coals, found certain variations in the yield of tarry matter when the temperature of carbonization ranged from below 500°C. to above 1000°C. Their data are plotted in Fig. 19, where it is seen that the yield of tar per gross ton of coal rises to a maximum at about 700°C. The experiments of Burgess and Wheeler (57) are not in agreement with the figures given by Lewes (17), whose maximum yield occurred about

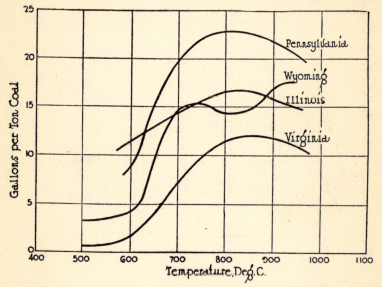

FIG. 20. YIELD OF TAR FROM AMERICAN COALS AS A FUNCTION OF TEMPERATURE

300°C. lower. No information was given by the latter authority regarding the composition of the coal used to secure his data, so that the disagreement cannot be explained. The specific gravity of the tar gradually increases with the temperature increase. This is to be expected, since the lighter hydrocarbons are destroyed through decomposition at the higher temperatures to form fixed gas, leaving the heavier, higher-boiling hydrocarbons and the carbon freed in the cracking.

Porter and Ovitz (96) investigated the tar distilled at various temperatures from several coals of the United States. Their figures, computed from a percentage basis to gallons of tar per net ton, are plotted in Fig. 20. Comparison of this illustration with Fig. 19 will disclose that, qualitatively, the data are in agreement with the results obtained by Burgess and Wheeler (57) on Welsh coals. In Fig. 20 it appears that, from the standpoint of securing maximum tar yield, the optimum temperature of carbonization is in the neighborhood of 800°C., although in commercial plants this figure appears somewhat high. Too much confidence cannot be placed in the quantitative value of these curves for they seem low for high volatile coals.

According to Fischer (119), the solid paraffins in primary tar represent one or two per cent of the tar and in this respect we find one striking difference between the tar obtained from brown coals and that obtained from bituminous coals. Fischer (120) found the tar from Saxon brown coal to contain as much as 29 per cent solid paraffins, while the tar from Rhenish brown coal yielded 13 per cent. In other respects, the two primary tars are quite similar.

Garbe (121) distilled a Shetland peat, containing 21.4 per cent moisture and 73.8 per cent volatile matter, at 500°C. in a Tozer retort and obtained a yield per gross ton of 33.6 per cent peat char; 4,500 cubic feet of 500 B.t.u. per cubic foot gas; 1.44 gallons of 0.7885 specific gravity motor spirit; 23.4 gallons of crude oil; and 16.3 pounds of ammonium sulphate. The peat tar contained 35.2 per cent moisture; 2.2 per cent light oil up to 170°C.; 19.8 per cent medium oil in the fraction 170°C. to 230°C.; and 37.8 per cent residuum above 230°C. The middle oil contained 22 per cent tar acids.

Garvin (112) reports that, on the average, distillation of Scottish shale yields 24.5 gallons of 0.860 specific gravity tar; 9,800 cubic feet of 270 B.t.u. per cubic foot gas; 35.7 pounds of ammonium sulphate; and 1,550 pounds of waste spent shale from each ton of raw material. Oil shales of the United States have tested all the way from less than 7.5 gallons of tar per ton, in the case of a Nevada sample, to over 60 gallons per ton, for a specimen from Colorado. The specific gravity of these tars varies also from 0.881 to 0.924. The average test yield of tar from eleven United States shales from six states was 37.2 gallons per ton.

Time Effect. The time element deserves important consideration in regard to the tar as well as with respect to the gas. If the distillation is slow and the tar vapors are removed slowly, secondary decomposition may occur with a corresponding decrease in the yield of oils and increase in the evolution of gas. But the tar yield is not the only outcome of slow carbonization. The structure of the tar is vastly changed. A tar produced in slow distillation contains a larger proportion of the aromatic derivatives and fewer members of the aliphatic series. The curve of tar yield against time is somewhat similar to that of gas evolution, shown in Fig. 14. We know, of course, from the differential calculus, that the derivative of this curve is the curve of the rate of yield of tar. Inspection of the slope shows that the rate of yield in gallons per minute, as plotted against time, should reach a maximum and then gradually fall off until a

TABLE 46

Comparison of slow and rapid carbonization in yield of tar

HOURS DURATION	ATMOSPHERE	TEMPERATURE	PER CENT	GALLONS TAR PER GROSS TON
		°C.		
5.25	Nitrogen	1,040	9.3	16.0
0.42	Nitrogen	1,040	10.5	18.1
0.33	Nitrogen	1,050	11.7	20.1
5.00	Coal gas	1,010	10.9	18.0
0.50	Coal gas	1,020	12.1	20.7
5.00	Coal gas	950	10.0	17.1
0.50	Coal gas	980	11.9	20.5

point may be reached where it will be uneconomical to prolong the process for the tar alone. In other words, the rate of yield curve for tar has been found by experiment to be similar to that for gas shown in Fig. 17. It should not be overlooked that, although the production of tar after a certain period may not be sufficient to warrant continuation of carbonization, the gas evolved may entirely justify prolongation.

The effect of bringing the charge up to maximum temperature in 5 hours, as compared with attaining the same temperature within a fraction of an hour, is shown by the results of Table 46, after Taylor and Porter (98). These experiments were conducted on Pennsylvania coal. It is seen that in every case the yield changed from about 16.0 gallons per gross ton of coal to about 20.5 gallons per gross ton when the period of attaining the maximum carbonization temperature was decreased from 5 hours to a much shorter period.

Pressure and Vacuum Effect. Some thirty years ago, Dewar and Redwood patented the distillation of petroleum under pressure to crack the heavy distillates into low-boiling and more valuable fractions. In 1910, Burton developed the pressure cracking system and now it is a well established industry. Attempts have been made to reduce the deposition of carbon by the introduction of catalysers and Bergius has proposed the hydrogenation of the hydrocarbons by carbonization under pressure in an atmosphere of hydrogen. Cracking, however, in low temperature carbonization processes, is ordinarily avoided in order to preserve the primary products of distillation. Hence, the retorts are usually operated at atmospheric pressure or

TABLE 47

Comparison of atmospheric and vacuum tar yields

TYPE OF TAR	GALLONS PER GROSS TON				
	West Virginia coal	Illinois coal	Pennsylvania coal	Utah coal	Oklahoma coal
Atmospheric.....................	5.2	9.6	15.0	17.7	27.5
Vacuum.........................	8.3	13.3	20.1	16.8	20.6

under slight vacuum, of hardly more than two inches of water, to overcome the resistance of the piping system. A discussion of the possibility of increasing the yield of lighter hydrocarbons, suitable as a fuel for internal combustion engines, by cracking the primary tar will be taken up under the subject of motor spirit.

A vacuum system assists in removal of the vapors and prevents condensation of the heavy tars in the retort. It also removes the air which is present, thus preventing oxidation, and preserves the primary tar by avoiding cracking. In 1905 and 1906, Simpson obtained patents which were afterwards incorporated in the Tozer retort for distilling in partial and complete vacuum. Little work has been done by way of investigation in this field, but Taylor and Porter (98) have examined certain coals of the United States when distilled at pressures below 4 cm. of mercury. A comparison of the tar yields from atmospheric and vacuum carbonization is instructive. The atmospheric distillation in Table 47 was carried out at 475°C. The figures, for convenience, have been converted from a percentage basis to gallons per gross ton.

The effect of temperature on the yield of vacuum tar was also investigated by the same authorities. In this case, different periods of distillation were used at different temperatures, so that the data

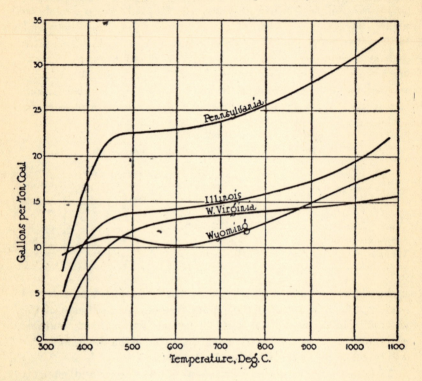

FIG. 21. YIELD OF TAR FROM AMERICAN COALS *in Vacuo* AS A FUNCTION OF TEMPERATURE

are not strictly comparable, but they are given in Fig. 21 because no other similar figures are available. The data are computed to gallons per gross ton. It will be noted that the yields in this illustration are higher than those indicated by Table 47. This is due, doubtlessly, to the systematic error pointed out above, as well as to an additional cause. In this case, the percentage tar obtained was determined by subtraction, rather than by direct observation, and, consequently, the cumulative errors of analyses fall entirely on the tar content. Figure 21 should be compared with Fig. 20, where the corresponding results of atmospheric distillation are shown. The main difference in the characteristic temperature versus yield curves of atmospheric and vacuum carbonization lies in the absence of a maximum on the vacuum system. The yield of tar, in the latter case, quickly rises until about 450°C. is reached, when little change in the quantity of tar produced is noticed during the next 150°C. temperature increase. Thereafter, the yield of tar increases with temperature rise even up to 1050°C.

Atmospheric and Moisture Effect. Taylor and Porter (98) investigated the effect of inert atmospheres on the quantity of tar produced. The presence of coal gas or nitrogen did not exert any

TABLE 48

Effect of moisture content on yield of low temperature tar

TAR	MOISTURE	
	1.2 per cent	9.6 per cent
Tar in dry coal............................	10.3	10.2
Tar in coal as used........................	10.2	9.2

decided influence on the yield. Thus, over a 5-hour period of distillation, 17.1 gallons of tar per gross ton were obtained in an atmosphere of coal gas at 950°C. and 16.0 gallons when pure nitrogen was introduced into the retort during carbonization at 1040°C.

Weathering of the coal before coking appears to have an effect on the quantity of tar evolved in carbonization. Thus, it was found that a Wyoming coal yielded 9.1 per cent of its weight as tar, when distilled as received, but only 6.2 per cent after air drying. It is a well known fact that weathering reduces the volatile content of the coal, both through escape of the occluded gases and through oxidation. It is not surprising, therefore, to find a larger evolution of tar immediately upon reception of the sample than after the coal has been exposed to the action of the air.

The moisture content of the coal does not have any influence on the amount of tar produced, when computed upon a dry coal basis, according to Porter and Ovitz (96).   Thus the yield of tar from a dry Pennsylvania coal, containing but 1.2 per cent moisture, as compared with another sample containing 9.6 per cent moisture, is given in Table 48.   The decrease in tar, when figured as a percentage of the coal as charged, is a fictitious decrease only, arising entirely from the selection of a base for computation which contains a smaller quantity of the tar-producing element.

Davis and Parry (97), it will be recalled, conducted experiments to determine the effect of superheated steam upon the carbonization products.   It has been shown that probably the temperature is not sufficiently high in the low temperature distillation process to cause any interaction between the steam and the primary volatile products, and, consequently, the principal effect of steam will be in preventing secondary decomposition by assisting in the quick removal of the products.   With Pennsylvania coal from the Upper Freeport bed, Davis and Parry (97) found that 33.0 gallons of tar per gross ton were obtained without the use of steam, whereas, the following yields were obtained when 88 per cent steam was passed through the retort: 30.8 gallons per gross ton at 475°C.; 33.3 gallons per gross ton at 550°C.; and 50.9 gallons per gross ton at 650°C.   At 550°C., which is the only temperature at which experiments were made on the same coal without the use of steam, apparently there was little effect on the yield.   It is evident that an enormous quantity of tar was evolved under steam distillation at 650°C.   Unfortunately, no information is at hand to determine whether this large yield is due to the presence of steam or is a peculiarity of the coal.

The tar produced in steam distillation at low temperatures is a little more viscous, but otherwise it does not appear essentially different from the tar obtained without the use of steam.   Its fractionation, however, shows it to have a marked difference in volatile content.   It contains a smaller percentage of light oils, but more of the heavier hydrocarbons.   This topic will be taken up again under a discussion of the fractionation of low temperature tar.

Constitution of Primary Tar.   Although low temperature tar obtained from lignite and brown coal may be solid at ordinary temperatures, due to a large proportion of solid paraffins, primary tar, in general, is lighter and more fluid than that from high temperature processes.   The specific gravity of primary tar usually ranges from 0.95 to 1.06, as compared with 1.2 specific gravity for high temperature tars, according to Fischer (119). The comparatively low density is due mainly to the presence of large proportions of liquid hydrocarbons and phenols. Low temperature tar usually has a strong odor of phenols and of hydrogen sulphide, but it never has the naphthalene odor of secondary tars. In transparent layers, its color ranges from orange to red. Fischer and Gluud (60) have pointed out another way in which low temperature tar resembles petroleum and differs from high temperature aromatic tars. They found that some of the hydrocarbons from primary tar exhibit a small but distinct optical activity. In a tar from Lohberg coal, freed of phenols, the optical rotation with sodium light through a 20 cm. tube varied from $+0.05°$, for the fraction 175°C. to 185°C., to the value $+0.30°$, for the fraction 225°C. to 235°C. Low temperature

TABLE 49

Decomposition of low temperature tar by distillation

FRACTION	RAW TAR		DISTILLATE	
	Fraction, per cent tar	Cresote, per cent tar	Fraction, per cent of distillate	Cresote, per cent tar
	per cent	*per cent*	*per cent*	*per cent*
70° to 250°C............................	18.5	2.7	37.0	3.00
250° to 300°C...........................	15.0	2.3	24.5	1.80
Over 300°C..............................	6.0	10.0	38.5	1.54

tars are usually soluble in the ordinary organic solvents, such as benzene, ether, acetone, chloroform, carbon tetrachloride, and petroleum ether, but its solution is usually accompanied by precipitation of resins.

It has been shown conclusively that distillation of the primary tar, during analytical procedure, distinctly alters its composition, especially that of the higher boiling compounds. Fischer (49) states that primary tar cannot be distilled without the part above 300°C. decomposing, the viscous lubricating oils suffering the greatest decomposition and the higher phenols being affected to a lesser degree. A specific case of this for low temperature brown coal tar has been given by Fischer (85) and is reproduced in Table 49. The distillation was carried out slowly for 8 hours, yielding 85.6 per cent oil, 4.7 per cent gas, 9.2 per cent coke, and a small amount of water. It will be observed that distillation so altered the constitution of the fraction from 70°C. to 250°C. as to increase its proportion from 18.5 per cent to 31.7 per cent of the original tar. The proportion of acids was simultaneously greatly decreased. Schneider (122) confirmed these results with tar from a bituminous coal.

Decomposition of primary tar during distillation is further indicated by the evolution of gas. Weindel (123) found that gas first was evolved at 270°C., reaching a maximum at about 335°C. The gas contained 7 per cent hydrogen sulphide, 4 per cent carbon dioxide, about 75 per cent methane and its homologues, and about 10 per cent ethylene and acetylene hydrocarbons. Edwards (124), and also Brittain, Rowe, and Sinnatt (125), detected the evolution of sulphur dioxide at the beginning of distillation and hydrogen sulphide at 170°C., when studying tar from the Coalite process.

It is quite evident that the evaluation of low temperature tars is a difficult task and that the method of separation by solvents must be used to avoid distillation as much as possible, but even this method of approach is not without its difficulty of solvent reaction. These troubles are augmented by the fact that most low temperature tars change color and character on standing. This has been attributed, by Jaeger (126), to oxidation by the atmosphere through the action of light, but the presence of bases are important factors. Parr and Olin (37) found, also, that the viscosity of the tar increased with standing, apparently the result of oxidation, for Brittain, Rowe, and Sinnatt (125) found no change when the tar was kept in darkness and out of contact with air.

As early as 1862, Williams (127) and Schorlemmer (128) seem to have made the first chemical examination of low temperature tar obtained from cannel coal. The latter of these investigators identified paraffin hydrocarbons. However, the first noteworthy research was conducted by Börnstein (95) in 1904. He fractionated primary tar from Westphalian coals, from 50°C. to 450°C., and found it conspicuously different from high temperature tar, being a thin liquid with little free carbon and containing no naphthalene or anthracene, but quantities of phenols and up to 2 per cent solid paraffins. With another Westphalian low temperature tar he found no solid paraffins, but something less than half of one per cent methylanthracene.

Pictet and Bouvier (51) (129) (130) (131), and also Pictet, Kaiser, and Labouchère (52), conducted a series of investigations, beginning in 1913, on primary tar obtained from vacuum distillation of a French bituminous coal, containing about 11 per cent ash, 70 per cent fixed carbon, and 19 per cent volatile matter. The fresh tar was composed of 68 per cent unsaturated hydrocarbons, 30 per cent saturated hydrocarbons, 2 per cent alcohols and 0.2 per cent bases. They found no phenols in the fresh tar, but detected some after the tar had remained standing a long time. As other investigators have found over 15 per cent phenols in fresh tar examined by them, it appears that Pictet and Bouvier must have had an exceptionally true primary tar. They established the presence of toluidine, pentamethylphenol, tetramethylphenol, xylenol, hydroquinoline, and isohydroquinoline.

Jones and Wheeler (42) examined the tar obtained from a Scottish and a Durham coal, distilled at 450°C. *in vacuo.* In the oils below 300°C., they found about 40 per cent unsaturated hydrocarbons; about 40 per cent saturated hydrocarbons, mostly naphthenes; about 7 per cent aromatic compounds, probably homologues of naphthalene; about 12 per cent phenols, chiefly cresols and xylenols; traces of pyridine bases, and a small amount of solid paraffins.

Identification of Compounds. Regarding particular chemical compounds that are found in low temperature tars, some quantitative determinations by Schültz and Buschmann (34) (35), and also by Fieldner (36), have been given under the chemistry of low temperature carbonization, discussed in Chapter I and compiled in Table 5 and Table 6, respectively. A qualitative list of compounds, actually identified in low temperature products, was given in Table 7, accompanied by references to the authorities who isolated them.

Among the aromatic hydrocarbons, Whitaker and Crowell (132) (134), when investigating a Pennsylvania coal, observed that benzene first formed at 500°C. and toluene at 400°C., but that maximum yields were not obtained until 800°C. for benzene, 700°C. for toluene, and 600°C. for xylene. Traces of benzene have been found by a number of observers, but most investigators have been unable to detect it in primary tars examined by them. Parr and Olin (37) found benzene, as well as toluene, zylene, and possibly mesitylene, in Illinois low temperature tar. Schültz (43) is the only authority who has reported considerable quantities of benzene hydrocarbons. He examined a tar obtained by distillation of Furst-Hardenberg coal in a rotary retort at about 480°C. Broche (53), however, examined tar from the same coal and found less than 0.4 per cent benzene, from which he concluded that the tar examined by Schültz was abnormal. Fischer and Gluud (39) detected a very small amount of benzene in tar from one coal examined by them.

Besides Parr and Olin, toluene in minute quantities was found by Jones and Wheeler (42) and its presence was confirmed by Frank and Arnold (133). The latter observers also found the three xylenes in the tar fraction from 120°C. to 180°C. Klein (135) found both toluene and xylene in the light oil from a large rotary retort, while Weissberger and Moehrle (46), and also Kruber (136) and Kaffer (137), found the higher homologues of benzene, of which pseudo-cumene, durene, and a few others have been identified.

Less than one per cent naphthalene seems to be present in low temperature tars, as compared with 4 per cent or 5 per cent in aromatic tars. According to Ruhemann (138), brown coal low temperature tar contains some naphthalene. Brittain, Rowe, and Sinnatt (125), Morgan and Soule (45)(48), as well as Weissberger and Moehrle (46), found it in tar from full-scale low temperature plants, while Parrish and Rowe (139) found small quantities in tar carefully distilled from coal at 600°C. Anthracene is present in even smaller proportions than naphthalene, but it has been reported as present by Brittain, Rowe, and Sinnatt (125) and by Weissberger and Moehrle (46), the last of which also established the presence of naphthalene homologues, such as the methylnaphthalenes, confirming the observations of Fischer, Schroeder, and Zerbe (47).

Among the saturated and unsaturated hydrocarbons, Fischer and Gluud (39) found pentane, hexane, many of their homologues, and possibly terpenes, among the low-boiling fractions of primary tar. Schültz, Buschmann, and Wissebach (38) established the present of ethylene, propylene, butylene, pentene, butadiene, and cyclo-pentadiene in the light oils, most of which were also found by Fieldner (36) in certain American low temperature tars, as shown in Table 6. Klein (135) also detected octylene and nonylene in large-scale primary tar.

Among the oxygenated compounds, acetone has been observed by Frank and Arnold (133), by Schültz (140), and by Broche (53). Acetaldehyde and indications of ketones were obtained by Brittain, Rowe, and Sinnatt (125), while Schültz (140) also identified acetaldehyde, as well as methylethylketone, and acetonitrile.

Free sulphur is probably present to a small extent in low temperature tar, although its presence is undesirable, but it cannot be avoided if the raw coal is one of large sulphur content. Schültz (43) detected methylmercaptan and dimethylsulphide, in addition to the simple sulphur compounds hitherto mentioned. Brittain, Rowe, and Sinnatt (125) found over 1.5 per cent combined sulphur in the crude full-scale low temperature tars examined by them.

Tar Acids. Heretofore it has been pointed out that one of the outstanding peculiarities of low temperature tar is its high acid content. These acids do not consist so much of phenol, itself, as of homologues of the series, such as the cresols, xylenols, and more complex phenol derivatives.

There has been a great variation in the amount of acids present in the tars examined by various authorities. Thus, Jones and Wheeler (42) found about 7.0 per cent; tests on the Tozer retort gave 10.2 per cent; Edwards (124) reported 10.8 per cent to 15 per cent; Morgan and Soule (48) determined 14.7 per cent; Davis and Galloway (141) found from 12 per cent to 19 per cent; The Fuel Research Board reported 17.8 per cent; Morgan and Meigham (142) 17.5 per cent; Davis and Parry (97) 18.2 per cent; tests on the Nielsen retort yielded 20 per cent; Brittain, Rowe, and Sinnatt (125) 26.6 per cent to 30.6 per cent; Parr and Olin (37) 27.9 per cent; and Church and Weiss (143) as much as 50.0 per cent.

The work of Morgan and Soule was conducted on tar from the Carbocoal process; Jones and Wheeler used vacuum tar; Church examined a tar from an Illinois coal of high oxygen content; Parr and Olin used Illinois coal; Davis and Parry used tar derived from Pennsylvania coal; and Edwards used English coals. The high yield obtained by Church does not seem extraordinary, when it is recalled that he used a coal of high oxygen content and that the phenolic compounds contain combined oxygen. In fact, it seems permissible to predict that, in general, coals which are highly oxygenated may be expected to give a larger quantity of the tar acids upon carbonization. The same may be said, perhaps, of coals which have been weathered through exposure to the atmosphere or retorted in the presence of a considerable amount of oxygen. Unfortunately no experimental data are at hand to substantiate this belief.

The bulk of low temperature tar phenols consists of complex hydrogenated and alkalated derivatives of ordinary high temperature tar phenols. They are largely saturated compounds. Morgan (144) states that on account of their long side chains the primary tar phenols are less soluble in water than those derived from aromatic tars.

Phenol, itself, is usually present in amounts of less than 0.5 per cent of the tar, as compared with twice that amount for high temperature tars. Its presence in small quantities has been established by Fischer and Breuer (145), by Brittain, Rowe, and Sinnatt (125), by Morgan and Soule (48), by Parrish and Rowe (139), and by Frank and Arnold (133). Schültz (43) and his co-workers (38) are the only investigators reporting as much as 1.35 per cent phenol in the crude tar. Pictet, who examined an exceptionally true primary tar, found no phenol but up to 2 per cent methylcyclohexanol, an unstable alcohol which decomposed into phenol upon standing.

All three cresols have been identified, but there seems to be no uniformity in the way in which they predominate. Gluud and Breuer (50) found that meta-cresol predominated; Brittain, Rowe, and Sinnatt (125) found about 46 per cent ortho-cresol, about 37 per cent meta-cresol, and about 16 per cent para-cresol; while Morgan and Soule (48) found 54 per cent para-cresol, 27 per cent ortho-cresol, and 19 per cent meta-cresol. Schültz, Buschmann, and Wissebach (38) have identified four of the zylenols, while Avenarius (147) has isolated a fifth.

Catechol was detected qualitatively by Morgan and Soule (48), by Edwards (124), and by Parrish and Rowe (139). Börnstein (95) also detected it, while Gluud (148) estimated the quantity of this compound in the tar from Lohberg coal, examined by him, to amount to 0.02 per cent of the coal. Brittain, Rowe, and Sinnatt (125) found catechol present in tar from the Coalite process.

Among the higher-boiling phenols, Morgan and Soule (48) reported the presence of naphthols, while Weindel (123) observed β-naphthol, and Edwards (124) reported both α-naphthol and β-naphthol. Gluud and Breuer (50) found trimethylphenols, the presence of which was confirmed by the researches of Fromm and Eckard (40) and of Pictet, Kaiser, and Labouchère (52). The latter experimenters also identified tetramethylphenol and pentamethylphenol. Marcusson and Picard (149) recorded the presence of solid phenols in primary tar from Upper Silesian coal, but Tropsch (150), who examined the low temperature tar of a coal from the same region, was unable to confirm this.

Among the sulphonated phenols, Schültz, Buschmann, and Wissebach (38) reported appreciable quantities of mercaptans and Avenarius (147) concluded that thiophenols were present. Parrish and Rowe (139) found 0.73 per cent sulphur in their crude phenols, while Brittain, Rowe, and Sinnatt (125) estimated the sulphur content of the crude phenols from Coalite tar to be less than one per cent.

Some idea of the distribution of the various constituents may be gained from a rough separation of the phenols made by Fischer and

TABLE 50

Distribution of phenols in low temperature tar acids

CONSTITUENT	AUTHORITY			
	(125)	(125)	(48)	(146)
	per cent	*per cent*	*per cent*	*per cent*
Phenol	0.11	0.18	0.6	0.70
Cresols	4.78	5.20	4.9	6.83
Xylenols	5.88	4.71	2.8	6.07
Higher phenols	7.07	8.75	5.1	4.75
Resins	8.68	10.92	1.3	15.49
Total phenols	26.6	30.6	14.7	33.8

TABLE 51

Tar acids in fractions of steam and ordinary low temperature tar

FRACTION	ORDINARY TAR	STEAM TAR
	per cent	*per cent*
0° to 175°C	14.5	8.4
175° to 225°C	46.0	40.0
225° to 275°C	30.0	26.3

others. They found from one per cent to 6 per cent cresols; about the same proportion of xylenols; 5 per cent to 25 per cent higher phenols; and 8 per cent to 15 per cent acid resins. The tar from the Fuel Research Board horizontal retorts yielded about half the acid content reported by Fischer, about 5 per cent cresols, 11 per cent xylenols, and the remainder was composed of the heavier derivatives of phenol. Parrish (117) has compiled a list, shown in Table 50, which gives the distribution of phenols among the tar acids in low temperature carbonization.

According to the results of Davis and Parry (97), introduction of steam into the retort during distillation of the coal considerably alters the quantity of tar acids produced in each fraction of the tar. Their data are given in Table 51 as percentages of the fraction. The tar examined was obtained in both cases by carbonization of Pennsylvania coal from the Freeport bed at 550°C. The yield is equivalent to 4.76 gallons of tar acids per net ton of coal, or 14.5 per cent of the crude tar, for dry distillation and 4.04 gallons per net ton, or 12.2 per cent of the crude tar, under steam distillation. The average yield per net ton from five Pennsylvania coals, tested by Davis and Parry (97), was 5.45 gallons. The specific gravities of the acids separated from the various fractions of tar were 1.021, 1.028, and 1.051 for the light, middle, and heavy oil cuts, respectively. The middle oil contained a preponderance of cresols and xylenols.

TABLE 52

Effect of temperature variation on yield of tar acids

FRACTION	TEMPERATURE		
	475°C.	350°C.	650°C.
	per cent	*per cent*	*per cent*
0° to 175°C.	10.0	8.4	9.9
175° to 225°C.	36.0	40.0	36.0
225° to 275°C.	22.5	26.3	25.0

Tar from the same coal, carbonized at different temperatures, was examined by the same investigators with a view of determining the effect of temperature variation on the production of tar acids. The results are reproduced in Table 52, which shows conclusively that increase of the temperature from 475°C. to 650°C. does not influence the yield to any extent. It is apparent that the acids are stable up to beyond 650°C. and that no decomposition occurred at that temperature. This experiment was carried out in the presence of steam, which, to a great extent, reduced the susceptibility to thermal decomposition.

Fig. 22 shows the variation of the percentage of tar acids, as a function of the average boiling point of the fraction, for low temperature tar from Pennsylvania coal, as determined by Davis and Parry (97), when compared with the same determinations on tar from the Carbocoal process, as found by Morgan and Soule (151). In the illustration, it will be noted that the maximum yield of tar acids occurs in the fraction whose average boiling point is 200°C., in the Freeport tar, whereas, in the Carbocoal tar, this maximum occurs 60°C. higher.

Tar Bases. The nitrogen bases are characterized usually by absence of the simpler members, although pyridine and the simple aliphatic amines have been detected in small quantities. The tar

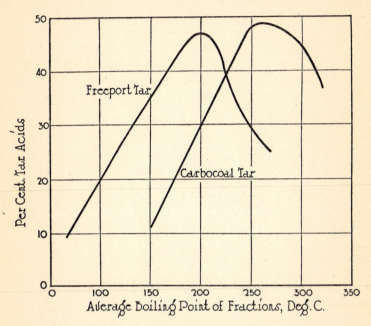

FIG. 22. DISTRIBUTION OF LOW TEMPERATURE TAR ACIDS AS A FUNCTION OF BOILING POINT

bases consist mostly of secondary and tertiary compounds and others of unknown composition.

Davis and Parry (97) found 1.23 per cent nitrogen bases in the low temperature tar from Pennsylvania coal; Davis and Galloway (141) found 2.8 per cent to 5.7 per cent in the tar distillate up to 275°C., representing 1.1 per cent to 2.3 per cent of the total tar; Edwards (124) found from 2.9 per cent to 5.8 per cent in the distillate up to 311°C., amounting to 1.3 per cent and 2.5 per cent, respectively, of the total tar; Jones and Wheeler (42) found less than one per cent; Parr and Olin (31) found 0.9 per cent; Pictet, Kaiser, and Labouchère (52) found as little as 0.2 per cent; Fischer and Gluud (152) found 0.46 per cent; Parrish and Rowe (139) found 2.7 per cent; Morgan and Soule (48) found 0.6 per cent in Carbocoal tar; and Brittain, Rowe, and Sinnatt (125) found from 2.45 per cent to 4.1 per cent in the total tar from the Coalite process. These figures, however, can

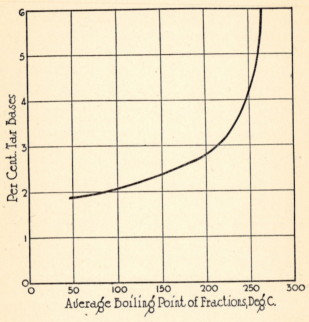

FIG. 23. DISTRIBUTION OF LOW TEMPERATURE TAR BASES AS A FUNCTION OF BOILING POINT

be misleading, as most of the determinations were made on fractions representing as little as 30 per cent of the total tar and the quantity of bases present in those distillates computed back on a total tar basis, whereas it is quite apparent that a large percentage of the bases remains in the tar residuum above 300°C. Indications are that the tar bases amount to from 3 per cent to 5 per cent of the total tar.

Gollmer (146) found among the primary amines in low temperature tar, analine, the toluidines, and the xylidines; the primary amines in all amounting to 4.5 per cent of the tar bases. Schültz, Buschmann, and Wissebach (38) confirmed the findings of Gollmer. Other investigators, however, found no primary amines, but Morgan and Soule (48) found 20 per cent secondary and 80 per cent tertiary amines; Brittain, Rowe, and Sinnatt (125) found 56 per cent secondary and 44 per cent tertiary amines; while Parrish and Rowe (149) found 15 per cent secondary and 85 per cent tertiary amines.

It has been observed generally that a large proportion of unsaturated compounds are found in the tar bases. Traces of pyridine have been observed by Gollmer (146); by Brittain, Rowe, and Sinnatt (125) in the tar liquor; by Fromm and Eckard (40); by Schültz, Buschmann, and Wissebach (38); and by Morgan and Soule (48).

TABLE 53

Percentage nitrogen bases in fractions of Coalite tar

FRACTION	SAMPLE NO. 1		SAMPLE NO. 2	
	Pressure	Bases	Pressure	Bases
	mm.	per cent	mm.	per cent
78° to 110°C...................	766	1.2	762	1.4
110° to 200°C..................	766	8.7	762	3.8
200° to 260°C..................	24	9.1	762	11.2
125° to 150°C..................	24	14.3	6	16.8
150° to 200°C..................	24	20.3	6	26.0
200° to 275°C..................		25.0	6	20.7
Residue........................		19.7		17.9
Loss...........................		1.7		2.2

Among the homologues of pyridine, Schültz and his co-workers found methylpyridines, dimethylpyridines, and trimethylpyridines; the presence of the latter being confirmed by Gollmer (146), while Morgan and Soule (48) found ethylpyridine and its hydrogenated derivatives. Brittain, Rowe, and Sinnatt (125) also found small amounts of diethylamine and triethylamine in the tar liquor. Schültz (38) and his associates established the presence of quinoline and its derivative, methylquinoline, while Pictet and his co-workers found a number of dihydroquinolines present.

The distribution of nitrogen bases in the fractions of low temperature tar, as determined by Davis and Parry (97), is given in Fig. 23, where the percentage yield is plotted against the average boiling point of the fraction. The determinations were made by washing the oil fractions, after removal of the tar acids, with 20 per cent sulphuric acid to remove the bases. The results shown in this curve agree with the fact discovered by Morgan and Soule (48), namely, that the pitch contains a larger proportion of bases than the lighter oil fractions.

Brittain, Rowe, and Sinnatt (125) fractionated two samples of Coalite tar under atmospheric and under reduced pressures and determine the percentage of nitrogen bases present in each fraction. The results are given in Table 53. It will be observed that the quantity of bases, present in the various fractions, is considerably greater than that shown in Fig. 23, but the general trend to larger proportion of bases as the boiling point of the fraction increases is in agreement with other experimenters. It is quite apparent that the proportion

TABLE 54

Distribution of sulphur in low temperature tars

FRACTION	PER CENT SULPHUR BY WEIGHT		
Authority..................	(125)	(125)	(139)
	per cent	*per cent*	*per cent*
Crude tar...........................	1.49	1.73	1.35
Neutral oil.........................	1.74	1.30	1.53
Acids...............................	0.77	0.95	0.73
Bases...............................	0.99	1.40	0.77
Solids..............................	3.82	10.20	1.19

of bases in a given fraction is more than doubled by vaccum distillation.

Tar Solids, Sulphur, and Liquor.   Many low temperature tars have been observed easily to form emulsions with the tar liquor, thereby entailing a great deal of trouble in bringing about demulsification. This tendency to emulsify has ordinarily been attributed to the low specific gravity of primary tar and to dust and other mineral matter carried over with the tar during distillation. In the course of their investigations, Brittain, Rowe, and Sinnatt (125) isolated a brown amorphous powder, precipitated from the tar fractions by various organic solvents. After removal of this solid powder, which amounted to as much as 0.94 per cent of the tar in one sample and 9.9 per cent of the tar in another, it was observed that emulsification of the samples did not take place. It was concluded that this solid material, present in the tar either as suspended powder or as partly in solution, was a contributing factor in emulsification. The existence of such a brown powder was confirmed by Edwards (124), who attributed its formation to changes in the tar vapor prior to condensation or to changes in the tar itself during storage, rather than to primary decomposition of the coal during carbonization.

Ruhemann (138) distilled low temperature tar from lignite and found sulphur in the various fractions to the amount of 3.5 per cent in the lower cuts and 1.9 per cent in the higher cuts. The neutral oil of the primary tar, examined by Marcusson and Picard (149), contained from 5.4 per cent to 6.3 per cent sulphur. Avenarius (147) and Schültz, Buschmann, and Wissebach (38) found sulphur in their tar acids. The nature of these sulphur compounds has already been discussed and need not be repeated here. Parrish (117) has compiled a table from the experiments of Brittain, Rowe, and Sinnatt (125) and of Parrish and Rowe (139) to show the distribution of sulphur in low temperature tars which were examined by them. This compilation is given in Table 54. The notably high sulphur contents of the tar solids suggests that it plays an important part in these substances.

The aqueous distillate from low temperature tar is usually straw yellow in color and has an acid reaction. According to Jones and Wheeler (42), the tar liquor contains both hydrochloric acid and ammonium chloride. Brittain, Rowe, and Sinnatt (125) made a careful examination of the tar liquor, from distillation of Coalite tars, and established the presence of acetic acid, formic acid, acetaldehyde, and certain ketones, which could not be identified. They also found traces of diethylamines, triethylamines, pyridine, and methylpyridine, while phenol, cresols, and xylenols were isolated.

Primary Tar Distillation. Following the procedure adopted in the evaluation of petroleum, a rough separation of the constituents of low temperature tar can be obtained by preliminary fractionation. Thus, the tar obtained from the distillation of five high grade Barnsley coals has been separated into three qualities of oil, according to the boiling points. The first cut, up to 170°C., is given as light oil, the second cut, from 170°C. to 245°C., is called middle oil and the last cut, from 245°C. to 315°C., is designated as heavy oil. The viscous residuum is mostly pitch. The results of the fractionation are given in Table 55.   On the average 6.9 per cent of the tar by volume is light oil, 30.5 per cent middle oil, and 18.4 per cent heavy oil.   The proximate analyses of the coal, whose tar yield is given in Table 55, from tests by Lewes as reported by Wellington and Cooper (89), was very similar to that of Pennsylvania coal, containing about 60 per cent fixed carbon and about 32 per cent volatile matter.

TABLE 55

Fractionation of low temperature tar from Barnsley coals

COAL	PER CENT VOLATILE MATTER IN COAL	GALLONS PER GROSS TON				
		Light oil	Middle oil	Heavy oil	Pitch	Total tar
Thorncliffe..............	33.1	1.94	9.20	5.57	14.3	31.0
Swilley.................	32.5	1.28	7.49	4.04	13.0	25.8
Flockton...............	31.1	2.08	8.20	3.98	9.7	23.9
Lidgett................	32.0	1.26	7.12	3.56	12.0	23.8
Parkgate...............	30.5	2.05	6.64	5.86	7.3	21.8

TABLE 56

Fractionation of low temperature tar from Warwickshire coal

FRACTION	PER CENT TAR	SPECIFIC GRAVITY	PER CENT OF FRACTION		
			Acids	Bases	Neutral oil
	per cent		*per cent*	*per cent*	*per cent*
Up to 170°C......................	5.1	0.850	10.2	1.7	88.1
170° to 230°C.....................	20.5	0.949	45.9	1.0	53.1
230° to 270°C.....................	14.4	0.981	49.5	3.5	47.0
270° to 310°C.....................	12.7	1.003	37.6	2.3	60.1
310° to 335°C.....................	10.1	1.132	33.2	2.4	64.4
Pitch...........................	36.1				

A Warwickshire coal, containing 10.3 per cent moisture, 35.3 per cent volatile matter, 40.8 per cent fixed carbon, and 13.5 per cent ash, was distilled at 600°C. in vertical retorts at the Fuel Research Station.   The tar from this experiment had a specific gravity at 15°C. of 1.029, contained less than one per cent mineral matter and 2.29 per cent water.   It was fractionated by Parrish and Rowe (139) with the results given in Table 56.   The percentage acids and bases are also shown.

In regard to experiments made upon coals of the United States, Parr and Olin (37) obtained a dark brown tar, which had a specific gravity of 1.069, from Illinois bituminous coal. Crude fractionation gave the following results: 17.2 per cent light oil up to 210°C., with a specific gravity of 0.966; 52.7 per cent heavy oil from 210°C. to 325°C., with a specific gravity of 1.032; and 30.1 per cent pitch over 325°C., with a specific gravity of 1.270. These fractions were refined and the yield between certain points computed as a percentage of the tar with the results shown in Table 57.

TABLE 57

Refinement of fractions of low temperature tar from Pennsylvania coal

FRACTION	PER CENT OF TAR
	per cent
Light oil:	
Phenols, etc.	5.7
Amines and bases	0.9
75° to 95°C.	0.38
95° to 125°C.	1.33
125° to 170°C.	4.77
170° to 200°C.	2.67
200° to 210°C.	1.32
Heavy Oil:	
Tar acids	22.2
210° to 250°C.	2.87
250° to 270°C.	13.55
Over 270°C.	1.53

Low temperature tars obtained from the Pittsburgh and Upper Kittanning beds of Pennsylvania at 550°C. to 650°C. have been fractionated by Davis and Parry (97). A comparison of the boiling ranges of low temperature tar, crude shale oil, and petroleum is given in Fig. 24. Examination of these curves discloses that below 250°C. none of the low temperature tars is as volatile as petroleum and that below 200°C. shale oil contains a larger percentage of volatile constituents than the tar. Above 200°C., the percentage by volume of the tar which distills exceeds that of the shale oil and, at a slightly higher temperature, even that of petroleum. The low temperature tar obtained from the Carbocoal process contains higher-boiling hydrocarbons than the other tars, as demonstrated by the position of the curve in the illustration.

Fig. 25, after Davis and Parry (97), shows the distillation range of tar from five Pennsylvania coals. All of these tars had about the same volatility, except Pittsburgh rooster coal, which contained more of the lighter oils with boiling points below 150°C. This particular tar gave a lower percentage of phenol and unsaturated compounds than the other samples. The specific gravity of these tar fractions increased from 0.882 at 175°C. to 0.992 at 275°C.

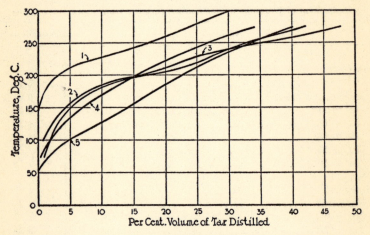

Fig. 24. Boiling Range of Low Temperature Tar, Shale Oil, and Petroleum

1 = Carbocoal tar.   2 = Upper Freeport tar at 600°C. to 650°C.   3 = Upper Freeport tar at 550°C.   4 = Shale oil.   5 = Petroleum.

Parr and Layng (102) distilled low temperature tar from Utah coal and found that 4.02 per cent distilled from 0°C. to 170°C.; 37.1 per cent from 170°C. to 300°C.; 34.7 per cent from 300°C. to 360°C.; leaving 22.8 per cent pitch and loss. The fraction from 170°C. to 300°C. was composed of 28.6 per cent tar acids, 4.6 per cent amines, and 22.4 per cent paraffins.

Giles and Vilbrandt (99) made a careful study of the low temperature carbonization products obtained at various temperatures from Farmville, N. C., coal. The effect of temperature upon the composition of the gas from this coal has already been seen in Fig. 12. The influence of temperature of carbonization on the volatility of the tar is nicely illustrated in Table 58. It will be observed that when

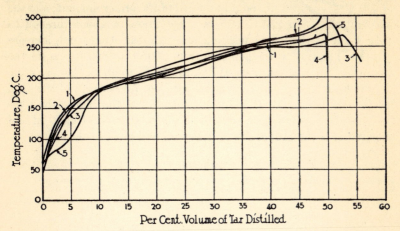

FIG. 25. BOILING RANGE OF LOW TEMPERATURE TARS FROM PENNSYLVANIA COALS

1 = Pittsburgh seam. 2 = Upper Freeport. 3 = Lower Freeport. 4 = Pittsburgh roof. 5 = Pittsburgh rooster.

TABLE 58

Fractionation of tar from North Carolina coal carbonized at various temperatures

FRACTION	TEMPERATURE OF CARBONIZATION					
	300°C.	360°C.	420°C.	540°C.	600°C.	600°C.
	per cent	per cent	per cent	per cent	per cent	per cent
70° to 170°C.	31.0	18.2	11.9	9.8	8.9	8.8
170° to 230°C.	25.6	30.6	25.8	10.6	10.0	8.1
230° to 270°C.	18.8	17.4	13.3	7.1	10.6	7.1
270° to 315°C.		12.4	13.3	7.9	7.2	6.9
315° to 355°C.		9.3	13.8	32.4	23.5	14.0
Residue	7.1	10.9	18.3	27.1	38.8	54.9

the temperature of distillation is advanced from 300°C. to 660°C. the proportion of the lower fractions as a percentage of the entire tar undergoes a decided decrease, while the proportion of the heavier fractions have a corresponding increase. Between the distillation

temperatures of 300°C. and 660°C., the percentage of the fraction
70°C. to 170°C. is reduced at the higher temperature to almost one-
fourth of its initial value; the percentage of the fraction from 170°C.
to 230°C. is reduced to about one-third of its former amount; and the
fraction 230°C. to 270°C. suffers a reduction to about three-fifths
of its value at the lowest temperature.   On the other hand, increase
of the carbonization temperature from 200°C. to 660°C. causes the
amount of the fraction from 315°C. to 355°C. to about double, while
the residuum above 355°C. is increased from 7.5 per cent of the total
tar to 54.9 per cent.   It is quite evident that the higher the temperature of carbonization, the less is the proportion of light oil and
the greater is the proportion of heavy oil and pitch in the tar.

TABLE 59

Fractionation of tar from Washington lignite carbonized at various temperatures

FRACTION	TEMPERATURE OF CARBONIZATION			
	300°C.	400°C.	500°C.	600°C.
	per cent	*per cent*	*per cent*	*per cent*
To 150°C. (light oil)..................	10.7	10.5	7.8	3.9
150° to 300°C. (medium oil)...........	42.5	41.7	41.5	40.9
Above 300°C. (paraffin oil)...........	33.4	33.2	29.8	27.8
Coke.................................	10.0	10.3	15.9	21.1
Loss.................................	3.4	4.3	5.0	6.8
	100.0	100.0	100.0	100.0
Soft paraffin.........................	1.8	1.9	1.4	0.5
Hard paraffin........................	5.0	5.2	2.1	0.6

We have already seen in Table 29 the effect of the temperature of
carbonization on the composition of the gas evolved from distillation
of Washington lignite.   Benson and Canfield (108) also fractionated
the tar condensed from these experiments.   The results are given in
Table 59.   The findings in this case agree with those of Table 58,
except that here the decrease in light oil fractions with increasing
temperature of carbonization is compensated by an increased proportion of coke.   With Washington lignite, the specific gravity of the
light oil fraction advanced from 0.807, when obtained at 250°C.,
to 0.821, when the coal was distilled at 600°C.   The specific gravity
of the middle oil fraction advanced from 0.905 to 0.955 at the same

temperatures, while that of the heavy or paraffin oil changed from 0.939 to 0.985.

In Table 27 there was shown the composition of gas obtained from carbonizing peat in vertical retorts, as determined in an investigation conducted by the Fuel Research Board (106), under conditions of temperature somewhat exceeding the limits ordinarily construed to fall within the category of low temperature distillation, but which will be reproduced here, as data on peat tar are decidedly lacking in

TABLE 60

Fractionation of peat tar by Fuel Research Board

FRACTION	TEMPERATURE OF CARBONIZATION	
	997°C.	843°C.
Per cent water collected......................	3.2	5.5
Specific gravity tar (dry)....................	0.997	0.986
B.t.u. per pound tar (dry)..................	16,500	16,210
Per cent free carbon.........................	0.62	0.17
Per cent ash................................	0.12	0.15
Per cent sulphur............................	0.10	0.10
Fractionation (weight):	*per cent*	*per cent*
To 170°C...................................	2.6	2.3
170° to 230°C...............................	14.3	13.6
230° to 270°C...............................	17.2	13.6
270° to 310°C...............................	21.0	24.5
310°C. to pitch.............................	7.1	16.9
Pitch......................................	34.7	25.6
Loss	3.0	3.5

the technical literature. The results of these tests, as applied to the tar, are given in Table 60.

The tar from peat was a thick and semi-solid mass which contained a high proportion of paraffin wax and only a small amount of ammoniacal liquor. The tar from the 843°C. test contained about 6.5 per cent paraffin wax which melted at about 52°C. The first fraction contained about 13.2 per cent bases and unsaturated compounds and 40.5 per cent tar acids, while the second fraction was composed of about 54.0 per cent bases and unsaturated hydrocarbons and 8.0 per cent tar acids. The last two fractions were solid at 10°C. and contained practically all the paraffin wax. A separate proportion of the 843°C. tar was submitted to vacuum distillation with the result that 0.45 gallons of purified and refined light motor spirit was obtained per gross ton of peat. The total peat tar, which was produced, represented about 20 gallons per gross ton. From a study of the effects of temperature on the proportion of the tar fractions, as demonstrated in Table 58 and Table 59, it would appear that under true low temperature conditions, peat tar would fractionate to about 7 per cent in the cut up to 170°C., about 31 per cent in the cut from 170°C. to 230°C., about 12 per cent in the cut from 230°C. to 270°C.,

TABLE 61

Fractionation of petroleum and shale oils

FRACTION	PENNSYL-VANIA PETRO-LEUM	SHALE OIL			
		Scotch	Indiana	Utah	Colorado
	per cent	*per cent*	*per cent*	*per cent*	*per cent*
Up to 50°C.	0.90	0.17	0.7	0.75	
50° to 75°C.	1.61	0.24	1.6	0.96	1.2
75° to 100°C.	4.08	1.18	2.6	0.71	1.1
100° to 125°C.	8.29	2.77	4.6	1.93	2.8
125° to 150°C.	5.46	4.06	4.7	3.18	4.4
150° to 175°C.	6.77	3.82	5.7	5.30	4.8
175° to 200°C.	5.82	4.56	6.2	4.42	5.3
200° to 225°C.	6.95	5.57	6.7	6.70	5.6
225° to 250°C.	6.42	7.33	6.6	7.35	6.4
250° to 275°C.	7.46	7.57	8.1	10.75	7.4
Total	52.76	37.10	47.5	39.95	39.0

and about 24 per cent in the cut from 270°C. to 335°C., with about 26.0 per cent pitch and loss.

According to Garvin (112), to whom the data in Table 61 are due, shale oils of the United States are less volatile than Pennsylvania crude petroleum and somewhat more volatile than Scottish shale oil. Up to 270°C., nearly 53 per cent of Pennsylvania petroleum distills over, as compared with about 48 per cent for Indiana shale oil, 40 per cent for Utah shale oil, and 39 per cent for Colorado shale oil. It is well to compare the results of Table 61 with those of Fig. 24, where it is quite evident that low temperature tars from bituminous coals are closely related to shale oil.

The data in Fig. 26 are plotted from figures reported by Garvin (112). The illustration gives a distillation analysis of the various fractions of Scottish shale oil and two distillation analyses of American gasolines for comparison. It is seen from the illustration that light oil fractionated from crude shale oil is considerably more volatile than ordinary gasoline, while the naphtha cut has a characteristic

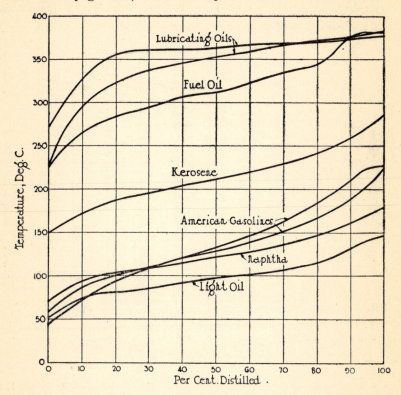

FIG. 26. BOILING RANGE OF SHALE OIL FRACTIONS AND OF AMERICAN GASOLINE

distillation curve very nearly resembling that of gasoline, except that it has a slight deficiency in oils boiling below 100°C. and contains slightly more of the oils boiling between 120°C. and 220°C. The lubricating oils, fractionated from shale oil, contain only about 25 per cent oils boiling below 340°C.

Steam Distilled Tar. It has been pointed out that, although the presence of steam in the retort during low temperature carbonization appears to have little effect on the quantity of tar produced, there is a decided change in the constitution of the product, as indicated by its fractionation.   It has also been shown that the major function of steam is the prevention of secondary reactions by rapid removal of the products of distillation from the carbonization chamber. Steam distilled tar should, therefore, contain more of the primary products of coal.   The curves in Fig. 27, after Davis and Parry (97), compare the distillation range of steam distilled tars at various

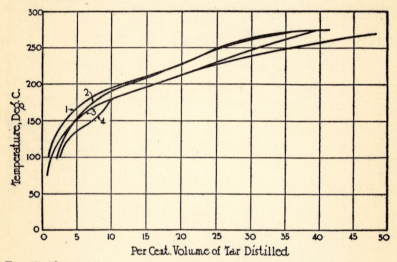

Fig. 27. Boiling Range of Steam Distilled Low Temperature Tar as a Function of Temperature

1 = 475°C. steam distilled tar.   2 = 550°C. steam distilled tar.   3 = 650°C. steam distilled tar.   4 = 550°C. atmospheric distilled tar.

temperatures with that obtained in atmospheric distillation at 550°C. The low temperature tar was distilled from Pennsylvania coal.   The volatility curve for atmospheric tar obtained at 550°C. lies entirely below the curve for steam distillation beyond fractions with a boiling point of 150°C.   This indicates that steam carbonization at low temperatures yields a tar with a larger percentage of higher-boiling constituents than the ordinary product.   It will be noted that under steam distillation the proportion by volume of lighter oils in the tar increases with temperature rise in carbonization, due no doubt to cracking effects.

Variations of the pressure under which fractionation is accomplished is a factor in determining the percentage of tar distilled at a given temperature. Fig. 28, after Davis and Parry (97), shows the effect of fractionation under 4 cm. of mercury pressure, when working with low temperature tar from Pennsylvania coal. In the first place, it will be seen that the steam tar is far more volatile than ordinary tar obtained at the same temperature. This is the reverse of the case when fractionation is carried on under atmospheric pressure, as shown in Fig. 27. Furthermore, above 275°C., the proportion of the steam tar distilled increases far more rapidly than does ordinary

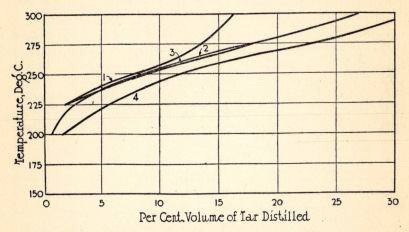

FIG. 28. BOILING RANGE OF VACUUM FRACTIONATED STEAM DISTILLED LOW TEMPERATURE TAR

1 = 550°C. atmospheric distilled tar. 2 = 475°C. steam distilled tar. 3 = 650°C. steam distilled tar. 4 = 550°C. steam distilled tar.

low temperature tar. The volatility of both steam and regular low temperature tars, when fractionated *in vacuo*, is decidedly less than when the distillation is carried out under ordinary pressures. At first thought, this would not be anticipated, because it might be supposed that reduction of pressure would lower the boiling point and, consequently, increase the volume of oil distilled at a given temperature. This would, of course, be the case, if the constituents of the tar existed in the same form in both the crude and the redistilled state. By comparing Fig. 27 and Fig. 28 it will be seen, however, that at 225°C.

only about 2 per cent of the tar is distilled in vacuum fractionation, whereas, about 6 per cent is obtained at the same temperature under ordinary distillation.   This behavior finds easy explanation in the fact that temperatures even as low as 225°C. cause transformation of the tar constituents from primary to secondary compounds.

The unsaturated hydrocarbons, which are present in the tar, must be accounted part of the refining loss, judging from the present standards of the petroleum industry.   Pennsylvania low temperature tar contains about 42 per cent unsaturated material in the light oil, 45 per cent in the middle oil, and 63 per cent in the heavy oil.   This is of importance, from the standpoint of motor fuel, because the unsaturated compounds must be removed before the oil is considered satisfactory for use in internal combustion engines, according to present standards.   Therefore, a low percentage of unsaturated material in the low boiling fraction will greatly increase the yield of motor spirit.

Low temperature tar is usually examined by determining the per cent of each crude fraction soluble in 10 per cent sodium hydroxide, which represents the amount of tar acids present in the cut.   Then the tar is treated with 95 per cent sulphuric acid, which removes the unsaturated hydrocarbons.   The residuum consists of the saturated compounds which are present in the fraction.   The Pennsylvania coals, studied by Davis and Parry (97), have been examined in this manner.   Using a tar obtained at 550°C., they found for ordinary low temperature tar the following percentages of saturated compounds in the various fractions: 50.5 per cent from 0°C. to 175°C.; 30.0 per cent from 175°C. to 225°C.; and 26.0 per cent from 225°C. to 275°C.   With steam distilled tar the quantity of saturated hydrocarbons in the various fractions was 53.1 per cent, 37.0 per cent, and 30.3 per cent, respectively, showing a slight increase.   The percentage of unsaturated compounds in the corresponding fractions of the same tars was 35.0 per cent, 25.0 per cent, and 44.0 per cent, respectively, for the ordinary primary tar and 38.5 per cent, 23.0 per cent, and 43.4 per cent, respectively, for the steam distilled tar. We see that no great change occurred in the proportion of unsaturated material in the fractions of low temperature tar by virtue of the presence of steam.   Under the discussion of tar acids, it was shown that the small increase in saturated compounds, noted above in the case of steam tar, is accounted for, not through any change in the amount of unsaturated material present, but through a reduction in the percentage of tar acids evolved in steam distillation.

The results of Davis and Parry (97) on the examination of low temperature tar from Pennsylvania coal carbonized at 550°C. showed that a larger amount of oil up to 275°C. was present in ordinary low temperature tar than in tar obtained by carbonization in the presence of steam. This higher yield of oil up to 275°C. is doubtlessly the result of some secondary reactions, prevented by the introduction of steam, as indicated by the presence of considerably more pitch in the ordinary tar than in the steam tar.

Full-Scale Retort Tar. Many additional factors enter into the

TABLE 62

Comparison of large-scale low temperature tars

FRACTION	FUEL RESEARCH BOARD (114)	TOZER (255)	NIELSEN (91)	CARBOCOAL (213)
Specific gravity of tar..................	1.033	1.060	1.076	1.070
Tar B.t.u. per pound.................	16,840		16,000	
Fractionation:	*per cent of crude tar*	*per cent of crude tar*	*per cent of crude tar*	*per cent of crude tar*
0° to 170°C.........................	9.1	6.0	4.8	4.2
170° to 230°C.........................	19.4	16.5	20.0	14.6
230° to 270°C.........................	12.8	9.0	14.5	13.8
270°C. to pitch.....................	11.8	36.0	24.0	18.2
Pitch...............................	46.6	32.5	35.0	49.8
Loss...............................	0.3		1.8	0.4

situation when large-scale operations are carried out, so that only rough estimations of commercial retorts can be drawn from comparatively small laboratory experiments. It is important, therefore, to study the products of large-scale carbonization processes when such data are available. In this connection, it should be pointed out that so much depends upon the coal used that it is important that some method of small-scale distillation be devised, so that by the application of certain factors of proportionality a fair idea may be gained as to what might be expected in large-size retorts. A discussion of several laboratory devices for this purpose has already been given in Chapter I, under the subject of assay. A more detailed examination of low temperature tars will be undertaken in the discussion of individual processes, but for present purposes a comparison of the low temperature tars, obtained by several different processes, will suffice. This comparison is given in Table 62. The various retorts, given in the table, represent different types. All are externally heated, except the Nielsen retort, which is a rotary kiln wherein the coal is carbonized by the sensible heat of producer gas. The Fuel Research Board and Tozer processes are horizontal and vertical static retorts, respectively. The Carbocoal system is a two-stage process, involving primary carbonization in a horizontal internally agitated retort, briquetting, and finally secondary carbonization in an inclined oven.

The Fuel Research Board (114) experiments were made with Dalton Main No. 2 coal as the charge. It will be seen that, not only

TABLE 63

Yield of oils from horizontal retort low temperature tar with Dalton Main coal

FRACTION	SPECIFIC GRAVITY 15°C.	VOLUME PER CENT TAR	GALLONS PER GROSS TON
To 160°C. (light naphtha)..	0.829	8.25	1.38
160° to 200°C. (heavy naphtha)........	0.870	4.59	0.77
200° to 270°C (burning oil)............	0.886	11.95	2.00
270° to 300°C. (gas oil)................	0.976	5.46	0.91
300° to 360°C. (light lubricants).......	1.005	5.10	0.85
Total oils...........................		35.33	5.91

is there a variation between the small and large-scale products, but also among the large-scale processes themselves. Especial attention is called to the low yield of the cut, 270°C. to pitch, obtained in the Fuel Research Board experiments, as compared with that obtained in other processes. Furthermore, the large amount of pitch obtained and the generally higher yield of lighter hydrocarbons are all indicative of cracking and secondary reactions in the Fuel Research Board horizontal retorts. The fractions of the tar, obtained from Dalton Main No. 2 coal in the Fuel Research Board horizontal retorts, can be classified according to their use in the trade. The classification in Table 63 gives in gallons per gross ton the quantity of oil that may be expected in these cuts. In addition to the yields reported in the table there was a refinery loss of 4.09 gallons per gross ton, a yield of 2.54 gallons per gross ton of tar acids, and a residuum of 67.5 pounds of pitch per gross ton. The temperature of carbonization was 600°C.

Four British coals, carbonized at low temperatures by the Fuel Research Board (114) in horizontal retorts, averaged 20.7 gallons of tar per gross ton, which yielded upon fractionation 10.3 gallons of crude oil per gross ton of dry coal retorted. This yield of crude oil was reduced to 5.8 gallons per gross ton, upon washing and refining, or a loss of about 44 per cent in the refinement process. It has been shown that low temperature tar contains 35 per cent to 40 per cent unsaturated hydrocarbons, which must be removed from the oils to render them of commercial value, according to the present standards of the petroleum industry, which is the chief competitor of low temperature carbonization as a source of liquid fuels. Thus, the un-

TABLE 64

Average yield of refined oils from British coals in horizontal retorts

FRACTION	GALLONS PER GROSS TON		
	Crude oil	Washed oil	Refined oil
0° to 170°C	1.98	1.72	1.52
170° to 230°C	3.31	1.68	1.60
230° to 270°C	2.50	1.28	1.20
270° to 310°C	2.54	1.62	1.50

saturated material becomes the major portion of the refining loss. Table 64 gives the original fractional yields in gallons of dry tar per gross ton, as well as the yields of washed and refined oils. The reduction in refining varies from about 25 per cent in the first fraction to about 50 per cent in the last.

Low temperature tar has a high fuel value, ranging from 16,000 B.t.u. to 16,500 B.t.u. per pound, but it has a low flash point. Attempts to remedy this fault have been made through removal of the light oils, but so far this procedure has rendered the tar too viscous for use. The question of mixing low temperature tar with mineral oils for use as a fuel has been raised. In a number of instances this has been found impractical because of their immiscibility. Thus, with American petroleums and shale oils, low temperature tar has

TABLE 65

Miscibility of low temperature tar with petroleum

PETROLEUM	SPECIFIC GRAVITY	PER CENT TAR	PER CENT SEPARATION	NATURE OF SEPARATION
American..........	0.902	90	9	Resinous and gummy
		50	19	Resinous and gummy
		35	18	Thick and gummy
		25	4	Black fluid
Burma	0.895	90	8	Resinous and gummy
		75	12	Semi-solid
		50	18	Thick fluid
		35	24	Thick fluid
		25		No separation
Mexican...........	0.936	90	5	Thick fluid
		75	10	Fluid
		50		No separation
		35		No separation
Persian...........	0.942	90		No separation
		75	10	Thick fluid
		50	20	Thick fluid
		25	25	Thick fluid
Shale.............	0.867	90	6	Semi-solid
		75	11	Semi-solid
		80	14	Thick black fluid
		30	5	Thick black fluid
Texas.............	0.926	90	11	Thick and gummy
		75	12	Thick and gummy
		50	20	Thick fluid
		35	18	Thick fluid
		25		No separation
Trinidad...........	0.968	90		No separation when heated during mixing
		50		
		25		

been found to be quite immiscible in all proportions, their mixtures causing a separation of a thick black gummy fluid. Burmese oil formed a stable mixture up to 25 per cent tar and Mexican oil did not give a separation until more than 50 per cent low temperature tar was present. Trinidad was the only petroleum which was miscible in all proportions and then only upon heating during the mixing process. Table 65 shows the results of experiments made on this problem by the Fuel Research Board (114).

A method of overcoming the immiscibility of low temperature tar with crude petroleum has been proposed by Lessing (153). The tar is mixed with petroleum, which causes a separation of the pitch, and the mixture is then subjected to steam distillation, which gives a sharp separation of the pitch and the oil. The distillate is finally fractionated into liquor, neutral oil, tar acids, bases, and pitch. The crude oil is approximately 81 per cent of the mixture and yields on distillation: 56.1 per cent neutral oil; 24.4 per cent tar acids; 0.2 per cent tar bases; and 16.9 per cent pitch.

Tar Cracking. Dalton (154) apparently made the first investigation of the pyrogenic decomposition of hydrocarbons, but no systematic effort was made to study this phenomenon until Bertholet (155) (156) (157) published the results of his researches, in which he found that methane, ethane, and ethylene decomposed into acetylene and other hydrocarbons. The polymerization of acetylene to form aromatic hydrocarbons has been discussed in Chapter I, under the subject of chemistry.

According to Williams-Gardner (158), the views of Bertholet, that acetylene plays an important part in the formation of cyclic compounds, are obsolete and the mechanism of the formation of aromatics must be modified to include, either the momentary existence of unsaturated residuums, which may be transformed by polymerization, hydrogenation, or broken down into carbon and hydrogen, or else the direct formation of olefines and methane, with or without the liberation of hydrogen and without the necessity of forming acetylene. The opinion of Williams-Gardner is substantiated by his own experiments, by the work of Anschutz (159), who obtained aromatic compounds, ranging from benzene to anthracene, from Russian oil residuums by condensation of the complex hydrocarbons without elimination of hydrogen, and by Haber (160) who found that n-heptane decomposed between 600°C. and 700°C. to form methane and the next lowest olefine, that is, amylene, without the formation of acetylene. This is also in agreement with the results of Thorpe and Young (161), who distilled solid paraffins under pressure and obtained amylene, pentane, hexylene, hexane, heptylene, heptane, octylene, octane, nonylene, nonane, undecylene, and undecane, all boiling below 200°C. The latter experimenters concluded, with others, that the decomposition give rise to olefines and lower paraffins with or without the evolution of hydrogen.

Jones (162) observed, from his study of the influence of temperature in cracking low temperature tars, that the mechanism of decomposition consisted essentially of the disintegration of the naphthenes, paraffins, and unsaturated hydrocarbons to form olefines, which condense at higher temperatures to form aromatic compounds. He found that the proportion of higher olefines, which appear in the gas from cracking, reached a maximum at 350°C. and almost disappeared at 750°C. At the latter temperature, naphthalene appeared in the gas and shortly afterwards there was a rapid increase in hydrogen evolution.

The effect of heat on the various constituents of primary tar was studied by Fischer (49), who concluded that the amount of phenol and its lower homologues, initially present in the tar, is augmented by decomposition of the higher members of the series at temperatures below 700°C., aromatic hydrocarbons of the benzene series being formed from the phenols above 700°C. According to Parrish (117), also, below 700°C. the effect of heat upon primary tar is to cause decomposition of the higher boiling constituents into lower boiling compounds of a similar type. The higher phenols, in particular, are sensitive to this cracking effect. In general, the higher the temperature, the greater is the proportion of lower members of a given series of compounds. Decomposition becomes more radical above 700°C., producing aromatic compounds, especially benzene, naphthalene, anthracene, phenol, and pyridine. Most of the higher phenols are entirely cracked into phenol, cresols, and xylenols. The tar bases also decompose to form pyridine and quinoline together with their homologues and derivatives.

The light and middle oils, reported in Table 70 as fractionated from Pennsylvania low temperature tar by Davis and Parry (97), were vaporized in a retort and passed through a cracking chamber which was heated to various temperatures at atmospheric pressure. The raw stock constituted the neutral fraction from 175°C. to 275°C. Table 66 shows the amount of motor spirit obtained from the cracked distillate and scrubbed from the cracked gas. A maximum yield of hydrocarbons boiling below 175°C. was obtained from the neutral oil at a cracking temperature of 750°C. The refining loss, due to the presence of unsaturated material and tar acids in the fraction, amounted to 56 per cent. Analysis of the fraction showed the presence of aromatic hydrocarbons, principally in the form of benzene.

The curves in Fig. 29, after Davis and Parry (97), show that the amount of oil recovered after cracking is almost exactly inversely proportional to the temperature and that the yield of light oil and gas increased with temperature rise, but at a decreasing rate. Comparison of Table 66 and Fig. 29 points out that, although the percentage

TABLE 66

Motor spirit yielded by cracking Pennsylvania light and middle neutral oils

TEMPERATURE	GALLONS PER NET TON COAL			
	Cracked distillate		Spirit from gas	
	Crude	Refined	Crude	Refined
°C.				
650	0.96	0.42	0.06	0.03
750	1.02	0.45	0.21	0.11
820	0.27	0.12	0.59	0.29

of motor spirit contained in the cracked oil reaches a maximum at 750°C., the yield of motor spirit in the gas has no such maximum, but continues to increase with the temperature.

When the anthracene oil fraction from 280°C. to 350°C. of Table 70 was subjected to similar cracking reactions at 800°C. and atmospheric pressure, about 50 per cent of the cracked oil was recovered, yielding per net ton of coal 0.12 gallon of crude light oil, boiling below 175°C. This was no increase from that obtained in the Hempel distillation of the anthracene oil before cracking, so that in cuts up to 200°C., at least, it may be said that little secondary decomposition took place in the anthracene oil fraction. About 47 cubic feet of gas per gallon were evolved during the heating at 800°C. and this yielded upon scrubbing 2.2 per cent of the fraction, or 0.09 gallon of crude light oil per net ton of coal.

Curtis and Beekhuis (163) conducted a number of cracking tests on the neutral oil of low temperature tar from the McIntire process and made from West Virginia coal, containing 3.0 per cent moisture, 36.0 per cent volatile, 50.5 per cent fixed carbon, and 10.5 per cent ash. The coal was carbonized at 620°C. Pressures varying from 100

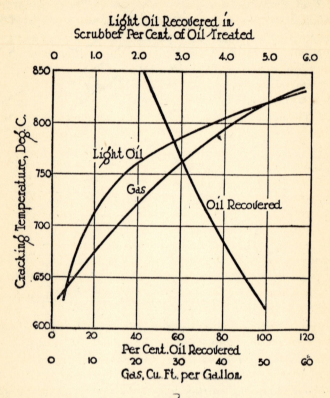

FIG. 29. LIGHT OIL AND FIXED GAS FROM LOW TEMPERATURE TAR AS A
FUNCTION OF CRACKING TEMPERATURE

pounds to 500 pounds per square inch were used in cracking. They found that decomposition was slow below 400°C. but that above 450°C. the formation of coke, accompanied by high gas yield, was rapid. Within the range of their observations, the effect of pressure variation on the rapidity and character of the cracking was slight. By cracking the kerosene fraction of the neutral oil, they found that the yield of oil boiling below 210°C. could be increased from 20 per cent of the neutral oil initially present to about 35 per cent.

Morrell and Egloff (164) cracked a typical low temperature tar from a West Virginia bituminous coal, which yielded about 25 gallons of crude tar per net ton. The crude tar, with a specific gravity of 1.074, was cracked at 100 pounds per square inch pressure and 452°C. temperature to yield 40 per cent cracked distillate with 0.8927 specific gravity. The gasoline fractionated from the cracked distillate amounted to 18.1 per cent of the intial crude tar, and had a specific gravity of 0.8299. The straight distillate from this low temperature tar analyzed 26.5 per cent tar acids, 3.3 per cent tar bases, 44.3 per cent unsaturated hydrocarbons, 9.5 per cent aromatic hydrocarbons, and 16.5 per cent naphthenes and paraffin hydrocarbons, while the cracked distillate from the straight distillate contained 21.3 per cent tar acids, 4.3 per cent tar bases, 27.0 per cent unsaturated hydrocarbons, 20.3 per cent aromatic hydrocarbons, and 27.3 per cent naphthenes and paraffin hydrocarbons.

The neutral oil from this same low temperature tar, having a specific gravity of 0.9484, when cracked at 175 pounds per square inch and 427°C., yielded 50 per cent cracked distillate of 0.8514 specific gravity, which fractionated to give 31.9 per cent of the initial crude tar as gasoline of 0.8090 specific gravity. Analysis of the neutral oil before cracking showed it to be composed of 2.7 per cent tar acids, 4.5 per cent tar bases, 60.6 per cent unsaturated hydrocarbons, 9.4 per cent aromatic hydrocarbons, and 22.8 per cent naphthene and paraffin hydrocarbons, while the cracked distillate analyzed 4.8 per cent tar acids; 4.8 per cent tar bases, 38.4 per cent unsaturated hydrocarbons, 19.4 per cent aromatic hydrocarbons, and 32.7 per cent naphthenes and paraffin hydrocarbons.

These data show a decided decrease upon cracking in the unsaturated compounds and a small increase in the aromatic hydrocarbons. The tar acids in the cracked distillate appeared to be mainly cresols. No naphthalene was present, either in the initial crude tar or in the cracked distillate. While only a trace of anthracene was found in the original low temperature tar, considerable quantities were found after cracking. This was thought remarkable, inasmuch as the temperature of cracking was only 452°C., whereas, anthracene, heretofore, had been regarded as a high temperature product.

Egloff and Morrell (165) also cracked the low temperature tar from an Ohio-Indiana bituminous coal at 100 pounds per square inch and 426°C. The crude tar had a specific gravity of 1.0794 and yielded upon fractionation 29.0 per cent neutral oil, 27.5 per cent tar acids, and 1.6 per cent bases. When cracked, this crude low

TABLE 67
Cracking tests on shale oil

CRUDE SHALE OIL	ORIGIN OF OIL SHALE		
	United States	Australia	France
Specific gravity..........................	0.8905	0.8756	0.8956
Pounds pressure........................	120	150	120
Liquid temperature, °C................	417	433	426
Vapor temperature, °C................	399	398	409
Yield:	*per cent*	*per cent*	*per cent*
Cracked distillate...................	82.0	55.6	61.0
Residuum..........................	0.0	35.4	27.7
Coke..............................	11.8	4.5	5.9
Gas................................	6.9	3.2	4.9
Distillate fractionation:			
Gasoline...........................	52.8%	50.1%	51.0%
Specific gravity....................	0.7499	0.7591	0.7762
Gas oil............................	24.6%	3.5%	7.6%
Specific gravity....................	0.8849	0.8740	0.8778
Gasoline analysis:	*per cent*	*per cent*	*per cent*
Unsaturated hydrocarbons..........	20.1	15.7	16.1
Aromatic hydrocarbons.............	24.9	26.0	28.8
Naphthene hydrocarbons...........	6.2	6.0	6.1
Paraffin hydrocarbons..............	49.8	52.3	49.0

temperature tar yielded 33.9 per cent gasoline, containing 35 per cent tar acids, or an acid-free yield of 22 per cent gasoline. The neutral oil from this same crude stock was cracked at 200 pounds per square inch and 455°C. to yield over 50 per cent high grade anti-knock motor fuel.

Shale oils from the United States, Australia, and France were cracked by Morrell and Egloff (166) under pressures ranging from 120 pounds to 150 pounds per square inch and at temperatures ranging from 398°C. to 433°C. to produce over 50 per cent of the raw stock as gasoline. This cracked gasoline was declared to be a motor fuel of high anti-knock value. The results of the cracking tests on shale oil are given in Table 67.

Cracked Tar Gas. The fixed gas, evolved during cracking, is of an entirely different nature from the gas which is evolved during carbonization of the coal. The latter is the result of destructive distillation, or primary modification of the fuel constituents, while the former is the outcome of secondary decomposition, induced through the medium of heat. An analytical study of the fixed gas from the neutral oil fraction from 175°C. to 275°C. at various crack-

TABLE 68

Analyses of gas evolved in cracking neutral oil fractions

CONSTITUENT	TEMPERATURE		
	650°C.	750°C.	820°C.
Cubic feet gas per gallon..............	9.0	33.0	50.0
B.t.u. per cubic foot..................	1,175	1,035	840
Analysis:	*per cent*	*per cent*	*per cent*
CO_2................................	0.3	0.2	0.0
CO..................................	0.8	0.5	2.1
CH_4................................	36.1	33.9	56.1
C_2H_4..............................	38.9	36.2	21.6
C_2H_6..............................	15.1	10.3	2.0
H_2................................	6.1	5.4	17.4
O_2................................	0.5	2.8	0.2
N_2................................	2.2	10.7	0.6

ing temperatures was made by Davis and Parry (97). This is the same oil fraction from Pennsylvania coal already referred to in Table 66 and Fig. 29, and which will be further discussed in Table 70. Analyses of the fixed gas which was evolved from cracking the neutral oil at various temperatures are given in Table 68.

The permanent gas, obtained from cracking at 800°C. the anthracene oil fraction from 275°C. to 350°C., was almost identical in composition with that liberated by the neutral oil when cracked at 820°C. The large percentage of hydrogen is indicative of much unsaturated material in the cracked oil and this was shown to be the case. The proportion of ethylene and of ethane decreased with rise in the cracking temperature, while the percentage of methane greatly increased. The small percentage of the oxides of carbon which was produced is worthy of notice, especially in comparison with the compositions of the gas from carbonization, as shown in Table 23 and in Fig. 10.

If low temperature neutral oil is essentially the same as petroleum gas oil, there is possibility of it finding a commercial outlet in that market. A great deal of information is thrown on that matter by an examination of the fixed gas obtained in the cracking of petroleum gas oil. Such an experiment has been conducted by Davis and Parry (97), the results of which are given in Table 69.

TABLE 69

Analyses of gas evolved from cracking petroleum gas oil

CONSTITUENT	TEMPERATURE		
	600°C.	700°C.	800°C.
Cubic feet gas per gallon............	12.0	24.0	63.0
B.t.u. per cubic foot.................	538	1,241	922
Analysis:	per cent	per cent	per cent
CO_2................................	1.3	0.2	0.0
CO...................................	0.9	0.6	0.5
CH_4................................	11.2	25.3	28.8
C_2H_4..............................	22.0	50.0	33.3
C_2H_6..............................	12.2	15.2	8.7
H_2.................................	1.5	4.6	5.1
O_2.................................	7.1	1.1	5.3
N_2.................................	43.3	3.0	18.3

The gas, evolved in cracking petroleum gas oil, has about the same thermal value as that obtained from the low temperature tar neutral oil, but a somewhat larger quantity of gas is produced. Far less hydrogen and methane is evolved from the former, but a very large percentage of nitrogen. It might be said, in general, that the two oils are not greatly different and that low temperature tar neutral oil is comparable with the petroleum gas oil fraction.

Hydrogenation. Upon consideration of the facts hitherto presented, it appears that primary tar normally consists of aliphatic hydrocarbons and phenolic compounds. Whatever small percentage of light aromatic compounds that is found to be present in the tar must be derived from reduction of these phenolic substances. This suggests the possibility of entirely reducing the tar acids to low-boiling oils for use as a motor fuel. This problem has been studied by Fischer (167) and by Fischer and Schroeder (168), who passed elementary hydrogen together with a mixture of phenols and hydrocarbons through a tube heated to 750°C. A great deal was found to depend upon the nature of the reaction tube, but they discovered that a tinned iron tube was suitable for commercial processing and avoided the excessive deposition of carbon which sometimes plugged the tube. The deposition of carbon was apparently accelerated by iron. However, if water gas was used as a source of hydrogen for hydrogenation, the tinned coating peeled away, as a result no doubt of the action of carbon monoxide in the gas. An iron reaction tube, coated internally with iron sulphide, was finally adopted by Fischer and Zerbe (169) to overcome this last difficulty. With the improved form of hydrogenating tube, little separation of carbon occurred and the phenols were reduced to benzene homologues. With cresols and xylenols, the conversion to motor fuel was up to 99 per cent and 72 per cent, respectively, of the theoretical.

Whether or not hydrogenation at high pressures and high temperatures, according to the Bergius process (170) (171) (172), is applicable to low temperature tar acids has not yet been demonstrated. According to Fischer (173), at the temperature of 400°C. employed in such circumstances, hydrogenation could be successful only at hydrogen pressures exceeding the dissociation pressure of hydrogen in the compounds to be produced. At lower temperatures of 200°C., the reaction velocity would be entirely too slow. The introduction of a catalyst to accelerate the reaction rate at lower temperatures necessitates excessive and expensive purification of the reaction gases to eliminate sulphur and avoid poisoning the catalyst. Fischer and Schroeder (174) obtained the conversion of the phenolic portion of primary tar into oils under pressure at 400°C. with nascent hydrogen, derived from sodium formate and from carbon monoxide and steam.

Sabatier and Senderens (175) showed that naphthalene vapor, mixed with an excess of hydrogen, could be passed over finely divided nickel at 175°C. to produce decahydronaphthalene, with a boiling point of 187°C., and at 200°C. to form tetrahydronaphthalene, with a boiling point of 205°C. Fischer (176) (177) obtained the partial liquefaction of naphthalene, to the extent of about 35 per cent, by treating it for about half an hour at 150 pounds per square inch pressure in the presence of aluminum chloride. From these experiments, it is apparent that naphthalene can be considered as a raw material for the manufacture of motor fuel. On account of the limited amount of naphthalene present in primary tar, however, it is doubtful if this process is important from the standpoint of low temperature carbonization, unless it be in the secondary treatment of cracked tar products.

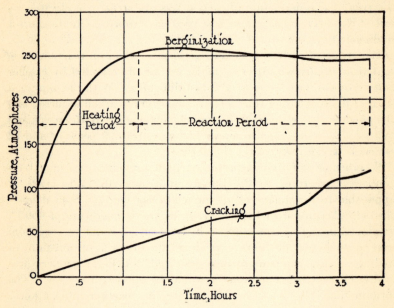

FIG. 30. REACTION PRESSURE OF BERGINIZATION AND CRACKING AS A
FUNCTION OF TIME

For the most part, cracked motor fuel contains a high proportion of unsaturated compounds, which, according to present standards, are more or less undesirable, due principally to unpleasant odors and darkening of the distillate. The method of hydrogenation, developed by Bergius (172), and commonly known as berginization, in which the distillate is cracked at the required temperature under a high pressure of elementary hydrogen, largely overcomes this difficulty and yields a distillate containing only a small percentage of unsaturates. Fig. 30, after Kling (178), shows the pressure developed in berginization and in cracking the same oil. It is obvious that, as the heating period is prolonged, the pressure of the cracked vapor becomes greater and greater. During berginization, however, there is a rapid increase of pressure during initial heating but, finally, when equilibrium has been reached, the pressure decreases at constant temperature, thereby indicating hydrogenation. Berginization appears to require close pressure and temperature control, as indicated by the negative experiments of Waterman and Perquin (179), who were unable to effect hydrogenation of paraffin wax at 435°C. and initial pressures of 600 pounds per square inch and of Skinner and Graham (180), who were unable to secure hydrogen absorption by low temperature tar, obtained at 600°C. from Fifeshire cannel coal and redistilled at 450°C., when the tar was treated under 1560 pounds per square inch hydrogen pressure at 411°C. for 4 hours. Bergius used initial pressures of as much as 1500 pounds per square inch, which rose in some cases to above 3000 pounds per square inch when the autoclave was heated to the required temperature.

Motor Fuel. Motor fuel is obtained directly from two sources in low temperature carbonization, the tar and the gas, and it can be obtained from three subordinate sources by special processing, such as cracking of the heavy tar fraction, hydrogenation of the tar acids, and liquefaction of the gas by high pressures and low temperatures.

The entire fraction up to 200°C., when freed of the tar acids, bases, and unsaturated material, may be used as an internal combustion engine fuel. This fraction consists mostly of higher paraffins, unsaturated hydrocarbons, and in some cases a small quantity of benzene and toluene. This cut may yield anywhere from one to 3 gallons of refined motor spirit per net ton of coal. Davis and Parry (97), in their work on the low temperature carbonization of Pennsylvania coals paid special attention to the yield of products valuable as motor fuel. Using the tar obtained from retorting Freeport coal at 550°C. in a stationary vertical retort, they examined the light oil fraction obtained from the tar and the possibility of cracking the higher-boiling hydrocarbons. The fractionation of this tar is given in Table 70.

The entire fraction, boiling under 175°C., was considered a crude light oil suitable as a motor fuel. It was found that 42 per cent of this cut consisted of unsaturated hydrocarbons and 17 per cent of tar acids, which must be removed in refinement before the oil could be sold to the trade. This means that the crude yield of 2.80 gallons must be reduced 59 per cent to 1.15 gallons of refined motor spirit obtained from this fraction.

The recovery of light oils in the gas is not a simple process. It can be accomplished by condensation, scrubbing, or adsorption. Fischer and Gluud (181) recovered the motor spirit from the low temperature gas in their experiments by scrubbing with paraffin oil and subsequent

TABLE 70

Fractional yields of oil from Pennsylvania low temperature tar

FRACTIONS	SPECIFIC GRAVITY	PER CENT CRUDE TAR	GALLONS OIL PER NET TON
0° to 175°C. (light oil)...............	0.853	8.5	2.80
175° to 225°C. (middle oil).............	0.962	16.0	5.26
225° to 275°C. (heavy oil).............	0.998	19.5	6.44
280° to 350°C.(anthracene oil).........		11.2	3.70

TABLE 71

Motor spirit yielded in scrubbing of low temperature gas

UNIT	HOURS OF SCRUBBING	
	5.0	8.1
Cubic feet gas scrubbed............................	60.0	49.7
Cubic feet gas scrubbed per hour..................	12.0	6.12
Cubic centimeters wash oil per hour...............	1608	1394
Cubic centimeters wash oil per cubic foot gas......	134	229
Concentration of spirit in wash oil........	1.60%	1.04%
Gallons crude motor spirit per gross ton.....	1.85	2.02
Gallons refined motor spirit per gross ton.........	1.67	1.74
Specific gravity refined spirit 15°C............ . .	0.731	0.731

rectification. They obtained a yield of 3.8 gallons to 2.0 gallons per net ton of coal carbonized, representing 1.23 per cent and 0.67 per cent of the coal, respectively. The Fuel Research Board (114) also carried out scrubbing experiments on the gas from low temperature carbonization in horizontal retorts, as shown in Table 71. They recovered 1.68 gallons of refined spirit per gross ton of coal. It had a specific gravity of 0.731 at 15°C. Dalton Main No. 2 coal, which gave 3,200 cubic feet of gas at the temperature of distillation, was used in the work of the Fuel Research Board. The duration of scrubbing, as well as the rate of washing, was varied in order to determine the influence of these factors on the quantity of light oil recovered.

The refining loss of motor spirit, obtained from low temperature gas, is less than that occurring in the light fraction of the tar. Scrubbing greatly reduces the percentage of hydrocarbons present in the gas and it has been pointed out, notably in Fig. 13 and elsewhere, that low temperature gas is in part characterized by a low proportion of unsaturated hydrocarbons. Consequently, it is anticipated that there should be a low refining loss in the light oils scrubbed from the gas. The rate of scrubbing with wash oil does not appear to have as

TABLE 72

Yield of light oils from low temperature investigations

INVESTIGATOR	CARBONIZATION TEMPERATURE	CRUDE LIGHT OIL PER CENT OF TAR	MAXIMUM TEMPERATURE OF CUT
	°C.	per cent	°C.
Parr and Olin (37)	750–800	17.2	210
Davis and Parry (97)	550	15.5	175
Gluud (23)	500	13.0	200
Runge (183)	730	12.5	
Fuel Research Board (114)	600	11.2	170
Davis and Berger (184)	600–650	6.8	175
Lewes (17)	400–500	3.1	170
Morgan and Soule (48)	730	0.6	173

great an effect on the amount of spirit recovered as the quantity of wash oil used per cubic foot of gas scrubbed.

Engelhardt (182) investigated the recovery of light oil from illuminating gas by activated charcoal, the condensed vapors being subsequently liberated by treatment with superheated steam. This same process was used by Davis and Parry (97) in the recovery of light oils from the gas evolved in the low temperature carbonization of Pennsylvania coals. They found that the efficiency of the charcoal was greatly reduced in the presence of hydrogen sulphide and water vapor. Thus, while up to 3 gallons of crude light oil per net ton of coal were recovered in ordinary distillation, only one gallon was obtained under steam distillation. By this method they recovered an average of 2.75 gallons of crude motor spirit per net ton of coal from six different coals. This light oil had a specific gravity of 0.740 and represented 0.838 per cent of the coal charged. It contained 23 per cent unsaturated hydrocarbons, so that the net yield of refined spirit was reduced to 2.23 gallons. A recent development, utilizing this same principle of adsorption, has been the introduction of silica gel in place of activated charcoal.

Table 72 shows the yield of light oils reported by a number of different investigators in low temperature carbonization. All of these experiments were made in externally heated retorts, except those of Gluud (23) and a few runs by Parr and Olin (37), in which cases internal heating was used. Lewes (17) used a gas coal; Runge (183) used a by-product coal; Parr and Olin (37) used Illinois coal; Davis and Berger (184) used Freeport coal; Morgan and Soule (48) used Pittsburgh Terminal coal; Davis and Parry (97) used coal from the Freeport bed; and the Fuel Research Board (114) used Dalton Main No. 2. Attention must be called to the fact that the yields in Table 72 are crude light oil and large reductions occur in refining, as has been pointed out, so that the yield of refined motor spirit will be considerably less. It is interesting to note the wide variation in the yields reported and caution must be sounded that some observers report their tar yields before dehydration and their crude tar yields are swelled by the moisture content. The high yields of Parr and Olin, and also of Gluud, are due in part to the fact that they included higher boiling hydrocarbons in their light oil fraction. The figure given by Davis and Parry includes the light oil obtained from both the tar and the gas.

The explosive range of low temperature motor spirit is over 20 per cent greater than that of petrol, while a mixture of equal parts of motor spirit and petrol has an explosive range 30 per cent greater than petrol alone and 35 per cent greater than benzol, according to the Fuel Research Board (114). The explosive range, expressed as cubic centimeters of fuel per cubic foot of air at 15°C., was 2.7 to 6.7 for benzol of 0.881 specific gravity; 2.5 to 7.3 for petrol of 0.723 specific gravity; 2.3 to 9.5 for low temperature motor spirit of 0.731 specific gravity; and 2.5 to 10.5 for a mixture of equal parts of petrol and motor spirit.

The motor spirit obtained from low temperature distillation of coal is miscible in all proportions with benzol and petrol for use as a fuel in internal combustion engines. With the growing use of alcohol in the field of motor fuels, something should be said concerning the miscibility of low temperature motor spirit with alcohol. The amount of low temperature motor spirit held in solution by alcohol depends largely upon the strength of the latter, thus, at 10°C., the Fuel Research Board (114) found 95 per cent alcohol held as much as 74.2 per cent motor spirit in solution, while 90 per cent alcohol held but 16.3 per cent and 85 per cent alcohol retained only 7.1 per cent. With a mixture of benzol and 95 per cent alcohol, in equal proportions, low temperature motor spirit is dissolved up to 60 per cent at 10°C. Even with refined spirit, there is a slight tendency for resinous matter to deposit on standing, thus darkening the fuel, but alcohol prevents deposit by dissolving the resins which separate.

It has been pointed out that Davis and Parry (97) recovered 1.15 gallons per net ton of refined motor spirit from the light oil fraction of low temperature tar which they obtained from Pennsylvania coal and 2.23 gallons per net ton of refined motor fuel from the low temperature gas, netting 3.38 gallons per net ton which were obtained directly without additional processing. It has also been pointed out that they obtained an additional 0.66 gallon per net ton by cracking the higher-boiling tar fractions. We have already seen that other Pennsylvania coals yielded 5.45 gallons per net ton of tar acids, 56.5 per cent of which consisted of phenol, cresols, and xylenols, which can be converted to motor fuel by hydrogenation at an efficiency of 72 per cent to 99 per cent of the theoretical maximum conversion, which ranges from 64 per cent to 87 per cent, depending on the initial and final products. On this basis, an additional 1.5 gallons to 2.5 gallons per net ton of motor fuel could be obtained. By employing these additional means, there appears the possibility of increasing the total motor fuel yield to 5.5 gallons or 7.5 gallons, or even more, per net ton of coal. The desirability of associating hydrogenation with low temperature carbonization, to effect an increase of motor fuel by hydrogenating the tar acids, has been stressed by Gentry (185), but Egloff and Morrell (165) see no reason at all why the tar acids should be removed from the motor fuel, as demanded by present standards.

Fuel Oil. Crude low temperature tar has a viscosity quite suitable for fuel oil, but according to Lander and McKay (186) its flash point is far too low. On the other hand, if sufficient low volatile constituents are removed by distillation to increase its flash point, the crude tar becomes too viscous for use as a liquid fuel. However, the tar may be fractionated in such a way as to obtain a distillate which meets all the requirements of a fuel oil, both from the standpoints of flash point and of viscosity. Furthermore, there is no evident reason why the fuel oil, if too viscous, cannot be heated before firing to increase its fluidity. The immisibility of low temperature tar with other fuel oils has already been dealt with.

CHAPTER IV

Low Temperature Coke

High and Low Temperature Coke. Agitation for a smokeless fuel, which would eradicate the civil nuisance of smoke, together with the shortage of oil in some countries of the world have been largely responsible for the development of low temperature carbonization. Added to this incentive was the shortage of hard coals during the Great War and the possibility of obtaining a substitute in the form of an easily burning coke. Although some small amount of information was in hand at that time, it was soon realized that insufficient data were available for undertaking large-scale operations in coking at low temperatures. Research was the obvious remedy and, in recent years, a great many investigations have been made in this field both in the United States and abroad.

In high temperature coking, such as occurs in the metallurgical and gas industries, only a very small percentage of volatile matter remains in the coal after carbonization, so that from 64 per cent to 74 per cent by weight of the charge is converted into coke. Low temperature distillation, on the other hand, does not remove entirely the volatile constituents from the coal and, therefore, the percentage yield by weight of coke may be expected to be somewhat larger than in the case of gas and metallurgical cokes. Low temperature ovens yield about 66 per cent to 76 per cent of the charge as coke. The proximate and ultimate analyses of the three types of coke given in Table 73 furnish an excellent basis for comparison.

The outstanding peculiarity of the low temperature carbonization residuum, from a chemical standpoint, is the large proportion of volatile matter remaining in the coke. To this fact must be attributed many, though not all, of the desirable properties of this material as a fuel. As a consequence of the high volatile content, we find a somewhat greater thermal value in the coke which has been subjected to less extreme measures of carbonization. The volatile matter often exceeds 12 per cent. The semi-coke, or low temperature coke, whose analysis is given in Table 73, represents the average of that obtained from six full-scale retorts. The large

129

percentage of hydrogen recorded for the semi-coke, as compared with the cokes from other sources, is present in the form of volatile hydrocarbons. Low temperature coke is also characterized by the presence of considerable oxygen. The experimenters make no comment on this peculiarity in their reports, but doubtlessly it arises from the existence of volatile oxygenated hydrocarbons, such as the organic alcohols and possibly the aldehydes and ketones in small quantities. It might be pointed out, at this time, that the nitrogen content of low temperature coke is greater than that of the high temperature varieties. This fact will be taken up under the subject of ammonia

TABLE 73

Analyses of low and high temperature cokes

CONSTITUENT	OVEN COKE	GAS COKE	LOW TEMPERATURE COKE
	per cent	*per cent*	*per cent*
Proximate analysis:			
Moisture............................	3.0	1.1	2.2
Volatile matter......................	0.5	1.9	7.6
Fixed carbon........................	86.5	85.5	80.5
Ash................................	10.1	11.6	10.6
B.t.u. per pound...................	12,180	12,375	12,480
Ultimate analysis:	*per cent*	*per cent*	*per cent*
Carbon.............................	86.4	85.6	77.9
Hydrogen...........................	1.1	0.4	2.2
Oxygen.............................	0.5	0.4	4.9
Nitrogen...........................	0.7	1.2	1.5
Sulphur............................	2.2	0.8	1.6
Ash................................	8.9	11.7	12.6

and nitrogen recovery. How nearly the problem of anthracizing bituminous coal is solved by the low temperature process of carbonization is demonstrated by comparing Table 1 and Table 2 with Table 73. It will be seen that semi-coke has a proximate analysis almost identical with that of anthracite and that the ultimate analyses are not greatly at variance.

Semi-Coke. In their experiments on the coking of Illinois coal, Parr and Olin (31) obtained a coke yield of 77.5 per cent for 3-hour periods of distillation and 72.5 per cent for 6-hour periods. This represents 1,550 pounds and 1,450 pounds of semi-coke per net ton of coal, respectively. By recalling that at a given temperature of carbonization the volume of gas evolved is a function of the duration of distillation, as shown in Fig. 14, it will be seen that the decrease in coke yield, resulting from extension of the retorting period arises from the removal of more of the volatile matter.

Pennsylvania coal, coked by Davis and Parry (97), produced an average of 72.2 per cent, or 1,444 pounds, of semi-coke per net ton of coal. Their yields ranged from 70.0 per cent to 74.8 per cent. On the other hand, Parr and Layng (101), from twelve experiments on Utah coals, similar in analysis to that of bituminous coal given in Table 1 and Table 2, obtained an average of 61.2 per cent, or 1,224

TABLE 74

Proximate analyses of low temperature cokes from United States coals

CONSTITUENT	ILLINOIS COAL	PENNSYLVANIA COAL	UTAH COAL
	Temperature		
	450°C.	550°C.	750°C.
	per cent	per cent	per cent
Fixed carbon........................	64.3	74.8	81.6
Volatile matter......................	25.9	9.0	9.1
Ash................................	9.1	15.7	9.0
Moisture...........................	0.34	0.53	0.64
Sulphur............................	1.66	1.86	0.34
B.t.u. per pound...................	13,350	12,800	12,780

pounds of semi-coke per net ton of charge. For the average yield of semi-coke, however, this latter figure is exceedingly low.

Table 74 gives the average proximate analyses of semi-cokes obtained from various bituminous coals of the United States. While it is recognized that these tests are for different coals, certain deductions can be made with regard to the influence of temperature. It will be observed that the percentage of fixed carbon, for example, increases as the temperature of distillation advances. Such a change is to be expected, since the higher the temperature, the less volatile matter remains in the residuum. Monett (100) also distilled Utah coals at 550°C. His yields of coke ranged from 1,464 pounds to 1,250 pounds per net ton, representing from 73.2 per cent of the charge to 62.5 per cent. The semi-coke had a thermal value ranging from

13,516 B.t.u. to 12,227 B.t.u. per pound and it contained from 0.86 per cent to 1.93 per cent moisture; 19.84 per cent to 10.46 per cent volatile matter; 81.67 per cent to 64.35 per cent fixed carbon; 14.81 per cent to 5.94 per cent ash; and 0.40 per cent to 1.09 per cent sulphur. Analyses of these Utah coals have been given in Table 15 and Table 16, while the composition of the low temperature gas obtained from them was discussed under the subject of American coals in Chapter II.

Table 75 shows the temperature variation of the constituents of Farmville, N. C., coal which originally contained 37.08 per cent volatile matter, 52.95 per cent fixed carbon, 9.03 per cent ash, and which had a heating value of 14,336 B.t.u. per pound, as determined

TABLE 75

Temperature variation of low temperature coke analysis for North Carolina coal

TEMPERATURE	COKE	VOLATILE MATTER	FIXED CARBON	ASH	B.T.U. PER POUND
°C.	per cent	per cent	per cent	per cent	
200	89.67	26.82	63.71	9.25	14,280
300	74.33	8.95	81.70	9.31	14,210
360	72.68	3.40	86.77	9.80	14,135
420	69.70	2.53	87.39	10.05	14,096
480	68.50	1.61	88.07	10.29	14,058
540	66.00	0.93	89.03	10.02	14,045
600	66.00	0.37	89.14	10.49	14,032
660	65.50	0.12	89.11	10.77	14,000

by Giles and Vilbrandt (99). We have seen already in Fig. 12 the manner in which temperature influences the composition of gas evolved from this coal and in Table 58 its influence on the volatility of the low temperature tar. It must be said that this particular coal is an exception and the percentage volatile remaining in the coke at a given temperature is of the order of that to be found in an average semi-coke at approximately 200°C. higher temperature. There is a decided change at 540°C., accompanied by a voluminous evolution of gas. Below that temperature, the change in the coke structure is uniform but slight, while above 540°C. to as far as 660°C. there is little apparent change in the residuum. The heating value of the coke is high. It has been pointed out before that Farmville,

N. C., coal decomposes very easily, so that only 8.95 per cent volatile matter is left at 300°C. Above 540°C., where the major decomposition occurs, less than one per cent volatile matter remains in the coke.

TABLE 76

Temperature variation of char analysis from Washington lignite

TEMPERATURE	CHAR	VOLATILE MATTER	ASH	B.T.U. PER POUND
°C.	per cent	per cent	per cent	
150	90.2	38.0	14.3	11,800
200	85.1	31.8	15.1	12,210
250	74.1	26.7	17.5	12,500
300	70.6	22.5	18.2	12,690
350	67.2	19.4	19.3	12,790
400	66.1	16.2	19.5	12,870
450	65.3	13.1	19.9	12,930
500	64.2	9.9	20.1	12,980
550	63.1	6.8	20.4	13,020
600	62.1	4.1	20.7	13,040

TABLE 77

Analyses of peat char from Fuel Research Board vertical retorts

CONSTITUENT	RAW PEAT	980°C. CHAR.	848°C. CHAR.
Proximate analysis:	per cent	per cent	per cent
Moisture............................	20.1		3.37
Volatile matter......................	49.6	3.13	9.96
Fixed carbon........................	26.7	78.87	82.69
Ash.................................	3.5	8.60	9.98
B.t.u. per pound....................	7,660	11,380	12,210
Ultimate analysis:	per cent	per cent	per cent
Ash.................................	3.6	9.49	10.33
Carbon..............................	57.6	85.78	84.81
Hydrogen............................	5.2	0.52	0.39
Sulphur.............................	0.51	0.60	0.61
Nitrogen............................	1.42	0.42	0.53
Oxygen..............................	30.8	3.19	3.33

In Table 29 and Table 59, the composition of the gas and the volatility of the tar from Washington lignite have already been discussed. Benson and Canfield (108) also determined in Table 76 the effect of temperature variation on the proximate analysis of the

char. Originally the air-dried lignite contained 39.4 per cent
volatile matter, which was reduced to 4.1 per cent at 600°C. The
percentage ash varies inversely as the percentage of volatile matter
remaining within the residuum. Up to 500°C., the lignite char was
dull black and it more or less retained its original form. From
500°C. to 600°C. the lumps had a metallic luster and swelled slightly
larger than the initial size.

It has been pointed out before, that the Fuel Research Board
(106) carbonized peat in vertical retorts, obtaining gas of the composition shown in Table 27 and tar of the character given in Table 60.
Both proximate and ultimate analyses of the peat char, obtained
from these experiments, are given in Table 77. The principal point
to be noted in the carbonization of peat is the increase in calorific

TABLE 78

Proximate analyses of low temperature cokes from full-scale processes

PROCESS	FIXED CARBON	VOLATILE MATTER	MOISTURE	ASH
	per cent	per cent	per cent	per cent
Fuel Research Board (114)	79.3	8.4	0.5	11.9
Coalite (187)	83.6	10.0		6.4
Maclaurin (188)	86.7	4.8		8.5
Carbocoal (189)	85.6	2.8	1.8	9.8
Nielsen (91)	70.7	11.5	1.9	15.9
Tozer (190)	75.5	10.3		12.3

value by removal of the large amount of moisture present. North
and Garbe (121) report a test on carbonizing Shetland peat at 500°C.
in Tozer retorts. The raw peat contained initially 21.4 per cent
moisture and 73.8 per cent volatile matter, yielding on distillation
char to the extent of 33.6 per cent of the original charge and containing 18.6 per cent volatile matter, 71.4 per cent fixed carbon, and
9.9 per cent ash.

In Table 78 are given the analyses of six cokes from full-scale low
temperature processes. The experiments of the Fuel Research
Board (114) were carried out in their horizonal retorts, while those on
Coalite (187) were in that company's vertical retorts. Coke from
the Maclaurin (188) retort was carbonized by internal heating
through the agency of the sensible heat of producer gas. Carbocoal

(189) was produced through primary distillation, briquetting, and subsequent secondary carbonization in an inclined retort. The semi-coke from the Nielsen (91) process was produced by carbonizing the coal in a rotary retort by means of the sensible heat from producer gas. The Tozer (190) process utilized a static cast-iron vertical retort.

Porosity. A great deal of the ease in combustibility of semi-coke depends on its high volatile content, but the coke structure also has a great influence. One of the main factors, from a physical viewpoint, is the area available for oxidation. Some of the desirable features, however, of low temperature coke can be attained only by allowing a certain proportion of the volatile matter to remain, notable among these is a low ignition temperature.

When coal is coked, it first reaches a fusion temperature and

TABLE 79

Variation of porosity of coke with the temperature of carbonization

COKE	TEMPERATURE	SPECIFIC GRAVITY	POROSITY
	°C.		per cent
Low temperature......................	550	1.59	44.7
Gasworks.............................	850	1.87	52.5
Coke oven...........................	1,100	1.87	48.0

becomes plastic. Then, as the temperature is raised, gases are evolved and form bubbles throughout the mass until it becomes a foam. These bubbles then break, allowing the gases to escape. Rigidity finally sets in upon cooling and leaves the cellular structure of the coke. If the plastic material is not confined by walls, the bubbles swell the mass and cause it to become light and porous. But the pressure developed against retaining walls compresses the material to form a dense coke. Upon consideration of combustibility, it would appear, that the more numerous and, hence, the smaller the pores, the greater is the area exposed for oxidation, and, therefore, the more easily the coke should burn. A point is reached, however, where the outside surface of the lump exposed to oxidation is so reduced by the pores as to neutralize the result. Consequently a point of apparent porosity is reached where there is maximum combustibility. We shall see later that combustibility depends more on the microscopic cells of the coke than on the large pores.

Table 79 shows that different temperatures of carbonization produce coke of different porosities. The determinations were made by Cobb and Greenwood (191), who used a coal with 1.27 initial specific gravity. From this table, it is evident that low temperature coke is less porous than either gasworks or coke oven coke. We shall see later that, nevertheless, semi-coke is far more reactive and combustible than either of the others for several reasons, but primarily because of a microscopic cellular structure.

Coherency. Coherency depends upon the presence of sufficient resinous bodies to act as binding material. In their absence, various methods have been resorted to in order to secure a coherent carbonization residuum. One method of frequent use, is the blending of coking and non-coking coals, so that the resins present in the former will serve to bind the entire mass. Non-coking bituminous coals give a coke which is very friable and unsuitable for transportation, while coking coals cause trouble in the design of low temperature retorts. A blended charge yields a residuum upon distillation that is sufficiently strong, from the mechanical standpoint, and free, in a large part, of the retort design annoyances. It occasionally happens that a good coke is obtained without blending, solely by using the product of the seam as a whole, but as this situation is not of common occurrence, efforts have been made to provide means for coking the non-coking coals, without resort to blending, in order to save transportation charges.

No indication whatever of a coal's coking qualities can be determined from its proximate analysis, for it depends entirely on the proportion of resinous material present. There are two types of coals, the swelling and the non-swelling, depending on whether or not the volume of the resultant coke is greater than or equal to the initial volume for the coal. The coke residuum of non-swelling coals is usually non-coherent and friable, while the swelling coals form a good coke upon carbonization. For this reason, these two classes of coals are often classed as non-coking and coking.

If the resins are in excess, other difficulties arise in the possibility of foaming, and, here again, a number of remedies have been proposed. Cruickshanks in 1841 is said to have been the first to propose the blending of coking and non-coking coals, so that the resinous deficiencies of the one can be balanced against the excesses of the other. This method is successful, but suffers the economic disadvantage of transportation. To avoid this objection, Roberts (192) suggested that coke breeze be blended with the retort charge. This proposal, however, reduces the quantity of virgin coal that is carbonized and, hence, the output of the plant.

Parr and Olin (31) found that the texture of the coke could be altered by means of exerting pressure during carbonization. When pistons were used for this purpose, however, the outer layers of the charge, which had undergone fusion, hardened and formed a shell surrounding the inner mass, which latter became excessively porous due to the inability of the gases to escape. Efforts to overcome this by use of additional pressure resulted in fracture of the hardened shell and the coke was withdrawn from the retort in small broken pieces. They then resorted to ramming the charge into the retort and applying the pressure entirely before carbonization with decidedly more success. The semi-coke thus produced had a very good crushing strength and fine texture.

Taylor and Porter (96) found that bituminous coal, which gave a friable coke at atmospheric pressures, even when slowly heated, gave a dense coke when carbonized *in vacuo* at a pressure of about 3 cm. of mercury. This is probably due to the fact that the gases evolved are sucked away before large bubbles can form in the fused mass.

Swelling. When coals contain a large proportion of resinous bodies, swelling occurs during coking. When first heated, these coals slightly contract. This probably results from the melting of certain constituents between 350°C. and 450°C. A secondary contraction usually develops later at much higher temperatures, during coking proper. This is attributed to the liberation of gaseous products. Between the two contraction periods, the coke expands as the result of entrapped bubbles of gas in the plastic mass. Expansion is rather slow at first until the center of the charge reaches a given temperature, at which point expansion increases enormously. This swelling is usually greater than the initial contraction and develops a pressure which is liable to injure the retort or, at least, to render discharge difficult. A great many of the past failures encountered in low temperature retorts may be attributed directly or indirectly to this phenomenon.

Audibert and Delmas (193) studied the intumescence of coal under various conditions of time, temperature, and rate of heating. Their method of determination was to place the finely ground coal in a heated metal cylinder, equipped with a counterpoised piston to transmit expansion and contraction of the charge to an indicating pointer. Fig. 31 shows the swelling of Loire coal, as a function of the time of heating, for various constant temperatures. This is a most interesting diagram. It discloses that at such low temperatures as 390°C. there is no swelling of the charge at all, but an actual shrinkage amounting to about 11 per cent. At 400°C., there is an

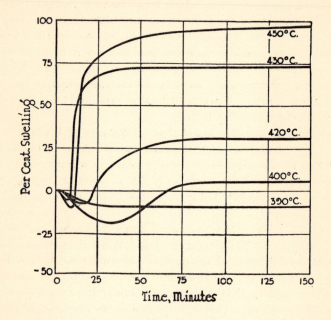

FIG. 31. SWELLING IN LOIRE COAL AS A FUNCTION OF TIME AND OF TEMPERATURE

initial contraction during fusion, amounting to as much as 20 per cent, at the end of 35 minutes heating, after which the coal expands and finally, after 75 minutes heating, reaches a steady volume about 6 per cent greater than its initial condition. As the temperature advances, the initial contraction, which always takes place at fusion, reaches a maximum at some temperature which is characteristic of the given coal. It then decreases gradually until at 450°C., in the case of Loire coal, the initial contraction amounts to only about 6 per cent at the end of approximately 10 minutes, after which the coal rapidly swells to an increase of 75 per cent over its original volume in 25 minutes, thereafter continuing to swell at a very slow rate. In this particular coal the swelling amounted to 95 per cent at the end of 150 minutes.

Fig. 32 shows for Béthune coal the variations of swelling, as a function of the temperature, for several different rates of heating.

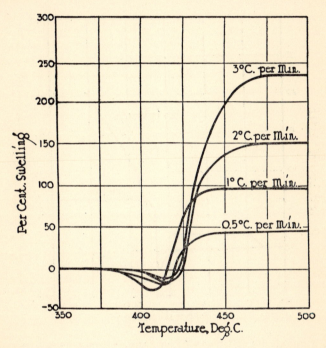

FIG. 32. SWELLING IN BÉTHUNE COAL AS A FUNCTION OF TEMPERATURE AND OF RATE OF HEATING

It is interesting to note how rapidly the swelling increases with the rate of heating when the same final temperatures are attained. This family of curves has a common characteristic, in that there is an initial period of contraction during fusion amounting to as much as 20 per cent of the original volume at 400°C. to 425°C., following which there is a rapid expansion at 425°C. to 450°C. which ceases rather abruptly and leaves the charge at constant volume. The final swelling of Béthune coal amounts to about 47 per cent at 440°C., when heated at 0.5°C. per minute; 95 per cent at 440°C., when heated at 1°C. per minute; 150 per cent at 475°C., when heated at 2°C. per minute; and about 225 per cent at 475°C., when heated at the rate of 3°C. per minute. Audibert and Delmas (193) concluded that for each coal there existed a rate of heating below which intumescence is not observed, whatever the final temperature

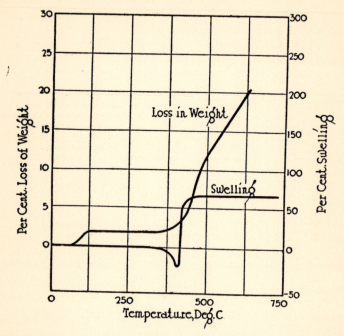

Fig. 33. Comparison of Loss in Weight and of Swelling in Durham Coal as a Function of Temperature

reached may be. However, the rate of heating may be so low as to render it impractical in practice to use this means of avoiding excessive swelling. Swelling is observed only at rates of heating in which fusion of the coal particles is complete, *i.e.*, when the coal becomes fused into a homogeneous mass, and intumescence never occurs when the rate of heating is so low that the charge retains the heterogeneous structure of coal particles in juxtaposition.

Fig. 33 shows the loss of weight of the charge, due to evolution of volatile matter at various temperatures for a Durham coal, together with the intumescence at the same temperature.   It is quite apparent that swelling, at the same rate of heating, always occurs at a higher temperature than that of initial softening and initial evolution of volatile matter.   The presence of microscopic cavities in the charge after heating led Audibert and Delmas (193) to conclude that swelling was only an apparent change and one which arose, not through changes in the condition of the solid material, but through the imprisonment of bubbles of volatile matter trapped within the plastic mass during thermal decomposition.

Preheating and Oxidation. Some coals, which in their natural state will not coke, can be made to do so by special thermal treatment

TABLE 80

Effect of preliminary heat treatment on low temperature coke

PRIMARY DISTILLATION AT 450°C.		SECONDARY DISTILLATION AT 700°C.
Time	Volatile matter in coal	Crushing resistance of coke
min.	*per cent*	
0	28.1	Spongy and friable
30	23.5	Spongy and friable
60	22.2	Spongy and friable
90	21.4	Spongy and friable
105	20.0	560 pounds per square inch
120	18.1	1,325 pounds per square inch
150	16.6	342 pounds per square inch
165	14.8	Powdery

to remove some of their volatile matter, according to Charpy and Godchot (194).   That is, by subjecting the coal to preliminary distillation at 450°C. and by subsequent carbonization at 700°C., it can be made to coke.   These experiments were made on Durham coal, which would not coke in its natural state under ordinary conditions.   From Table 80, it is seen that a good coke was obtained after 2 hours of preliminary carbonization at 450°C. when the volatile matter of the coke had been reduced to 18 per cent.   Primary distillation, as a means of inducing coking, has also been studied by Illingworth (195), whose results confirm what has already been said.

Audibert and Delmas (193) investigated the effect of preheating and partial oxidation on intumescence in coal during carbonization.

Fig. 34 shows the swelling of Varennes coal, as a function of the temperature, for various periods of preheating *in vacuo* at 350°C., and when finally heated to the required temperature at the rate of 1°C. per minute. This temperature of preheating is within 15°C. of the softening temperature of this coal at the particular rate of heating used. In every case, no matter how long the preheating, the initial contraction of the charge during fusion apparently remains. Varennes coal, when untreated, swelled about 65 per cent at 465°C., but when heated for 4 hours *in vacuo* the swelling property of the coal was entirely destroyed and the residuum at 525°C. had practically

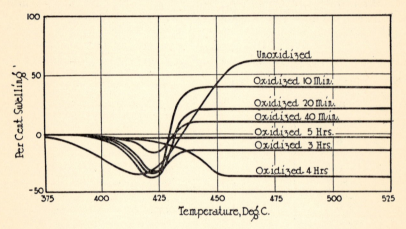

FIG. 34. SWELLING IN VARENNES COAL AS A FUNCTION OF TEMPERATURE AND OF OXIDATION

the same volume as the initial coal. When preheating was prolonged to 4.5 hours, there was a resultant contraction of about 22 per cent at the final temperature. The influence of preheating is attributed to the fact that, even at temperatures below the fusion point, carbonization reactions must have an appreciable velocity and that such chemical changes as occur within the coal, upon preheating under the above conditions, are not usually accompanied by loss in weight to any extent.

Destruction of a portion of the excess resin by oxidation is another means which may be employed to effect coking in certain coals. Bone (195) showed that the resins could be completely destroyed by prolonged oxygenation, even at as low a temperature as 108°C.

Roberts (196) found that by heating a non-coking coal for a very long time at this temperature it could be made to coke. Here it is not clear whether the effect is one of oxidation or evolution of the undesirable constituents. At any rate, this method does not promise great commercial favor, because of the length of time required in the operation, unless carried out at higher temperatures.

Fig. 35 shows the swelling, according to Audibert and Delmas (193), in Varennes coal, as a function of the temperature, for various periods of oxidation. The oxidation was carried out at 120°C. in air and subsequently heated to the required temperature

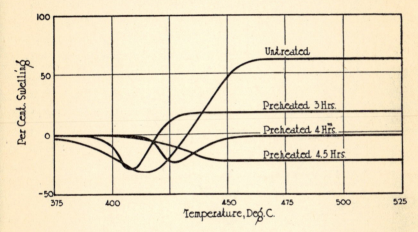

FIG. 35. SWELLING IN VARENNES COAL AS A FUNCTION OF TEMPERATURE AND OF PREHEATING

at the rate of 1°C. per minute. Preoxidation, even for short periods, exerts a considerable effect. The swelling at 500°C. is reduced from about 65 per cent in the unoxidized coal to 50 per cent after 10 minutes oxidation, and to about 10 per cent after 40 minutes oxidation. Oxidation for 4 hours causes a contraction to the extent of about 38 per cent, while 5 hours oxidation entirely destroys the fusing property of the coal. The influence of oxidation on the intumescence of coal is attributed to the fact that oxygen fixation transforms some of the coal constituents into more refractory substances.

Parr (87) separated the lignitic and bituminic portions of the coal by extracting the latter with xylene and then heated both the fresh and oxidized materials at various temperatures to determine the volume and character of the gas yielded. In Fig. 36 is shown the volume of carbon dioxide evolved from both the fresh and the oxidized lignitic residuum, when heated at various temperatures up to 350°C. The same data for the bituminic extract are given in Fig. 37. Table 81 gives the composition of all four gases collected up to 300°C. A

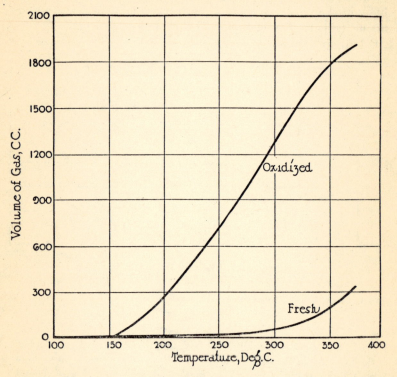

FIG. 36. EVOLUTION OF CARBON DIOXIDE FROM ILLINOIS COAL LIGNITIC
RESIDUUM AS A FUNCTION OF TEMPERATURE

study of this table, in connection with the two preceding diagrams, shows the striking difference between the behavior of the fresh and the oxidized lignitic material, as compared with the fresh and oxidized bituminic material, when all are heated to the same temperature. Up to 350°C., little carbon dioxide is ordinarily evolved from the fresh lignitic residuum, but this amount is increased over six fold when the material has been oxidized. On the other hand, oxidation has very little effect on the quantity of carbon dioxide evolved from the bituminic extract up to 350°C. The gas analyses show a reduction in hydrogen content after oxidation of the material in both cases, but a much greater reduction in the case of the lignitic residuum than in the

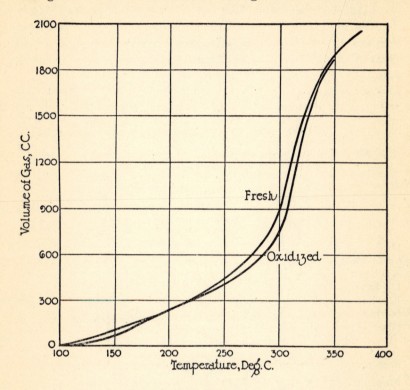

FIG. 37. EVOLUTION OF CARBON DIOXIDE FROM ILLINOIS COAL BITUMINIC EXTRACT AS A FUNCTION OF TEMPERATURE

sample of bituminic extract. The same observation applies also to methane. It is quite evident from these experiments that the reduction of coking power by oxidation can be attributed primarily to changes in the constitution of the lignitic material of the coal.

Coke Reactivity. A number of different experimenters have sought to devise a means for measuring the reactivity of coke, thus Koppers (197) (198) sought to measure its reactivity by the rate at which a particular coke reduced carbon dioxide to the monoxide; Bunte (199) (200) assumed coke reactivity to be proportional to the temperature at which it begins to react with oxygen; Fischer, Breuer, and Broche, (201) considered the reactivity to be inversely proportional to the temperature at which the coke begins to reduce dioxide to the monoxide of carbon; while Bahr (202) determined the reactivity of coke by measuring both the kindling point of the coke and temperature of reduction in an atmosphere of carbon dioxide. Bahr (202) observed that the kindling temperature of carbonaceous materials ranged from 230°C., with low temperature coke, to 410°C., with electrode carbon; that the reaction temperature varied from 480°C., with charcoal, to 820°C., with graphite; and that the re-

TABLE 81

Effect of oxidation on composition of gas from lignitic and bituminic constituents of coal

ANALYSIS	LIGNITIC RESIDUUM		BITUMINIC EXTRACT	
	Fresh	Oxidized	Fresh	Oxidized
	per cent	*per cent*	*per cent*	*per cent*
Carbon dioxide	63.0	87.6	79.2	75.8
Carbon monoxide	19.9	11.8	5.1	13.2
Hydrogen	4.3	0.2	8.3	7.2
Methane	5.4	0.2	4.9	2.1
Ethylene	2.1	0.0	2.1	0.0
Oxygen	3.1	0.2		
Illuminants	2.1	0.1	0.5	1.8

activity ranged from 99 per cent, for charcoal, to 4.4 per cent, with graphite. The addition of 3 per cent iron oxide was found to increase the reactivity of 950°C. coke from 17.5 per cent to 58.4 per cent, at the same time affecting neither the kindling temperature nor the reaction temperature to any extent.

Davis and Greene (203) investigated the reactivity of pulverized cokes in air, carbon dioxide, and water vapor at 950°C. Table 82 gives analyses of the cokes which were tested, together with the experimental determinations. The low temperature coke was made by heating coal for 30 minutes at 750°C. with superheated steam. The beehive coke was dense and hard in structure, whereas the low temperature coke was soft and porous. Before submitting the coke samples to test, the specimens were crushed and sized to pass a 10 mesh and to remain on a 20 mesh sieve. In Table 82 the coke reactivity in air is expressed as the percentage of the theoretical maximum amount of carbon gasified, the reactivity in carbon dioxide is reported as the percentage of carbon dioxide reduced to the monoxide, and the reactivity in steam is given as the sum of the percentages of hydrogen and carbon monoxide. The kindling temperature was

TABLE 82

Reactivity of coke in various atmospheres

CONSTITUENT	LOW TEMPERATURE COKE	GASWORKS COKE		BEEHIVE
		Rochester	Buffalo	
	per cent	per cent	per cent	per cent
Proximate analysis:				
Moisture............................	2.8	1.3	0.7	0.7
Volatile matter......................	10.6	2.5	1.6	1.7
Fixed carbon........................	75.4	86.3	86.1	86.7
Ash.................................	11.2	9.9	11.6	10.9
B.t.u. per pound....................	12,000	12,770	12,530	12,620
Ultimate analysis:	per cent	per cent	per cent	per cent
Hydrogen...........................	2.7	1.1	0.6	0.7
Carbon.............................	77.4	85.4	84.4	85.0
Nitrogen...........................	1.7	1.4	1.1	1.0
Oxygen.............................	6.4	1.5	1.7	1.4
Sulphur............................	0.6	0.7	0.6	1.0
Ash................................	11.2	9.9	11.6	10.9
Reactivity:	per cent	per cent	per cent	per cent
Air................................	72.4	65.4	62.8	63.3
Carbon dioxide......................	62.5	6.0	3.3	4.8
Water vapor........................	29.0	13.9	10.2	11.8
Kindling temperature...............	130°C.	290°C.	320°C.	300°C.

taken as that at which carbon dioxide was first formed. The results indicate that the kindling temperature of low temperature coke is less than half of that of the other cokes, that the reactivity of low temperature coke is 11 per cent to 14 per cent greater than the other cokes in an atmosphere of air, nearly 950 per cent greater in carbon dioxide, and finally 110 per cent to 190 per cent greater in water vapor.

Coke Combustibility. Coke may burn either from the external surface or externally and partially internally, depending upon its structure. Semi-coke, obtained from horizontal retorts at 600°C., burns on the surface and for some distance into the interior and makes a very attractive fire. On the other hand, low temperature coke made by fusion, briquetting, and secondary carbonization burns mainly at the surface and deposits thereon a fine ash, which must be brushed away frequently to maintain a nice looking fire. These are factors to be considered when semi-coke is used as a domestic fuel.

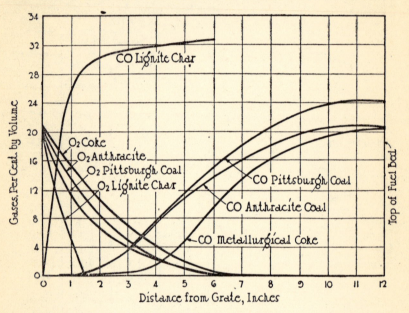

FIG. 38. PROPORTION OF OXYGEN AND CARBON DIOXIDE IN COMBUSTION
GASES FOR VARIOUS FUELS

Kreisinger, Ovitz, and Augustine (204) investigated the combustibility of various fuels in hand-fired furnaces, when burned at approximately 25 pounds per square foot per hour, by determining the mean percentages of carbon monoxide and of free oxygen for various distances above the grate. Some of their results are shown in Fig. 38, from which it is apparent that metallurgical coke is the least combustible and lignite char the most combustible of the fuels studied. Low temperature coke strongly resembles lignite char, from which we may conclude that its combustibility in furnaces will greatly exceed that of bituminous coal and in no way resemble the behavior of ordinary cokes.

Thau (205) has pointed out the common error of assuming that combustibility increases with porosity, having in mind principally those pores which are visible to the naked eye and not those of microscopic character, which have been shown elsewhere to contribute greatly to combustibility. Combustibility depends on two characteristics of the coke, structure and volatile matter. While in ordinary coking practice it is true, within limits, that the denser coke is the more combustible, at the same time, when judging the reactivity of a coke on this property, its purity must also be considered. The ash content of the coke plays a much greater part in reducing combustibility than is ordinarily believed. It is quite impossible to judge a coke by its structural density without a knowledge of its chemical composition. It is common experience that often a spongy coke is less combustible, despite its apparent porosity, than a more consolidated sample; the reason for this peculiar situation being that combustion is a surface phenomenon and it is the reactivity of the multitude of microscopic cells that is of importance rather than the large pores.

Thau (205) also points out that the general belief that silvery appearance of coke, caused by a graphitic deposit, is wholly a desirable condition is erroneous. While the graphitic deposit adds greater strength to the coke, when used for some purposes where it has to sustain a great burden, at the same time the vitreous carbon coating is less reactive than the carbon layers beneath and it tends to reduce combustibility in two ways, first, by its own inactivity, and second, because it plugs the highly reactive surface cells. Thau (205) is quite convinced that the combustibility of low temperature coke is due wholly to its cell structure, which is maintained by the presence of a small amount of volatile, which volatile is driven off as combustion proceeds to leave additional minute cells which are free from vitreous carbon and are highly reactive. The volatile matter present in low temperature coke serves principally to reduce the coke's ignition temperature.

On account of its high combustibility, should it be possible to strengthen low temperature coke in some manner, so that it could withstand the burden in metallurgical operations, it would be of great industrial importance. A number of attempts have been made to

do this, with more or less indifferent success, by applying pressure
to the charge either during or after carbonization.

Coke Strength. The strength required of a coke varies greatly
with the purpose for which it is produced.   For use in blast furnaces
and cupolas, where the weight of the burden which it must sustain is
tremendous, a high crushing strength is necessary.   The strength
of a coke depends upon its structure and a strong structure usually

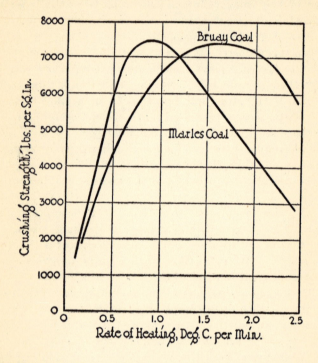

FIG. 39. CRUSHING STRENGTH OF COKES AS A FUNCTION OF RATE OF HEATING

requires high temperatures with the resultant deposition of graphitic
carbon. Thus, despite the greater reactivity of low temperature
coke, the superior strength of the high temperature product gives the
latter favor in metallurgical processes.

A variety of different schemes have been tried to increase the
strength of semi-coke, all of which are variations or combinations of
three methods, application of pressure, blending of the charge, and
temperature regulation.   In the use of pressure to this end, recourse

has been made to its application during carbonization by mechanical means or by weight of the supernatant charge, and to briquetting before, after, or between stages of carbonization. Some little success has been attained by blending different coals to reduce foaming in the fusing stage, but a more fruitful effort has been made in blending a certain amount of coke breeze with the raw coal. Record has been made of a case where the crushing load on a piece of coke, less than one square inch in cross-section, was increased from 250 pounds, when 20 per cent coke breeze was mixed with the charge, to 425

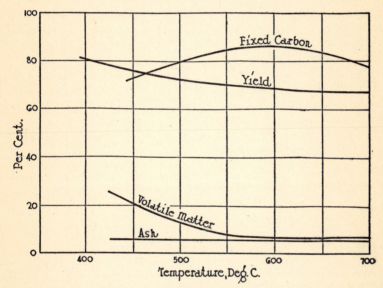

Fig. 40. Yield and Analysis of Semi-Coke under Steam Distillation as a Function of Temperature

pounds, when 35 per cent coke breeze was blended. The addition of breeze, however, is open to the objection that it reduces the daily throughput of raw coal.

Audibert and Delmas (193) determined the influence of rate of heating on the crushing strength of coke produced from a number of different coals, the data regarding two of them being reproduced in Fig. 39. These cokes were made at 900°C. Experiments by Audibert and Delmas (193) indicated that all coals examined by them attained a maximum strength at a given rate of heating, rising rapidly to this maximum as the rate of heating increases and declining slowly from the maximum as the rate of heating is further increased.

Temperature Effect. Davis and Parry (97) found that the introduction of steam during carbonization at 550°C. has no appreciable influence on the coke yield.   They obtained 70.7 per cent of the coal as coke when it was dry distilled and 70.8 per cent when large quantities of steam were admitted.   Variation of temperature, however, under steam distillation does have considerable influence on the amount of coke obtained.   Fig. 40 shows the coke yield obtained from steam carbonization at various temperatures, together with the proximate analyses of the cokes produced from Pennsylvania coal of the Freeport bed.   The ultimate analyses and calorific value

TABLE 83

Ultimate analyses of low temperature steam cokes

CONSTITUENT	TEMPERATURE		
	475°C.	550°C.	650°C.
	per cent	*per cent*	*per cent*
Carbon..............................	81.4	83.9	83.9
Oxygen...............................	4.7	3.7	3.7
Hydrogen............................	3.8	2.7	2.5
Nitrogen.............................	2.0	2.1	2.0
Sulphur..............................	1.0	1.1	1.0
B.t.u. per pound.....................	13,900	13,820	13,610

of this low temperature coke, carbonized at three different temperatures, are given in Table 83.   The yield of coke gradually decreases with rise of temperature for two reasons.   In the first place, a greater percentage of the volatile constituents is removed, which reduces the weight of the yield.   This is confirmed by the decrease in the proportion of volatile matter remaining in the coke.   In the second place, it has been pointed out that steam reacts with the coal to form the dioxide of carbon at approximately 550°C.   Consequently, the yield of coke would be decreased by the percentage of carbon dioxide generated.   That this is a factor in reducing the amount of coke obtained is verified by the fact that the percentage fixed carbon in the coke attains a maximum at about 550°C., after which it decreases on account of gasification.

From Table 83, temperature is seen to have no great effect on the ultimate analysis of the coke, other than its influence on the percentage of carbon. The reduction in oxygen and hydrogen content is due to removal of the phenolic derivatives and volatile hydrocarbons. The coke produced under steam distillation at 475°C. was black and spongy. Considerable swelling had occurred and the residuum was filled with blowholes. The carbonized product from distillation at 550°C. was of much denser structure. The layer next to the retort wall was rather porous, but of a grayish color, indicating more complete carbonization. The action of the steam was evidently responsible for the external porosity. The coke obtained at 650°C. was practically the same as that produced at 550°C., except that it was slightly lighter in color.

TABLE 84

Percentage of smoke producing constituents removed from United States coals

TEMPERATURE	PENNSYLVANIA COAL	ILLINOIS COAL	WYOMING COAL	VIRGINIA COAL
°C.	per cent	per cent	per cent	per cent
500			2.1	0.3
600	6.5	7.8	2.9	1.4
700	15.8	9.7	10.7	6.7
800	18.1	12.2	10.7	11.3
900	17.5	11.9	12.7	9.5

Semi-Coke Uses. As a whole, semi-coke is fairly dense and of good texture, although some of it is quite friable. Samples tested by the United States Bureau of Mines (101) indicate that it is adapted to the usual screening and sizing processes for preparation as a domestic fuel. The coke produced, of course, varies very greatly with the raw coal used, but there is no doubt that a few of the low temperature carbonization residuums are suitable for metallurigical purposes. The high percentage of volatile hydrocarbons remaining in the low temperature coke supplies a free-burning constituent, which is readily ignited and which will maintain fire without special attention. In this respect, the semi-coke is superior to anthracite. The percentage of smoke-producing elements, consisting of tar and heavy hydrocarbons, which can be removed from American coals at various temperatures of carbonization, as determined by Porter and

Ovitz (96), is given in Table 84. It has been pointed out that one of the purposes of low temperature processes was to produce a smokeless fuel, and how nearly this purpose has been attained is made evident by the table. The semi-coke obtained as a carbonization residuum is an ideal smokeless fuel.

Parr and Olin (31) conducted some experiments on semi-coke gasification, using a small Otto gas producer equipped with a wet scrubber, the results of which are given in Table 85. This producer

TABLE 85

Comparison of low temperature coke and anthracite as gas producer fuel

ITEM	LOW TEMPERA-TURE COKE	ANTHRACITE
Test conditions:		
Duration of test: hours..........................	6.3	7.0
Temperature of exit gases......................	380°C.	725°C.
B.t.u. per pound fuel...........................	11,660	12,980
Pounds water decomposed per pound fuel........	2.42	0.191
Pounds water decomposed per pound gas........	0.0588	0.0350
B.t.u. per cubic foot gas........................	121	97
Cubic feet gas per pound fuel	62.3	76.2
Grate efficiency.................................	98.2%	84.3%
Hot gas efficiency...............................	74.4%	56.8%
Cold gas efficiency..............................	64.9%	53.9%
Gas analysis:	*per cent*	*per cent*
Carbon dioxide..................................	4.2	8.8
Carbon monoxide................................	21.1	18.2
Oxygen...	0.3	0.9
Hydrogen.......................................	11.8	8.7
Methane..	1.5	1.0
Nitrogen..	61.0	62.4

was designed to operate on pea size anthracite coal. Using anthracite, the normal capacity was 4500 cubic feet of gas per hour. The semi-coke, which they used as a fuel, was obtained from carbonizing screenings of Illinois coal at 550°C. It was light and porous and showed no tendency to pack on the fuel bed. Analysis showed it to contain 18 per cent volatile matter and 71 per cent fixed carbon. The residuary gases, evolved from the secondary carbonization of this primary coke, were remarkably free from heavy condensation products.   This suggested that producer gas made by the gasification of semi-coke would be sufficiently free from tar to render it suitable as a fuel for internal combustion engines.   For comparative purposes, data obtained from the operation of the same producer, using a Pennsylvania anthracite coal, as determined by Garland and Kratz (206), are also given in Table 85.

The great increase in efficiency attending the use of low temperature coke as a gas producer fuel is the notable feature of Table 85. The higher thermal value of the gas from semi-coke is shown by the analysis to be the result of a low percentage of diluents, such as carbon dioxide, nitrogen, and oxygen, in the gas.   Little tar was produced during the operation of the producer with semi-coke as a fuel. As a whole, the tests were entirely successful and little attention was required during the runs.   The lightness of the low temperature coke and its slight tendency to arch made it necessary to poke the charge about once an hour and, in this respect, it required somewhat more attention than anthracite.   However, this semi-coke contained more volatile matter than the usual product, which fully accounts for such minor difficulties as were experienced.   There was a remarkable freedom from ash and clinker trouble.

Lander and McKay (186) reported some tests conducted at the Fuel Research Station in a small gas producer to determine the suitability of low temperature coke for complete gasification, as compared with high temperature coke from vertical retorts.   Since the tar had, for the most part, been removed from the semi-coke, it is reasonable to anticipate the success of using this fuel as a charge for gas producers.   The low temperature coke gave 23 per cent higher consumption of carbon than the high temperature product and yielded under the same conditions twice the percentage of carbon monoxide and less dioxide than the high temperature gas coke.   The high velocity of consumption is indicative of high reaction velocity, which accounts for the increase of 25 per cent in temperature of the producer hot zone.

Domestic Fuel.   One of the greatest potential markets for low temperature coke is that of a household fuel.   Semi-coke is ideal for this purpose, since it is clean, ignites easily, and burns readily with little attention.   Fireplaces and other domestic heating appliances emit a large portion of their heat by radiation.   Fishenden (207) has investigated the radiation efficiency of low temperature coke, as compared with coal ordinarily used.   Three tests were made on various types of open grates.   In the first test, a radiation efficiency of 19.7 per cent was obtained for low temperature coke, as compared with 17.3 per cent for bituminous coal; the second test showed the semi-coke to have a radiation efficiency of 24.0 per cent and the bituminous coal 19.5 per cent; the third test gave corresponding figures of 30.8 per cent and 24.2 per cent.   This shows that in open grates the radiation efficiency of low temperature coke is 20 per cent to 25 per cent greater than that of bituminous coal.

In kitchen boilers, Fishenden (207) also found low temperature coke to be more effective than bituminous coal.   Three different tests were conducted likewise.   In the first test, the radiation efficiency of semi-coke was 17.3 per cent, as compared with 13.1 per cent for bituminous coal; the corresponding figures for the second test were 20.7 per cent and 14.5 per cent; while in the third trial the low temperature coke gave 41.0 per cent radiation efficiency and the bituminous coal 31.0 per cent.   In ordinary kitchen ovens, however, the coke does not show any increase in efficiency over coal, but probably in an oven designed to take better advantage of the increased radiation this could be improved.   The advantage of low temperature coke over coal, aside from its smokeless quality, lies in its superior radiation, which is most apparent when the distance from fuel bed to boiler or oven is small.   When they are far apart, the advantage of the coke diminishes and the longer luminous flame of the coal gives better results.

Power Char.   An ideal fuel for pulverization should contain about 10 per cent volatile matter and be easy to grind.   One of the principal difficulties in installations utilizing powdered fuel is the wear on the pulverization mills.   Coke residuum from the low temperature process is comparatively easy to crush and prepare for the furnace.   For these reasons, low temperature coke is peculiarly suitable for pulverized fuel.   Gentry (208) has stressed the importance of semi-coke as a pulverized fuel for central electric stations and pointed out that the fuel can be prepared by grinding before or after carbonization or between operations of a multi-stage process.   A number of methods have been devised, notably by McEwen and Runge, in which the coal is carbonized in finely divided particles, thus entirely eliminating or reducing the pulverization ordinarily required after distillation.

It is well to consider the specific case of a bituminous coal which contains 32.2 per cent volatile matter, 57.8 per cent fixed carbon, 2.8 per cent moisture, and 7.2 per cent ash, with a heating value of 13,800 B.t.u. per pound. Such a coal ordinarily contains about 5.4 per cent hydrogen, which causes a loss on combustion of 628 B.t.u. per pound. Before pulverization, it is considered expedient to dry the coal to a moisture content of about 1.7 per cent water, in order to reduce the power required for grinding. The 1.7 per cent moisture in the fuel after drying causes a further loss of 22 B.t.u. per pound on burning. These losses reduce the heat available in the boiler furnace to 13,150 B.t.u. per pound. A modern large pulverized fuel boiler has an over-all efficiency of about 88 per cent, calculated on the gross heating value of the coal, or 92.4 per cent, figured on the net heating value, as delivered to the furnace. Hence, 12,174 B.t.u. per pound are absorbed by the boiler. A year's operating experience at the Columbia Power Station (209) showed that on the average 0.94 per cent of the coal was required to dry the fuel, with 3.9 per cent average initial moisture, to an average of 1.7 per cent moisture before grinding. Proportioned for a coal with 2.8 per cent initial moisture, 65 B.t.u. per pound must be deducted for drying. At the same power plant 16.2 k.w.h. per ton were required to operate the mills which, since the station operated on 12,495 B.t.u. per kilowatt hour, amounts to 102 B.t.u. per pound required for pulverization. These additional deductions for preparation of the fuel give a new figure of 12,007 B.t.u. per pound, or 87.0 per cent of the calorific value of the raw fuel, usefully absorbed by the boiler.

An average externally heated low temperature coke made from the bituminous coal considered above will have a thermal value of 13,400 B.t.u. per pound. Such a semi-coke will contain no moisture, as discharged from the retorts, but may absorb as much as 1 per cent upon standing, thereby causing a combustion loss of 13 B.t.u. per pound. The residual hydrogen in the low temperature coke amounts to about 2.0 per cent, which represents a combustion loss of 233 B.t.u. per pound. Deduction of the hydrogen and moisture losses gives 12,168 B.t.u. per pound, available in the furnace when the same boiler efficiency as used for the raw coal is applied. Semi-coke needs no drying before pulverization, so that no deduction need be made for that item, while the heat required for carbonizing the coal will be charged to the cost of processing for by-products. The consensus of opinion of those who have had experience in grinding semi-coke is that it will require 20 per cent less power for pulverization than the raw coal.   On this basis a deduction of 81 B.t.u. per pound must be made for grinding, giving finally 12,087 B.t.u. per pound usefully absorbed in the boiler.   This amounts to 87.6 per cent of the heat in the semi-coke usefully absorbed, as compared with 87.0 per cent for the coal from which the semi-coke was made.   Similar calculations made for a semi-coke obtained from an average partial gasification low temperature process, with 13,200 B.t.u. per pound calorific value and 1.5 per cent hydrogen, show about the same results.   It may be concluded, therefore, that low temperature coke, pound for pound, has a furnace efficiency in the pulverized form slightly exceeding that of the raw coal from which it was made.

Moreover, there are further economies, that may be expected from the use of pulverized low temperature coke as a boiler fuel, which may be of importance exceeding that of its increased furnace efficiency.   In the first place, semi-coke can be stored indefinitely in the powdered form without danger of spontaneous combustion, so that mill house operating costs can be reduced somewhat by allowing the mills to run at a much better load factor.   Furthermore, the friability and softness of semi-coke will require less mill maintenance than raw coal.   Here record must be made of the fact, commonly misunderstood, that low temperature coke is in no way comparable to high temperature coke, which is known to be brittle and excessively abrasive.   The firing of pulverized fuel in boilers requires an excessively large furnace volume to secure complete combustion, because of the long flame.   The length of a pulverized coal flame depends solely upon rate of combustion, which in turn depends on three things, temperature of the furnace, turbulence to bring fresh air for oxidation, and combustibility of the fuel.   The high combustibility of low temperature coke has already been pointed out, so that it is quite apparent that, for given furnace temperatures and given conditions of mixing, the rate of combustion of semi-coke is greater than raw coal and its pulverized fuel flame correspondingly shorter.   In fact, certain experiments have shown that the flame of pulverized semi-coke was so short that it was necessary to mix a certain proportion of raw coal to lengthen the flame in boilers designed with large furnace volume.   These results demonstrate that by using pulverized semi-coke in place of the raw coal, considerably smaller furnaces can be used for boilers of the same capacity, or, vice versa, for a given furnace volume, increased combustion rates will permit the boilers to be designed for greater capacity. Either increased capacity for a given furnace size or reduction in furnace size for a given boiler capacity will effect material saving in capital expenditure, which will ultimately be reflected in the cost of power. A further discussion of this subject will be given in Chapter VIII under the subject of by-product recovery in central stations.

The safety with which powdered semi-coke can be stored without fear of explosion is of importance in marine power plants. The limited space on shipboard and on locomotives also makes the short flame of low temperature pulverized coke and its associated small furnace volume of considerable importance to the transportation industry.

Low temperature coke briquets, made by the Carbocoal process, have been tested as a fuel in both locomotives and marine installations. It was demonstrated that the fuel was smokeless and that it evaporated from 8.5 pounds to 12.8 pounds of water per pound of fuel per hour, from and at 212°F., when fired at rates ranging from 100 pounds to 27 pounds of fuel per hour per square foot of grate surface, respectively. A maximum rate of 166 pounds of low temperature briquets per square foot of grate surface per hour was fired for short periods with no greater draft than was required by ordinary bituminous coal.

CHAPTER V

Nitrogenous and Other By-Products

Distribution of Nitrogen. According to Fieldner, Selvig, and Paul (210), the nitrogen content of coals of the United States varies from 0.32 per cent, in a sample from California, to 2.15 per cent, in a sample from Maryland. The Utah coal which was coked at low temperatures by Parr and Layng (101) contained 1.40 per cent nitrogen. Porter and Ovitz (96) found the following percentages of nitrogen in the coals distilled by them: Pennsylvania, 1.23 per cent; Illinois, 1.31 per cent; Virginia, 1.07 per cent; Wyoming, 1.06 per cent; and Utah, 1.16 per cent; while the bituminous coals carbonized by Taylor and Porter (98) contained nitrogen to the following extent: Pennsylvania, 1.53 per cent; Illinois, 1.55 per cent; West Virginia, 1.45 per cent; and Wyoming, 1.49 per cent. In Table 16, the average percentage of nitrogen found in coals of the United States has already been given. As a rule, these coals have from 1.1 per cent to 1.6 per cent nitrogen, which corresponds to 24.5 pounds and 36.0 pounds of nitrogen per net ton of coal, respectively. On the basis of 100 per cent theoretical yield, this amounts to from 30.0 pounds to 43.5 pounds of gaseous ammonia per net ton, or 115 pounds to 169 pounds of ammonium sulphate per net ton of raw fuel.

The efficiency of the nitrogen recovery depends largely upon the process of carbonization used. When the coke is completely gasified and the by-products recovered, as in some producer processes, the yield of ammonium sulphate attains as much as 85 pounds per net ton, which is 61.5 per cent of the theoretical. It is interesting to note from Table 86, which gives the average recovery of ammonium sulphate in the three methods of coal carbonization, that the greatest efficiency of recovery is obtained in gasworks practice and the lowest efficiency in low temperature carbonization, metallurgical coke ovens occupying an intermediate position. We shall see later that the reason for this resides in the fact that the low temperature retorts operate at too low a temperature to drive the nitrogen from the coke in quantities and that the metallurgical coke ovens operate at such a high temperature, in order to get a good coke structure, that the ammonia evolved is partly decomposed by the heat.

The nitrogen is present within the coal in a number of forms. Under destructive distillation some of it appears in the gas as free nitrogen, some as ammonia, and some as cyanogen. A small amount of the nitrogen appears in the tar, as nitrogen bases, and a large proportion ordinarily remains in the coke. The nitrogenous products found in low temperature tar have already been fully discussed in Chapter III, under the subject of tar bases. Table 87, after Lewes

TABLE 86

Efficiency of ammonium sulphate recovery

SOURCE	AMMONIUM SULPHATE PER NET TON	EFFICIENCY
	pounds	*per cent*
Gasworks....................................	22	16.0
Coke ovens..................................	20	14.5
Low temperature ovens......................	12	8.8

TABLE 87

Distribution of nitrogen in coal among its products of distillation

PRODUCT	PER CENT OF COAL	PER CENT OF NITROGEN
Coke...	0.933	58.3
Gas (N_2)...................................	0.312	19.5
Liquor (NH_3)..............................	0.174	17.1
Tar (bases).................................	0.054	3.9
Cyanogen $(CN)_2$...........................	0.019	1.2

(17), quoting McLeod, gives the distribution of nitrogen among the volatile products and residuum of carbonization. This table presents the interesting fact that the major portion of nitrogen remains in the carbonization residuum and a large part is lost in the gases which are evolved, so that, in any event, hardly more than 30 per cent of the total nitrogen is recoverable in a useful form. It has been shown in Table 73 that the percentage nitrogen in the coke after distillation is greatest for low temperature coke and least for that made in metallurgical coke ovens.

The gas evolved in low temperature carbonization contains considerable elementary nitrogen.   Thus, Parr and Layng (101) reported 3.87 per cent of the gases which they obtained from Utah coals at 750°C. to consist of this gas.   Davis and Parry (97) found that the Pennsylvania coals which they examined averaged 5.83 per cent nitrogen in the gas.   The gas evolved in the manufacture of Coalite runs considerably higher in nitrogen content, 9.28 per cent having been recorded by Parr and Olin (31).

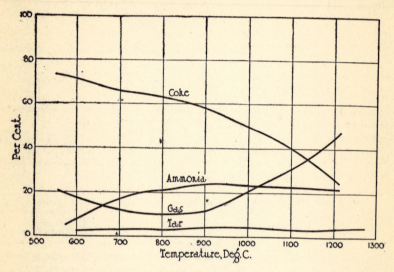

FIG. 41. YIELD OF PRODUCTS FROM SILESIAN COAL AS A FUNCTION OF TEMPERATURE

Effect of Temperature. The percentage distribution of the nitrogen in coal among its products of distillation varies with the temperature of carbonization.   Simmersbach (211) studied the effect of temperature upon the distribution of the elementary nitrogen with the results shown in Fig. 41.   These experiments were made upon Silesian coal with a total nitrogen content of 1.39 per cent. Reference to the illustration shows that the maximum percentage of nitrogen occurs in the ammonia at 900°C., while the minimum percentage of nitrogen in the gas occurs a hundred degrees lower. Heating of the coal beyond 900°C. decreases the nitrogen remaining in the carbonization residuum but does not increase the percentage of ammonia. The additional nitrogen evolved merely goes to increase its content in the gas. The nitrogen content of the tar remains about constant, irrespective of the temperature beyond about 600°C. It is interesting to note that, even at a temperature of 1200°C., over a quarter of the nitrogen contained in the coal remains in the coke.

We have already seen in Table 25 the variation in the proportion of free nitrogen in the gas which was evolved from Lancashire coal distilled up to 400°C. by Burgess and Wheeler (104). Lignites and peats usually contain much more nitrogen than bituminous coals and a large part of it appears as free nitrogen in the gas upon destructive distillation. We have seen in Table 27 that as much as 20 per cent of the gas which was evolved from the carbonization of peat in vertical retorts was free nitrogen. Again, in Table 29 the results of Benson and Canfield (108), on the distillation at various temperatures of Newcastle lignite from the state of Washington, show as much as 42.7 per cent free nitrogen in the low temperature lignite gas. After 400°C. temperature of carbonization in this particular case, there is apparently no increase in the percentage of free nitrogen in the gas, at least up to 600°C.

In Fig. 13, it is seen from the results of Taylor and Porter (98) in heating Wyoming coal for long periods at 350°C., that, after 25 hours of distillation, practically all the ammonia had been removed from the coal, whereas the production of saturated hydrocarbons, hydrogen, and the oxides of carbons continued even to coking periods of 200 hours. Consequently, the longer the period of distillation at this temperature, the less the proportion of ammonia to be expected in the gas.

Giles and Vilbrandt (99), in their distillation of Farmville, N. C., coal at temperatures ranging from 200°C. to 660°C., found that the ammonium sulphate produced, expressed as percentages of the original coal, amounted to 0.17 per cent at 200°C.; 1.23 per cent at 300°C.; 2.20 per cent at 420°C.; 2.25 per cent at 540°C.; and 3.00 per cent at 660°C. Analyses of the semi-coke obtained by Benson and Canfield (108), when distilling a Washington lignite at temperatures ranging from 150°C. to 600°C., showed the carbonization residuum to contain 2.9 per cent nitrogen at 150°C.; 2.5 per cent at 250°C.; 1.4 per cent at 350°C.; 0.9 per cent at 450°C.; and 0.5 per cent at 600°C.

Ammonium Sulphate. The authorities differ so greatly in the yields of ammonium sulphate which they have obtained in their experiments on low temperature carbonization that a tabulation of their average results, given in Table 88, will serve valuable comparative purposes. The average of the yields given in this table is almost exactly 14 pounds of ammonium sulphate per gross ton of coal, which is the value recommended by the Fuel Research Board, after their extensive experiments on many different coals, as the most reliable yield to be expected in low temperature carbonization. In order to pay for recovery, the ammoniacal liquor must be approximately 1.7 per cent ammonia or 8 ounce strength. This means a recovery of 14 pounds per ton. Otherwise, it is necessary to scrub the primary liquor with fresh gas until it reaches that concentration, which of

TABLE 88

Comparison of ammonium sulphate yields in low temperature experiments

AUTHORITY	COAL	RETORT	TEMPER-ATURE	$(NH_4)_2SO_4$ PER TON
			°C.	pounds
Parr and Layng (101)	Utah	Horizontal	750	20
Armstrong (212)	Barnsley	Coalite	650	18
Davis and Berger (184)	Pennsylvania	Vertical	650	18
Fuel Research Board (114)	Dalton	Horizontal	650	14
Lewes (17)			500	12
Curtis (213)	Virginia	Carbocoal	500	8
Davis and Parry (97)	Pennsylvania	Vertical	550	7

course means a larger operating expense and its consequent reduction of profit.

It is quite obvious from Table 88 that, with one exception and within the temperature limits of low temperature carbonization, the higher the temperature the greater is the yield of ammonium sulphate. The experiments of Burgess and Wheeler (104), on the carbonization of Silkstone coal at temperatures ranging from 450°C. to 900°C., as given in Table 23, show that at the temperatures of 500°C. to 700°C., inclusive, about 1.5 per cent of the gas evolved consists of ammonia. At 750°C., which, under these conditions, appeared to be extremely favorable to the formation of ammonia, there was a copious evolution, which thereafter decreased with temperature rise.

Table 89 gives the temperature variation of ammonium sulphate yield, as determined from the experiments of Lewes (17) and of Simmersbach (211). The latter used Silesian coal, which is by no means typical, for the yields quoted by Simmersbach are much higher than ordinarily obtaining between 600°C. and 900°C. The figures given by Lewes, who used a good gas coal, are perhaps more representative of ordinary coals. The yields are from charges subjected to carbonization over a period of 6 hours. These figures are more than 30 per cent lower than those given by Simmersbach in the low temperature range, but they are more representative of the conditions obtaining in full-scale operation.

TABLE 89

Temperature variation of ammonium sulphate yield

	SIMMERSBACH (211) SILESIAN COAL		LEWES (17) GAS COAL
TEMPERATURE	Per cent N in coke	$(NH_4)_2 SO_4$, per cent of coal	$(NH_4)_2 SO_4$, per cent of coal
°C.			
500			0.536
600	1.27	0.515	0.669
700	1.22	1.194	0.758
800	1.21	1.401	0.892
900	1.14	1.588	1.160
1,000	1.00	1.525	1.071
1,100	0.83	1.520	0.892
1,200	0.53	1.504	

Fig. 42 gives the data of Table 89 in pounds of ammonium sulphate per gross ton of coal. In the illustration, it is seen that the yield of ammonium sulphate reaches a maximum at 900°C., according to both authorities. An average bituminous coal may be said to yield considerably less ammonium sulphate when carbonized at low temperatures, from 500°C. to 700°C., than when distilled at high temperatures over the range of 900°C. to 1100°C. It will be noted in the illustration, that the curves showing the yields of ammonium sulphate decrease after attaining their maximum. It will be pointed out shortly that this drooping of the yield curve is the direct result of decomposition of the ammonia. Temperature serves to drive the remaining nitrogen from the coke, as indicated by Table 89 and Fig.

42, but not so much in the form of ammonia as in the form of elementary nitrogen, that is, in the absence of protective gaseous atmospheres.

Thermal Decomposition. That the yield of ammonia attains a maximum at a certain temperature under given conditions and thereafter decreases as the temperature of carbonization rises, has already been demonstrated. The reduction in the percentage of ammonia in the gas when it is subjected to superheating has also been noted in Table 36, as well as the decomposition of ammonia effected by

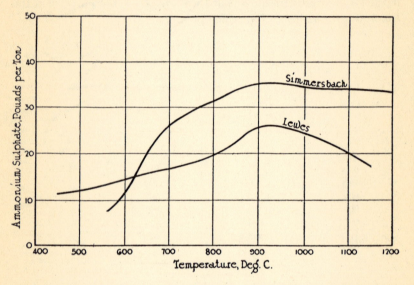

FIG. 42. YIELD OF AMMONIUM SULPHATE AS A FUNCTION OF TEMPERATURE

passing the gas over a small incandescent surface, as shown in Table 37, and by the catalytic action of hot brick contact surfaces, recorded in Table 38. Presently, the subject of ammonia decomposition by active brick surfaces will be taken up again.

A study of the equilibrium conditions surrounding the chemical equation,

$$2\,NH_3 \rightleftarrows N_2 + 3\,H_2 \qquad [22]$$

will explain clearly this phenomenon. This reaction, when proceeding from right to left, is an exothermic one and takes place with the liberation of 24,000 calories of heat (116). We can predict immediately, therefore, from thermochemistry, that low temperatures are favorable to the stability of ammonia.

The effect of temperature variation on ammonia decomposition was investigated by Ramsay and Young (214). Their first experiments consisted in passing the gas through a porcelain tube, filled

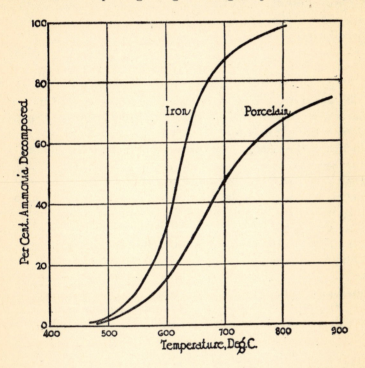

FIG. 43. CATALYTIC EFFECT OF IRON AND PORCELAIN ON AMMONIA DECOMPO-
SITION AS A FUNCTION OF TEMPERATURE

with broken pieces of the same material. In the second series of experiments, an iron tube was substituted for the porcelain tube for the purpose of investigating the effect of the tube material as a catalytic agent. The results are plotted in Fig. 43. It is seen from the illustration that decomposition of the ammonia begins below 500°C., attains a maximum rate from 600°C. to 700°C., and is practically complete at 800°C. The catalytic effect of the surface of the tube is very pronounced. Thus, iron increased the decomposition at a given temperature often as much as 100 per cent over that obtained in the presence of porcelain. It must be remembered that the equilibrium of Equation [22] is a dynamic one and the effect of a catalytic agent is to accelerate the rate of reaction in one of the directions, the net result being an increase or a decrease in the percentage of ammonia which may exist under given thermal conditions.

The data in Fig. 43 apparently disagree with the results of Simmersbach and of Lewes given in Table 89 and in Fig. 42. The maximum yield of ammonia occurs at 900°C. in Fig. 42, which is beyond the temperature prescribed in Fig. 43 for complete dissociation of the ammonia. Presently, we shall see that this can be readily accounted for by the retarding influence exerted by certain other constituents of the gas. In any case, the quantity of ammonia yielded is considerably less than the actual amount formed and the reduction of the yield at high temperatures must be attributed to its decomposition. The nitrogenous matter in coal is doubtlessly present in many forms. Some of the constituents of the coal give ammonia on simple distillation, while others react with the moisture and hydrogen which is present to form ammonia-yielding compounds.

Rate of Decomposition. Foxwell (215) (216) made an extended study of the thermal dissociation of ammonia in coke ovens. He used in his experiments a silica reaction tube, coated with a thin layer of carbon. Using such a tube packed with coke, Foxwell studied the concentration of ammonia at various temperatures and found that the decomposition was a second order reaction, whose rate of reaction, therefore, was expressible by the equation,

$$\frac{dx}{dt} = k\,(a - x)^2 \qquad [23]$$

where x is the amount of ammonia decomposed in time, t, and a is the initial concentration of ammonia expressed in millimeters of mercury partial pressure. From Equation [23] we may solve for the velocity constant, k, as follows:

$$k = \frac{1}{t}\left(\frac{1}{a-x} - \frac{1}{a}\right) \qquad [24]$$

Despite the heterogeneous reaction, occurring in the thermal dissociation of ammonia in coal gas, it was found that a bimolecular coefficient adequately expressed the results, even though it is difficult to interpret its meaning. Perhaps the presence of coal gas and water vapor exerted an influence which disguised the true character of the reaction.

The temperature variation of the reaction velocity constant was found to agree with Arrhenius' empirical equation,

$$k_2 = k_1 \, \epsilon^{A \left(\frac{1}{T_2} - \frac{1}{T_1} \right)}$$ [25]

where $A = 13{,}300$ and k_2 and k_1 are the constants at temperatures, T_2 and T_1, respectively. The calculated and measured values of the velocity constant, k, for various temperatures, when coke is used as the contact material, are given in Table 90, from which it is seen that the temperature increase of the velocity of the reaction is

TABLE 90

Temperature variation of ammonia decomposition velocity constant

TEMPERATURE	MEASURED k	CALCULATED k
°C.		
520	0.00013	0.000049
600	0.00025	0.00023
655	0.00056	0.00056
755	0.00215	0.00225
850	0.00673	0.00673

comparatively slow. Foxwell (215) (216) found that the ammonia decomposed to some extent below 600°C., contrary to the findings of other investigators.

It has been noted in Table 38 that hot brick surfaces catalyze the decomposition of ammonia and it has been pointed out that, since the equilibrium given in Equation [22] is dynamic, the effect of a catalyst is merely to accelerate the reaction rate which must be reflected in a variation of the coefficient, k, of Equation [23] and Equation [24]. This is indeed the case. Table 91 gives the analyses of four different bricks, two of which are silica bricks and two of which are siliceous bricks. The table gives for each type of brick a sample low in ferric oxide and a sample high in ferric oxide. The great influence of silica and ferric oxide on the velocity constant, k, is quite apparent. It can be concluded that silica brick has a much smaller decomposing influence than siliceous brick and that, from the standpoint of preservation of ammonia, the presence of iron is highly undesirable.   All the brick samples had substantially the same porosity.   Later we will discuss the results of Mott and Hodsman (217), who studied the influence of contact materials on the decomposition and oxidation of ammonia in various gaseous atmospheres.

Since brick contains many of the oxides found in coal ash, it might be anticipated that the constitution of the ash would have an important bearing on the decomposition of ammonia evolved from the coal.   Under the subject of catalysis in Chapter I, it has already been pointed out that Lessing (81), Lessing and Banks (82), and

TABLE 91

Effect of brick composition on ammonia decomposition

CONSTITUENT	SILICA BRICK		SILICEOUS BRICK	
	Low iron	High iron	Low iron	High iron
Velocity constant, k..........................	0.000433	0.000103	0.00502	0.0123
Analysis:	*per cent*	*per cent*	*per cent*	*per cent*
SiO_2...............................	94.69	94.45	83.29	73.68
Al_2O_3..............................	1.29	1.65	14.17	19.78
Fe_2O_3..............................	1.31	0.50	0.52	3.90
TiO_2...............................	0.15	0.13	0.66	0.66
CaO...............................	1.93	2.74	0.32	0.45
MgO...............................	0.16	0.12	0.10	0.07
Na_2O...............................	0.28	0.15	0.12	0.58
K_2O...............................	0.25	0.62	0.64	0.82

Marson and Cobb (83) investigated the effect of ash analysis on the solid residuum from distillation.   Foxwell (215) (216) made a number of experiments to define the influence of coke ash on the ammonia decomposition velocity constant.   He used a Durham coal, containing 8.10 per cent ash in his experiments, to which various ingredients were added in different samples for the purpose of ascertaining the effect of each substance.   The analyses of the ash from eight specimens is given in Table 92, along with the mean velocity constant for each sample at 755°C.   Sample No. 1 was the ash of a gas coke alone; Sample No. 2 was the ash of the Durham coal alone; Sample No. 3 contained an addition of 5 per cent impure pyrites

from a coal seam; Sample No. 4 contained an addition of 3 per cent
rutile; Sample No. 5 contained an addition of 5 per cent orthoclase
felspar; Sample No. 6 contained an addition of 5 per cent ferric
oxide; Sample No. 7 contained an addition of 3 per cent ignited
line; and Sample No. 8 contained an addition of 10 per cent ignited
lime.

The velocity constant given in Table 92 is the mean value for
periods of contact ranging from 0.78 second to 4.24 seconds, within
which time intervals the constant was found to be independent of

TABLE 92

Effect of coke ash analysis on ammonia decomposition velocity constant

CONSTITUENT	ASH SAMPLE							
	1	2	3	4	5	6	7	8
Velocity constant, k..................	0.00215	0.00193	0.00242	0.00203	0.00186	0.0293	0.00565	0.00608
Analysis:	per cent	per cent	per cent	per cent	per cent	per cent	per cent	per cent
SiO_2.........................	39.07	47.53	35.80	33.60	54.43	34.00	33.40	18.65
Al_2O_3......................	33.63	27.65	20.10	19.60	23.62	14.50	19.70	11.00
Fe_2O_3......................	16.20	13.00		9.20	7.80		9.45	5.31
FeS..........................			35.20			10.30		
Fe...........................						32.30		
TiO_2........................	1.25	1.30	1.19	30.00	1.04	0.90	1.25	0.55
CaO..........................	4.24	4.95	6.20	3.47	2.70	4.45	32.50	62.30
MgO..........................	0.96	0.72	0.51	0.51	0.45	0.52	0.52	0.30
Na_2O........................	0.26	0.26	0.14	0.18	0.19	0.18	0.17	0.09
K_2O.........................	1.47	1.09	0.92	0.77	7.50	2.95	0.75	0.45
SO_3.........................	3.26	3.83		2.70	2.20		2.85	1.82

the time of contact. Examination of the table discloses that rutile
and felspar have practically no catalytic effect, whereas iron in
certain forms and lime have a most vigorous influence. During
carbonization, pyrites and ferric oxide are converted to ferrous
sulphide and metallic iron, respectively. Ferrous sulphide increases
the reaction rate only slightly, whereas the addition of about 3.75
per cent metallic iron, reduced from ferric oxide, increased the
reaction rate fifteen fold. Consequently, if the iron is present in
the coal as pyrite, its catalytic effect will be negligible, but, if it is
present as ferric oxide, the decomposition of ammonia will be tre-

mendously accelerated. The result of the addition of lime was not anticipated and is somewhat inexplicable. The addition of lime is a well known practical method of increasing ammonia yield in carbonization practice, but these experiments showed that the addition of 3 per cent lime more than doubled the rate of dissociation, which was further increased only slightly by larger additions of the same material.

Some significant results were obtained by Foxwell (215) (216) when one per cent salt was added to the coal. In this case, the value of the reaction velocity constant, k, did not remain constant when the period of contact varied, as in the case of materials previously tested. As the period of contact increased, the value of k decreased in the following manner: for 1.14 seconds, $k = 0.00200$; for 1.20 seconds, $k = 0.00142$; for 1.33 seconds, $k = 0.00131$; and for 3.86 seconds, $k = 0.00093$. These data show that, when the period of contact is long enough, the salt acts as a negative catalyst and retards the dissociation of ammonia. The influence of salt is attributed to its reaction with water vapor and carbon dioxide to form sodium carbonate with the liberation of hydrochloric acid, the latter being the retarding agent. Explanation of the decrease in velocity constant, as the period of contact is lengthened, has been suggested to reside in the disappearance of the hydrogen chloride, as time progresses, by its reaction with the ash constituents to form hydrogen sulphide, ferrous chloride, and other compounds. The presence of hydrogen sulphide in the gas was indicative of this explanation. Foxwell (215) (216) attempted to ascertain the effect of hydrochloric acid concentration on the ammonia decomposition velocity constant and obtained some results that are difficult to interpret. He found that the velocity constant decreased from about 0.0030 to about 0.00060, as the ratio of hydrogen chloride to ammonia concentration increased from zero to 0.1, at which point there was an abrupt change. Thereafter, the velocity constant rose to a maximum of about 0.0015 at a concentration ratio of 0.4, finally decreasing to about 0.00035 at a concentration ratio of unity. The decrease up to a concentration ratio of 0.1 is explained by the negative catalytic effect of hydrogen chloride; the rise to a maximum at a concentration ratio of 0.4 is attributed to the positive catalytic effect of metallic iron, produced by the reaction of hydrochloric acid with ferrous sulphide to form ferrous chloride, which in turn reacts with moisture to form ferrous oxide, the latter being finally reduced by hydrogen to metallic iron; while the reduction of velocity constant up to a concentration ratio of unity can be conceived as the result of the formation of ammonium chloride, which is stable at temperatures above 800°C., thus decreasing the effective quantity of ammonia available for dissociation.

Ammonia Oxidation. An extensive investigation on the factors which influence the destruction of ammonia by oxidation in the carbonization of coal was carried out by Greenwood and Hodsman (218) (219). A knowledge of this phenomenon is clearly important, because of the likelihood of indrawn air in a leaky retort and because of the part played by water vapor and materials of construction in retarding or promoting ammonia oxidation. It is very well known that the oxidation of ammonia is exceedingly sensitive to catalysts, both with respect to the velocity of oxidation and with respect to the products of the reaction. Ammonia may react with oxygen to yield elementary nitrogen and water, or it may react to form nitric oxide and water. Under the conditions obtaining during carbonization, the formation of gaseous nitrogen upon oxidation is the more likely of the two to occur, but conceivably, by the use of certain catalytic agents, the ammonia could be oxidized almost quantitatively to the oxide. Apparently, ammonia is completely unstable in the presence of oxygen at all temperatures, so that neither of the above mentioned reactions is reversible under ordinary, or indeed under any known, conditions. Consequently, the decomposition of ammonia by oxidation cannot be regarded as limited by conditions of equilibrium or by the law of mass action. Under given physico-chemical conditions with a given catalyst there is always a temperature at which the tendency to form nitric acid from the reaction of ammonia and oxygen is at a maximum. Above and below this optimum temperature the tendency is to form free nitrogen, probably as a result of the interaction of nitric oxide that is produced and fresh ammonia to form elementary nitrogen and water. This sufficiently accounts for the fact that nitrates and nitrites are never found in the gas liquors.

Greenwood and Hodsman (218) (219) observed that the catalytic effect of a porous firebrick, which contained 1.4 per cent of ferric oxide, decreased from a marked activity, in the initial passage of gas, to about 25 per cent of its former value, after prolonged flow of gas. Thus, its effectiveness diminished from about 82 per cent of the ammonia oxidized, after 10 liters of gas had passed over the catalyst, to about 25 per cent decomposed, after 120 liters had flowed through the reaction tube, the decay of activitiy apparently following an exponential law.   This fatigue of the brick catalyst cannot be attributed to poisoning by other constituents of the gas, for the same

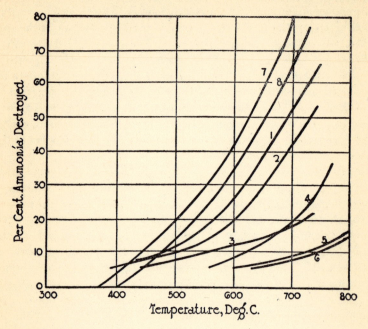

FIG. 44. CATALYTIC EFFECT OF REFRACTORY MATERIALS IN VARIOUS ATMOSPHERES ON AMMONIA DECOMPOSITION

1 = Dry air with fireclay.   2 = Moist air with fireclay.   3 = Dry air with silica.   4 = Silica with nitrogen containing 1 per cent to 2 per cent oxygen. 5 = Firebrick with coal gas containing 1 per cent to 2 per cent oxygen.   6 = Silica with coal gas containing 1 per cent to 2 per cent oxygen.   7 = Chattered firebrick with dry air.   8 = Chattered firebrick with moist air.

phenomenon was observed when pure air was passed.   The author suggests that an explanation may be found in surface adsorption and occlusion of gas within the minute pores.

Greenwood and Hodsman (218) (219) passed ammonia, mixed variously with dry and moist air, nitrogen, and coal gas, over different contact materials for quite a range of temperatures with the results illustrated in Fig. 44. A blank experiment was made with the ammonia mixed with dry air and passed over silica, representative of a relatively inactive contact material, to determine the temperature range over which oxidation takes place when catalysis is minimized. Below 500°C., very small quantities of nitrous acid, but never nitric acid, were detected, while above that temperature only free nitrogen was produced by the reaction. The introduction of a nitrogenous atmosphere, containing from one per cent to 2 per cent oxygen, caused a retardation of oxidation below 700°C., due to the reduction in oxygen concentration, but above that temperature this effect was not noticeable. When an atmosphere of coal gas, containing one per cent to 2 per cent oxygen, was substituted in place of air, with silica as the contact material, oxidation of the ammonia was so effectively retarded that it was zero at 600°C. and less than 15 per cent had been destroyed up to 800°C. When firebrick was substituted for silica as the contact agent, in the presence of coal gas there was only a slight increase in oxidation. On the other hand, when fireclay was used as the catalytic agent in air, the oxidation of ammonia was tremendously accelerated, as seen in Fig. 44. From zero decomposition at 450°C. with silica, the oxidation was raised to about 8 per cent with fireclay and from about 25 per cent oxidation at 750°C. with silica to about 70 per cent with fireclay. When, however, moist air was substituted for dry air in the presence of fireclay contact material, there was a decrease of about 20 per cent in the proportion of ammonia oxidized. All of the experimental data were reduced to a contact time of 7 seconds.

The results indicated that, under the conditions of the experiment up to temperatures of 800°C., there was very little oxidation of ammonia in the presence of coal gas, but that at the end of the passage the entire oxygen present had been removed, presumably by combination with the hydrogen or by reaction with the hydrocarbons of the coal gas. Had the entire ammonia present been oxidized, only a fraction of the oxygen would have been absorbed in this reaction. Even at 600°C., absolutely no ammonia was oxidized in an atmosphere of coal gas containing oxygen, although at this temperature the oxidation amounted to about 12 per cent and about 8 per cent in atmospheres of air and nitrogen, respectively. From these experiments, it is apparent that when ammonia is heated with oxygen in the presence of coal gas, oxidation of the hydrogen and hydrocarbons takes precedence over oxidation of the ammonia, and, if any of the latter is destroyed at all, it must be attributed to thermal dissociation rather than to oxidation.

The presence of moisture when a mixture of air and ammonia was passed over silica had very little effect, decreasing the oxidation but 2.5 per cent at 750°C. The presence of moisture in coal gas caused no difference whatever in the amount of ammonia oxidized. However, it is seen from Fig. 44 that when moisture was admitted to the

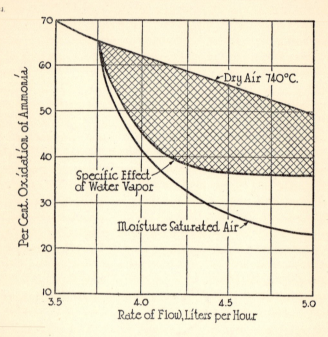

Fig. 45. Oxidation of Ammonia in Dry and Moist Air as a Function of the Rate of Flow

mixture of air and ammonia there was a material retardation in oxidation with fireclay as the contact material. The addition of 2.8 per cent water vapor caused a reduction of the percentage ammonia oxidized at 740°C. from 64.0 per cent to 52.3 per cent. The influence of water vapor on the stability of ammonia in the presence of oxygen can be attributed to two factors, viz.: the increased rate of gas flow with the consequent shortening of the period of contact with the active surfaces and the specific effect of the water vapor.

The curves in Fig. 45 show severally the variation of oxidation at 740°C. with the rate of flow for a mixture of ammonia and dry air; the variation of oxidation at the same temperature, as a function of the rate of flow, when the air is saturated with moisture; and, by subtraction, the resultant curve, which may be regarded as showing the specific action of the water vapor. The preservative influence of moisture on the oxidation of ammonia was marked only in the case of contact surfaces exhibiting active catalytic effects, and then the activity of the catalyst was only partially retarded. The most plausible explanation of this behaviour is found in the supposition that a unimolecular film of moisture forms on the catalytic surface, thus restricting the access of ammonia and oxygen to the active material.

Mott and Hodsman (217) investigated the influence of water vapor, and also the character of the contact materials, on the decomposition of ammonia at various temperatures. Their experiments were performed with a mixture containing about 1.5 per cent ammonia, which is the same order of concentration for that gas found in carbonization practice. Fig. 44 shows the decomposition of ammonia by oxidation, as a function of the temperature, when heated with dry and moist air and passed over chattered brick which had previously seen hard service in ovens where salty coals were coked. This brick had been badly corroded, iron from the coal ash having been volatilized as the chloride and deposited within the brick for some distance as the metal or as the oxide. Analysis showed this brick to contain 79.84 per cent silica, 11.49 per cent alumina, 1.31 per cent titania, 3.95 per cent ferric oxide, 0.60 per cent lime, 0.12 per cent magnesia, and 2.47 per cent alkalies, by difference. The high iron content of this brick probably largely accounted for its high catalytic action. These curves should be compared with those in Fig. 44 for a Farnley brick, designated as fireclay, from which it is observed that the iron in the chattered firebrick doubtlessly deposited as the more active metallic form, whereas in the fireclay it probably existed in combination with silicates. The presence of about 3 per cent water vapor lowered the oxidation at a given temperature much more than could be accounted for by reduction in time of contact, thereby confirming previous experiments indicating a specific action of water vapor.

Nitrogen and Hydrogen Atmospheres.   Mott and Hodsman (217) continued their work on the effect of contact surfaces on the oxidation and dissociation of ammonia in different atmospheres.   The results in atmospheres of coal gas, hydrogen, and nitrogen, with and without the presence of oxygen, are shown in Fig. 46.   In these experiments the chattered firebrick, previously referred to, was used as the contact material.   The data were all calculated to the same period of contact.

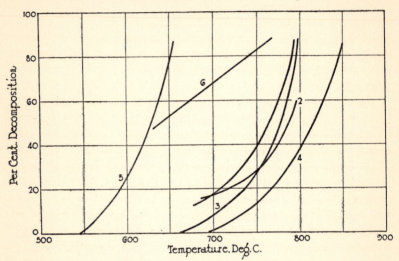

FIG. 46. CATALYTIC EFFECT OF CHATTERED FIREBRICK ON THE DESTRUCTION OF AMMONIA AS A FUNCTION OF TEMPERATURE

1 = Oxygen-free coal gas.   2 = Dry coal gas containing 1.2 per cent oxygen. 3 = Dry hydrogen.   4 = Mixture of moist coal gas and hydrogen.   5 = Oxygen-free nitrogen.   6 = Nitrogen containing 1.2 per cent oxygen.

When a mixture of dry hydrogen and ammonia, to the extent of about 1.5 per cent, was passed through the reaction tube, dissociation began at about 660°C. and rose rapidly until at 800°C. it was practically complete.   Under these conditions the velocity of dissociation increases rapidly with the temperature, the velocity constant k, of equation (23) increasing from 0.00074 at 675°C. to 0.0059 at 750°C. and to 0.081 at 800°C.   At 700°C. the decomposition amounted to about 9.5 per cent; at 750°C. to about 26 per cent; and at 800°C. to about 86 per cent.   When a nitrogenous atmosphere was substituted in place of hydrogen, dissociation began as low as 550°C. and reached nearly 80 per cent at 650°C. When 1.2 per cent oxygen, mixed with nitrogen, was used, the dissociation curve was apparently a linear function of the temperature, increasing regularly from about 46 per cent at 625°C. to about 90 per cent at 775°C. The dissociation of ammonia is tremendously greater in the presence of nitrogen than in atmospheres of hydrogen, the two curves being roughly parallel and about 150°C. apart. In nitrogen the ammonia was almost completely decomposed at 660°C., whereas decomposition was just measurable at that temperature with hydrogen. It could of course be argued, from the law of mass action, that changes in the hydrogen concentration would be far more effective in preserving the ammonia than changes in the nitrogen concentration. This, of course, is true near the equilibrium condition, but it is neither necessary nor probable under conditions where the reverse reaction is negligible. Quite surprisingly, the presence of 1.2 per cent oxygen in the nitrogen above 650°C. has a preservative influence on the ammonia. Whether or not this beneficial result is due to initial dissociation and reaction of the hydrogen to form water vapor with its inhibitory influence, or to an entirely different mechanism, such as direct oxidation, is a matter of conjecture. Finally, when an atmosphere of dry coal gas was used, the destruction of ammonia amounted to 18 per cent at 700°C., and was about complete at 800°C.; but when 1.2 per cent oxygen was present in the gas, the decomposition was only 62 per cent at the higher temperature. Here the benefit derived from the presence of oxygen is clearer, for water vapor is doubtlessly formed by the preferential oxidation of hydrogen in the coal gas.

Further experiments by Mott and Hodsman (217) on the decomposition of ammonia, when passed over coke, gave results similar to those derived from the use of chattered firebrick as the contact surface, but the decomposition at a given temperature under a given atmosphere was considerably less, showing the coke to be a far more inactive catalyst than the chattered brick. They concluded that, since carbon has been shown to be an indifferent catalytic agent, the quantity and quality of the coal ash remaining in the coke is more likely to influence the decomposition of the ammonia. We have already seen that Foxwell (215) (216) demonstrated that the composition of the ash, indeed, had a great effect on ammonia dissociation.

Monkhouse and Cobb (220) observed that, of the total nitrogen present in the coal, only 10 per cent to 25 per cent is obtained as ammonia, the greater portion, amounting to 40 per cent or 80 per cent, remaining in the coal and the rest being found in the gas as free nitrogen or as cyanogen. Many factors, such as temperature of distillation, nature of the coal, and rate of carbonization, affect the liberation of ammonia during coking. Temperatures above 500°C. are necessary for a good yield of ammonia and the higher the temperature, the less nitrogen remains in the coke. In general, the older the geologic age of the fuel, the less the proportion of total nitrogen obtained as ammonia. Finally, the slower the rate of distillation, the more nitrogen is evolved as ammonia, provided the vapors are quickly removed.

TABLE 93

Ultimate analyses of coal and cokes tested for liberation of ammonia

FUEL	COAL	TEMPERATURE OF COKE		
		500°C.	800°C.	1100°C.
Analysis:	*per cent*	*per cent*	*per cent*	*per cent*
Moisture............................	5.4	3.3	2.3	0.3
Carbon.............................	73.3	82.4	88.2	93.1
Hydrogen...........................	5.1	3.0	0.9	0.6
Nitrogen............................	1.67	1.87	1.34	0.58
Oxygen..............................	8.2	3.6	1.1	9.7
Sulphur.............................	1.75	1.41	1.40	1.30
Ash.................................	4.7	4.5	6.22	4.9

In their study of the liberation of nitrogen from coke as ammonia, Monkhouse and Cobb (220) used a Yorkshire bituminous coal which contained 5.4 per cent moisture, 34.0 per cent volatile matter, 56.0 per cent fixed carbon, and 4.7 per cent ash. The ash consisted of 25.1 per cent silica, 33.5 per cent alumina, 10.1 per cent ferric oxide, 13.1 per cent lime, 12.9 per cent sulphuric oxide, and 5.1 per cent alkali oxides. Ultimate analyses of the raw coal and the three cokes obtained from it are shown in Table 93. The 500°C. coke was considered representative of low temperature coke, the 800°C. coke resembled gas coke, and the 1100°C. coke was comparable to by-product oven metallurgical coke. The table shows clearly that the nitrogen present in the carbonization residuum was reduced as the temperature advanced. The ammonium sulphate equivalent of nitrogen in the raw coal was 176.3 pounds per gross ton of coal; that in the 500°C. coke was 197.5 pounds per gross ton of coke, or 138.3 pounds of ammonium sulphate per gross ton of coal; the 800°C. coke contained nitrogen equivalent to 141.5 pounds of ammonium sulphate per gross ton of coke, or 66.5 pounds per gross ton of coal; while the 1100°C. coke had 61.2 pounds equivalent ammonium sulphate per gross ton of coke, or about 34 pounds per gross ton of coal. These cokes were heated at various temperatures in different atmospheres to determine the specific action of different gases on the production of ammonia.

TABLE 94

Effect of reheating coke in nitrogenous atmosphere

ITEM	TEMPERATURE OF FURNACE		
	600°C.	800°C.	1000°C.
500°C. coke:			
Per cent total coke nitrogen as ammonia.....	3.1%	8.56%	0.06%
Pounds of ammonium sulphate per ton coke .	6.2	17.0	0.1
Per cent total nitrogen as ammonia..........	2.5%	6.7%	0.05%
Pounds ammonium sulphate per ton coal	4.3	11.9	0.1
800°C. coke:			
Per cent total coke nitrogen as ammonia.....	0.34%		
Pounds of ammonium sulphate per ton coke .	0.5		
Per cent total coal nitrogen as ammonia.....	0.17%		
Pounds ammonium sulphate per ton coal	0.3		

Table 94 shows the results of heating the different representative cokes in the presence of nitrogen. The amount of ammonia evolved from the 1100°C. coke under these conditions was so small as to be negligible. The 500°C. coke had 1.34 per cent nitrogen remaining after reheating to 1000°C., while the 800°C. coke had 1.02 per cent remaining after reheating to the same temperature. This table should be compared with Table 95, which gives a nitrogen balance for the tests of these cokes when they were heated to the final temperature of 1000°C. in an atmosphere of nitrogen. Reheating the 800°C. coke in stages to 1000°C., removed 30 per cent of the coke nitrogen, but, if any ammonia was formed, practically all of it was decomposed under these conditions, as only 0.2 per cent was recovered.

TABLE 95

Nitrogen balance after reheating coke to 1000°C. in nitrogenous atmosphere

ITEM	500°C. COKE	800°C. COKE
Calculated to coke total nitrogen:	per cent	per cent
Nitrogen as ammonia on reheating...............	11.7	0.3
Nitrogen in coke residue.........................	60.4	70.2
Free nitrogen and unaccounted for..............	27.9	29.5
Calculated to coal total nitrogen:	per cent	per cent
Nitrogen removed by coking.....................	21.6	49.7
Nitrogen as ammonia on reheating..............	9.6	0.2
Nitrogen in coke residue........................	47.3	35.3
Free nitrogen and unaccounted for..............	21.9	14.8

TABLE 96

Effect of reheating coke in hydrogenous atmosphere

ITEM	TEMPERATURE OF FURNACE		
	600°C.	800°C.	1000°C.
500°C. coke:			
Per cent total nitrogen as ammonia..........	12.47%	20.30%	1.47%
Pounds of ammonium sulphate per gross ton coke..	24.6	40.1	2.9
Per cent total coal nitrogen as ammonia.....	9.8%	15.9%	1.1%
Pounds ammonium sulphate per gross ton coal	17.2	28.1	2.0
800°C. coke:			
Per cent total nitrogen as ammonia..........	0.44%	2.64%	0.79%
Pounds of ammonium sulphate per gross ton coke..	0.6	3.7	1.1
Per cent total coal nitrogen as ammonia.....	0.22%	1.32%	0.40%
Pounds ammonium sulphate per gross ton coal..	0.4	2.3	0.7

Monkhouse and Cobb (220), with the idea of minimizing dissociation, next determined if any more ammonia could be obtained from the low temperature coke by heating it in stages to 800°C., as compared to heating it directly to 800°C., in an atmosphere of nitrogen. The results indicated that the ratio of ammonia to free nitrogen was slightly greater in the multi-stage heating than in direct heating, so that there was some little reduction of dissociation.

Monkhouse and Cobb (220) also reheated the cokes obtained by them at different temperatures in an atmosphere of hydrogen, thereby obtaining a distinctly different result from the use of nitrogen. Table 96 gives the results of heating the 500°C. and 800°C. cokes in stages to 1000°C. in the presence of hydrogen and Table 97 gives a nitrogen balance for the same conditions. The 1100°C. coke was heated in hydrogen up to 1000°C., but no ammonia whatever was

TABLE 97

Nitrogen balance after reheating coke to 1000°C. in hydrogenous atmosphere

ITEM	500°C. COKE	800°C. COKE
Calculated to coke total nitrogen:	per cent	per cent
Nitrogen as ammonia on reheating..............	34.2	3.9
Nitrogen in coke residue.......................	28.2	59.0
Free nitrogen and unaccounted for.............	37.6	37.1
Calculated to coal total nitrogen:	per cent	per cent
Nitrogen removed by coking...................	21.6	49.7
Nitrogen as ammonia on reheating..............	26.8	2.0
Nitrogen in coke residue.......................	22.1	29.7
Free nitrogen and unaccounted for..............	29.5	18.6

evolved. The nitrogen remaining in the 500°C. coke, after treatment up to 1000°C., was 0.65 per cent and that remaining in the 800°C. coke was 0.84 per cent.

The illustration in Fig. 47 shows graphically the difference between the effect of nitrogen and hydrogen atmospheres on the production of ammonia by reheating the low temperature coke to drive off the nitrogen. At 1000°C., in an atmosphere of nitrogen, the ammonia recovery ceased to increase appreciably with rising temperature, due doubtlessly to the increased rate of dissociation. The marked influence of an hydrogenous atmosphere on the yield of ammonia is seen by the fact that, when the low temperature coke was reheated at 1000°C. in an atmosphere of hydrogen, 34.2 per cent of the nitrogen in the coke was recovered as ammonia, with 28.2 per cent of the

nitrogen originally present remaining in the coke residuum, as
compared with 11.7 per cent recovered as ammonia in an atmosphere
of nitrogen, with 60.4 per cent of the original nitrogen remaining in
the coke after treatment.   In all cases, the rate of ammonia recovery
was more rapid when the various cokes were reheated at 800°C.
than at either the lower temperature of 600°C. or at the higher temperature of 1000°C.   If hydrogen aided the formation of ammonia
in nitrogenous compounds evolved at the higher temperatures, it
was rapidly decomposed.   It is quite conclusive that hydrogen

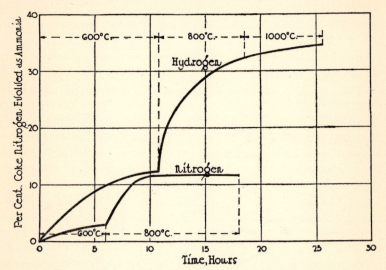

FIG. 47. EVOLUTION OF AMMONIA FROM LOW TEMPERATURE COKE IN
ATMOSPHERES OF HYDROGEN AND OF NITROGEN

exerted on the coke a specific action which favored the formation of
ammonia, as compared with the indifferent action of such inert
atmospheres as nitrogen.

One remaining phenomenon has its influence on the quantity of
ammonia yielded.   That is what has been called the secondary
production of ammonia by the action of hydrogen gas on the incandescent coke.   Tervet (222), in his experiments, passed a current
of hydrogen over incandescent coke and found that the ammonia
yield was increased 100 per cent.   The action of hydrogen on the
soft coke is such as to attack the nitrogen which it contains and to

form increased quantities of ammonia. Hydrogen did not attack hard coke at all and the effect on medium coke was much less pronounced than when the soft variety was used. A yield as high as 94 pounds of ammonium sulphate per gross ton was reported upon carbonizing the charge of soft coke slowly at 1000°C. in an hydrogenous atmosphere. It seems probable, therefore, that, over the range 500°C. to 800°C., hydrogen gas has a specific action capable of liberating additional quantities of ammonia, as well as of acting as a preservative of the ammonia otherwise formed.

Steaming. The use of steam during carbonization is well known to increase greatly the yield of ammonia in high temperature processes, but its effect in low temperature methods is questioned among the authorities. The Fuel Research Board maintains that here again the principal function of the steam is to sweep the retort clean of gaseous products, thus removing the ammonia as quickly as possible from the conditions favorable to its decomposition. They maintain that little or no increase in nitrogen, evolved as ammonia, can be expected through the use of steam in low temperature processes, although in coals of low moisture content it might assist in the recovery of small quantities of ammonia which would remain uncondensed and make scrubbing necessary. We have already seen in Table 43 the influence of increasing percentages of steam on the analyses of low temperature gas, the nitrogen content being decreased from 13.8 per cent in dry distillation to 7.6 per cent when 20 per cent steam was passed into the retort. This reduction in free nitrogen in the gas doubtlessly arises from a reduction of the thermal dissociation of ammonia.

Porter and Ovitz (96), in comparing the yield of ammonium sulphate obtained from dry and moist coals, substantiated the opinion of the Fuel Research Board that high moisture content increases the efficiency of ammonia recovery. They found that, when computed upon a basis of dry coal, a yield of 25.3 pounds of ammonium sulphate was obtained per gross ton of dry coal, as compared with 26.9 pounds of ammonium sulphate, recovered when the same coal was carbonized while moist.

The experiments of Mott and Hodsman (217) demonstrated that the presence of 25 per cent steam at 850°C. completely prevents dissociation of the ammonia, which ordinarily is completely decomposed at a temperature 50°C. lower. At 785°C. they found that 72 per cent of the ammonia ordinarily dissociated, but with 12.5 per cent water vapor only about 8 per cent decomposed.

Davis and Parry (97), using Pennsylvania coal of the Freeport bed, found that the use of 88 per cent steam during carbonization at 550°C. increased the yield of ammonium sulphate 43 per cent.   The variation of ammonium sulphate yield at various temperatures under steam distillation, as determined by them, is given in Table 98.   At 550°C. without steam, they obtained only 10 pounds of ammonium sulphate per net ton, the gas evolved containing 8.2 per cent nitrogen and 1.9 per cent nitrogen remaining in the coke.

It is seen in Fig. 46, from the experiments of Mott and Hodsman (217), that when one per cent to 2 per cent ammonia was passed through the reaction chamber in an atmosphere of coal gas, containing 1.2 per cent oxygen, the oxidation amounted to about 17 per cent at

TABLE 98

Temperature variation of ammonium sulphate yield under steam distillation

PRODUCT	TEMPERATURE		
	475°C.	550°C.	650°C.
Ammonium sulphate per net ton...	4.5 pounds	10.0 pounds	18.3 pounds
Nitrogen in gas evolved............	16.7%	8.2%	2.1%
Nitrogen remaining in coke........	2.0%	2.1%	2.0%

700°C. and to about 41 per cent at 750°C., whereas, when oxygen-free coal gas was used the decomposition was 18 per cent and 61 per cent at the corresponding temperatures.   At first sight, this appears astonishing, but reflection shows that in every case where oxygen was present in the coal gas it had entirely reacted with the hydrogen and hydrocarbons to form water, which undoubtedly exerted an inhibitory effect on the ammonia decomposition, it having already been demonstrated that under such conditions the oxidation of ammonia is prevented by the preferential oxidation of the hydrogen and the hydrocarbons.   When a mixture of coal gas and hydrogen, containing about 3 per cent moisture, was used, the inhibitory effect of water vapor was even more marked than in the case of an atmosphere of air, as shown by the two upper curves in Fig. 44.   At 700°C., the presence of 3 per cent water vapor reduced the ammonia decomposition from about 17 per cent to about 3 per cent and at 800°C. from about 95 per cent to about 38 per cent.   The reduction in the time of contact, through presence of the steam, could account for a difference of only about 2 per cent.

Monkhouse and Cobb (220), having ascertainèd that reheating the 1100°C. coke in dry hydrogen up to 1000°C. was without effect in removing the nitrogenous material of the coke in the form of ammonia, investigated the influence of using a mixture of steam and hydrogen, the former being present to the extent of 65 per cent.   The results are shown in Fig. 48, from which it is seen that the presence of moisture caused a slow but steady evolution of ammonia up to 800°C. At 1000°C. the evolution of ammonia increased greatly, doubtlessly because of gasification, according to well established principles of

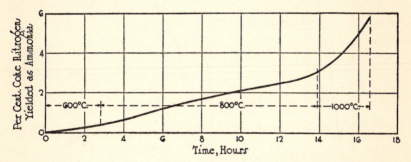

FIG. 48. EVOLUTION OF AMMONIA FROM HIGH TEMPERATURE COKE IN AN ATMOSPHERE OF HYDROGEN AND STEAM

ammonia production with excess steam, as used in the Mond system. It has been stated that, in such reactions, the carbon-nitrogen ratio of the fuel remains constant during gasification, which demonstrates that the production of amnonia in gasification processes with the use of steam is accompanied by simultaneous consumption of the carbon surrounding the nitrogenous materials.

The successive action of nitrogen, hydrogen, and steam was tried on low temperature coke to ascertain how far the nitrogen remaining in the coke from one treatment could be removed by application of gaseous atmospheres of more specific action.   The experiments were made on 500°C. low temperature coke at a reheat temperature of 800°C.   Heating was continued with each gaseous atmosphere until the evolution of ammonia practically ceased.   Two curves, giving the results of these experiments, are reproduced in Fig. 49, one for successive heatings with nitrogen, hydrogen, and steam, and one for only nitrogen and steam. At the end of the nitrogen stage, 10.1 per cent of the coke nitrogen had been yielded as ammonia; 19.6 per cent was evolved as free nitrogen; and 70.3 per cent remained in the coke residuum. When hydrogen was then introduced, an additional 32 per cent of the nitrogen was gasified, of which 31.0 per cent appeared as ammonia, the decomposition being practically

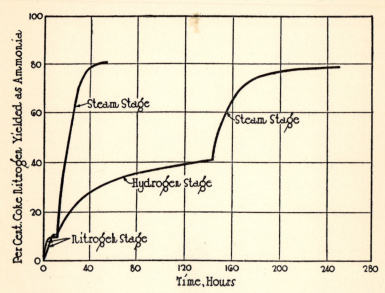

FIG. 49. EVOLUTION OF AMMONIA FROM LOW TEMPERATURE COKE BY SUCCESSIVE HEATING AT 800°C. IN VARIOUS ATMOSPHERES

nil under these conditions. Steam, diluted with 37.5 per cent nitrogen, was next admitted to the retort. Due to the water gas reaction, the quantity of gas yielded in this case exceeded that of the gas admitted, in fact, when the experiment was discontinued, it was found that this reaction had progressed to complete gasification, so that only the coke ash remained. In this final stage 38.3 per cent of the nitrogen originally present in the coke was removed, 38.1 per cent being ammonia and the rest free nitrogen. It is clearly seen that large additional quantities of the coke nitrogen can be removed by heating in atmospheres of hydrogen and of steam after treatment in nitrogen and, furthermore, that removal of the ammonia in hydrogenous and steam atmospheres is accompanied by very little decomposition. The latter is attributed to the fact that the ammonia present was so diluted by the other gases that equilibrium was not attained. Very little ammonia would have survived at 800°C., if equilibrium conditions at that temperature had been reached. As a matter of fact, the concentration of ammonia, itself, plays a more important part than that of either hydrogen or nitrogen on the rate of

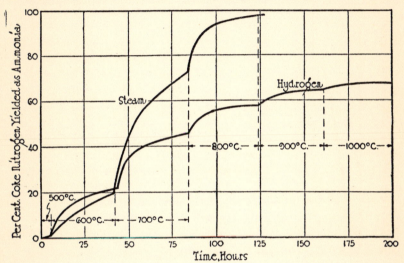

Fig. 50. Evolution of Ammonia from Low Temperature Coke Heated Successively at Various Temperatures

ammonia decomposition at a given temperature, the rate of decomposition being higher, the higher the concentration. Fig. 49 also shows the effect of omitting the hydrogen stage, the same amount of ammonia being obtained by this procedure in 40 hours of treatment as was removed in 240 hours when the hydrogen stage was introduced.

In a later research, Monkhouse and Cobb (221) investigated the use of hydrogen and steam in obviating the formation of free nitrogen, instead of ammonia, when the same cokes as used before were heated. Fig. 50 shows the effect of reheating 500°C. low temperature coke in 40-hour stages in two gaseous atmospheres. The steam contained

40 per cent nitrogen as the carrier gas.   After 40 hours of heating in the presence of steam at the final temperature, only ash remained, the carbon having been completely gasified.   At the end of the 800°C. stage, 9.1 per cent of the nitrogen originally present had been evolved as the uncombined gas when hydrogen was used, as compared with only 1.7 per cent at the same temperature, when steam was used, practically no dissociation of ammonia occurring in the latter case.

A careful examination of Fig. 50 shows that, whereas the evolution of ammonia in hydrogen at a given temperature had a gradually declining rate as time went on, the evolution of ammonia in steam proceeded at a constant rate after the initial rapid evolution at the beginning of each temperature stage.   In the former case, the curves are logarithmic in shape, while in the latter case, they are hyperbolic.   As the temperature is increased at each stage, there is an initial large evolution of ammonia which accompanies the temperature rise, even in an inert atmosphere.   Simultaneously, there is taking place a gasification of the coke carbon by the water gas reaction, which is of secondary importance at the beginning of an increased temperature stage, but which ultimately becomes the controlling reaction and accounts for the characteristic linear portion of the steam atmosphere curve.   In Fig. 51 is shown an enlarged curve of the lower part of Fig. 50, being the evolution of ammonia from low temperature coke at 600°C. in various atmospheres.   It is seen that, due to the characteristic shape of the steam curve, it falls below that of hydrogen for the first 35 hours of heating at this temperature.   At temperatures above 700°C., the steam curve will fall entirely above the others, as the temperature becomes more favorable to the water gas reaction.

An experiment, conducted by Monkhouse and Cobb (221) on the use of nitrogen, saturated with 63 per cent steam, in effecting the removal of nitrogen from 1100°C. high temperature coke, showed that, when the reheat temperature was 800°C., only 1.36 per cent of the coke nitrogen was removed, whereas 95.4 per cent evolved as ammonia at 900°C.   After about 90 hours treatment, 10 hours of which were at 800°C., 70 hours of which were at 900°C., and the remaining 10 hours at 1000°C., 97.3 per cent of the coke nitrogen was removed as ammonia and 2.7 per cent as free nitrogen.   The liberation of ammonia from high temperature coke, in the presence of steam at a given temperature, was much slower than from low temperature coke, due to the great reactivity of the 500°C. coke and to its ease of gasification.

Sulphur Distribution.   Analyses of many coals of the United States by the United States Bureau of Mines, as compiled by Fieldner, Selvig, and Paul (210), show that the amount of sulphur present ranges from as low as 0.11 per cent, in the case of a sample from

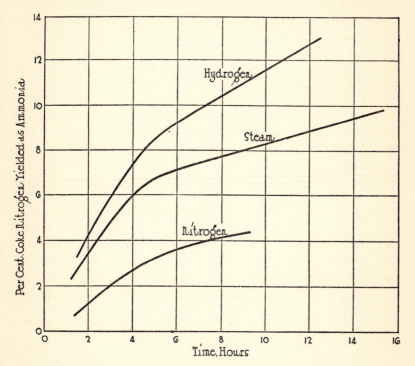

FIG. 51. EVOLUTION OF AMMONIA FROM LOW TEMPERATURE COKE IN VARIOUS ATMOSPHERES AS A FUNCTION OF TIME

Alaska, to as much as 11.68 per cent, for a specimen from the roof of a vein in Colorado.   A great many of the bituminous coals of the United States have from 0.5 per cent to 4.5 per cent sulphur, the average sample containing approximately 2.0 per cent.   The disadvantges of high sulphur content in coke are well known.   When used for domestic purposes, the fumes, liberated upon combustion, are objectionable to smell and are injurious to property.   When coke is completely gasified, the sulphur again presents the same difficulties, for it appears as hydrogen sulphide in the gas. We have already seen in Table 32 and Table 33 that, even at temperatures as low as 450°C., considerable quantities of sulphuretted hydrogen may be found in the gas from low temperature distillation.

Both inorganic and organic sulphur occur in coal. The inorganic sulphur is present mostly in combination with iron, either as pyrites or as marcasite, both of which have the same chemical formula. The former usually predominates. Free sulphur is occasionally found and also small quantities of sulphates. The organic sulphur had its origin in the protein of the plant and animal life of which coal is the degradation product, according to the theory discussed in

TABLE 99

Distribution of sulphur among different classes of compounds

CONSTITUENT	COAL SAMPLE				
	1	2	3	4	5
	per cent	*per cent*	*per cent*	*per cent*	*per cent*
Resinic sulphur.................	0.34	0.16	0.77	0.50	0.10
Humous sulphur................	0.87	0.51	0.70	0.95	0.45
Sulphate sulphur...............	0.05	0.25	1.31	0.31	0.01
Pyritic sulphur.................	0.85	0.31	2.06	1.36	0.29
Total sulphur.................	2.11	1.23	4.84	3.12	0.85

Chapter I, under the subject of the origin of coal. Powell and Parr (223) examined a number of different coals to ascertain the distribution of sulphur between inorganic and organic compounds. They found sulphur in both the resinic and humous bodies, whose proximate analyses were given in Table 4, and whose extraction has been discussed in Chapter I, under the subject of destructive distillation. On the average, the sulphur of coal is about equally distributed between organic and inorganic compounds. Table 99 gives the distribution of sulphur among different classes of compounds, as determined by Powell and Parr (223). All the specimens were of Illinois coal, except sample No. 5 which was from Tennessee.

The variation of the amount of sulphate which was present in the various samples is interesting, in view of the different ages of the coals after mining. During storage, oxidation of the coal, as a whole, includes oxidation of the sulphur compounds, and the iron pyrites may oxidize to such an extent that, after two or three years standing, sulphate may become the major sulphur compound. The sulphur content of Sample No. 3 in Table 99 contained less than 0.01 per cent sulphate, when freshly mined, as compared with 1.31 per cent, after standing two years in a flask.

Thermal Transformations. When coal is carbonized, the sulphur divides between the volatile products and the solid residuum. The ratio of volatile to residual sulphur varies between wide limits, but remains fairly constant for a given coal. The factors underlying the volatility of the sulphur are not well known. Undoubtedly, certain constituents of the coal, other than the sulphur, have a marked influence in this respect, but probably the most decisive factor is the relative amounts of the different sulphur compounds that are present in the coal. The sulphur compounds in the volatile matter from distillation are largely in the form of hydrogen sulphide, or tiophene derivatives, while the residual sulphur in the coke is principally of an unknown organic nature with traces of sulphides. When the coke from coal Sample No. 4 of Table 99 was examined by Powell and Parr (223) they found that 1.37 per cent sulphur remained, of which 0.30 per cent was sulphide and the rest organic. They found that the sulphate was entirely reduced, not to sulphide, but probably to form unknown organic sulphur compounds. The pyritic sulphur was totally decomposed, part being volatilized and part remaining as sulphide. Probably the resinic sulphur of the coal was left in the coke, but in a different form, while the humous sulphur was partly volatilized and partly left as residuum of changed form.

Powell (224) extensively investigated the reactions of coal sulphur in the coking process. When mineralogical pyrite is heated, very little decomposition is observed at 500°C., but at 1000°C. it is entirely decomposed into equal proportions of free sulphur and sulphide sulphur. If moisture, or other hydrogen-yielding compounds are present, the free sulphur will be partially converted to hydrogen sulphide. When mineralogical pyrite is mixed with an equal amount of coal and heated to the same temperature, it is found that half of the total sulphur appears as ferrous sulphide, about half as much again is evolved as sulphuretted hydrogen, while the remainder is divided in the ratio of about two to one as free and organic sulphur, respectively. It has been demonstrated by Campbell (225), and verified by Powell (224), that the ferrous sulphide residuum is pyrrhotite, or magnetic sulphide of iron, which is not a definite chemical compound, but a solid solution of sulphur in ferrous sulphide.

According to Powell (224), the total sulphur in the coal is the most important factor bearing on the sulphur content of the coke and a careful scrutiny of the percentage of organic and inorganic sulphur contents of the raw coal did not reveal any constant relation to the sulphur content of the coke produced therefrom. This practically nullifies any statement as to the relative importance of removing organic and pyritic sulphur before carbonization.

Temperature Effect. The transformation of sulphur compounds at various coking temperatures was studied by Powell (224), who used a number of different coals. The results of his heating a Tennessee coal, containing 4.25 per cent sulphur, are given in Table 100, from a critical study of which, it is possible to draw a number of conclusions regarding the reactions undergone by the sulphur compounds during coking. From Table 100, it is seen that the pyritic sulphur is rapidly decomposed between 400°C. and 500°C. and that the sulphates, which have gradually disappeared as the temperature increases, are almost entirely decomposed at 500°C. As the temperature advances, there is a gradual increase of sulphide sulphur in the coke and there is a gradually increasing proportion of volatile sulphur compounds found in the gas and tar. At first, the organic sulphur present in the coal varies inversely as the temperature, but, between 400°C. and 500°C., a radical change takes place with the formation of increasing amounts of organic sulphur, as the temperature of carbonization is further advanced. It is interesting to note from Table 100, that, from the region of low temperature distillation to the region of high temperature carbonization, the only sulphur remaining in the coke is in the form of sulphides or of organic compounds.

It should be noted, that, starting with an initial sulphur content of 4.25 per cent at 500°C. 2.95 per cent sulphur remained in the coke and this was further reduced to 2.65 per cent at 1000°C. Gentry (226) has pointed out that the high temperature zone in processes of low temperature carbonization by partial gasification is largely responsible for removal of sulphur in that type of retort, as compared with the ordinary externally heated designs. At the same time, there is an increase in sulphur present in the tar and gas to counterbalance the decrease in this constituent of the coke.

When Powell (224) heated Pocahontas, a West Virginia low sulphur bituminous coal, to 500°C., he found that the initial sulphur, consisting of 0.08 per cent pyritic, 0.01 per cent sulphate, and 0.47 per cent organic sulphur, was transformed to a residuum with 0.01 per cent pyritic, 0.43 per cent organic, and 0.04 per cent sulphide sulphur, 0.06 per cent of the sulphur volatilizing as hydrogen sulphide, and 0.02 per cent distilling into the tar. At 1000°C., 0.27 per cent organic and 0.09 per cent sulphide sulphur was found in the solid residuum, while 0.17 per cent appeared as sulphuretted hydrogen and 0.03 per cent was found in the tar. The difference in the transformations

TABLE 100

Effect of temperature on distribution of sulphur in Tennessee coal

CONSTITUENT	TEMPERATURE					
	0°C.	300°C.	400°C.	500°C.	600°C.	1000°C.
	per cent	*per cent*	*per cent*	*per cent*	*per cent*	*per cent*
Pyritic sulphur.....................	1.75	1.75	1.42	0.31	0.00	0.00
Sulphate sulphur....................	0.71	0.55	0.44	0.01	0.01	0.00
Organic sulphur.....................	1.79	1.63	1.51	1.70	1.87	1.81
Sulphide sulphur....................	0.00	0.13	0.44	0.93	0.82	0.84
Hydrogen sulphide sulphur..........	0.00	0.19	0.39	1.20	1.39	1.44
Tar sulphur.........................	0.00	0.00	0.05	0.10	0.16	0.16

taking place among the sulphur compounds of Tennessee coal and of Pocahontas coal may be explained by the fact that the latter contained very little pyritic sulphur and practically no sulphate. Further results from the treatment of Pennsylvania coals from the Pittsburgh and Upper Freeport beds are reproduced in Table 101 principally for reference, as it will be observed that the transformations do not differ greatly from those taking place during the carbonization of Tennessee bituminous coal.

Powell (224) next submitted a mixture of Joliet coking coal to study. This consisted of a mixture of 65 per cent Pocahontas, 20 per cent Kentucky, and 15 per cent washed Illinois coals. The sulphur, which was present in the raw mixture, amounted to 0.82 per cent, distributed as 0.26 per cent pyritic and 0.56 per cent organic sulphur.   After carbonization at 500°C., the sulphur in the coke consisted of 0.12 per cent pyritic, 0.44 per cent organic, and 0.08 per cent sulphide, while the volatile products contained sulphur to the extent of 0.02 per cent in the tar and 0.16 per cent as hydrogen sulphide in the gas.   At 1000°C., the residual sulphur was distributed as 0.49 per cent organic and 0.06 per cent sulphide, while the volatilized sulphur consisted of 0.02 per cent in the tar and 0.25 per cent as hydrogen sulphide.   The general transformations in this mixed coking coal are the same as those already discussed.

When an Indiana coal containing 1.38 per cent sulphur, distributed as 0.70 per cent pyritic, 0.03 per cent sulphate, and 0.65 per cent

TABLE 101

Effect of temperature on distribution of sulphur in Pennsylvania coals

CONSTITUENT	PITTSBURGH COAL			UPPER FREEPORT COAL		
	Temperature					
	0°C.	500°C.	1000°C.	0°C.	500°C.	1000°C.
	per cent	per cent	per cent	per cent	per cent	per cent
Pyritic sulphur.....................	0.79	0.32	0.00	0.47	0.33	0.00
Sulphate sulphur...................	0.23	0.00	0.00	0.07	0.01	0.00
Organic sulphur....................	0.70	0.74	0.98	0.67	0.58	0.66
Sulphide sulphur...................	0.00	0.23	0.16	0.00	0.09	0.12
Hydrogen sulphide sulphur.........	0.00	0.38	0.53	0.00	0.17	0.40
Tar sulphur.......................	0.00	0.05	0.05	0.00	0.03	0.03

organic, was washed, the total sulphur then amounted to 1.18 per cent, allocated as 0.25 per cent pyritic, 0.03 per cent sulphate, and 0.90 per cent organic.   Powell (224), in comparing the results with washed and unwashed Indiana coal, concluded, first, that in the raw coal, where the inorganic sulphur predominated, a larger quantity of metallic sulphides are converted into the organic form than in the washed coal, and, second, that in the washed coal, where the organic sulphur predominated, more of the organic sulphur is decomposed into hydrogen sulphide than in the raw coal.

These extensive investigations on the transformation of sulphur constituents of coal during carbonization establish five classes of primary reactions.   First, there is the complete decomposition of the pyrite and marcasite to ferrous sulphide, pyrrhotite, and hydrogen sulphide. This reaction reaches its maximum between 400°C. and 500°C., but begins at about 300°C. and is complete at about 600°C. Second, there is the reduction of sulphates to sulphides, which is complete at 500°C. Third, the organic sulphur decomposes to form hydrogen sulphide. Fourth, a small part of the organic sulphur decomposes to form volatile sulphur compounds, which are collected in the tar. Fifth, a portion of the ferrous sulphide and pyrrohotite that is formed apparently enters into combination with the carbon to form organic sulphur compounds in the neighborhood of 500°C. This last reaction has also been noted by Parr (227). In addition to these five primary reactions, there are a few additional secondary reactions, such as the formation of hydrogen sulphide by the attack of hydrogen in the gas on the organic sulphur compounds and the reduction of hydrogen sulphide by red-hot coke to form carbon disulphide. Lewes (17) has already shown that carbon disulphide is never a primary decomposition product of the distillation of coal and Powell (224) concurs in this conclusion.

Desulphurization. Powell (224) has shown that from one-fourth to one-half of the coal sulphur can be removed by washing and that there is a corresponding reduction of sulphur in the coke. However efficient this method of processing, Fraser and Yancey (228) pointed out that washing removes only a part of the sulphur that is present as pyrites, but does not eliminate the finely disseminated pyritic nor the organic sulphur. Besides washing, a number of methods have been proposed to desulphurize coke, all of which involve the elimination of sulphur compounds as volatile components or conversion of the sulphur to a soluble form which may be leached. To the first class belong such proposals as the introduction of steam, air, chlorine, carbon monoxide, and hydrogen during coking, while the second class involves the use of such addition agents as sodium chloride, sodium carbonate, and manganese dioxide. Most of these schemes, however, have never become commercial, because of cost or of inefficiency in sulphur reduction. It has been pretty well shown, in the foregoing tables, that most of the sulphur remaining in the coke is inorganic in nature, so that any method of desulphurization must attack the sulphur-carbon compounds.

Powell (229), noting the quantitative method for sulphur determination of Oteha (230), in which nascent hydrogen was used to attack the sulphur, studied the elimination of sulphur from coke by passing hydrogen through the coking mass.   His first experiments were made on Pittsburgh coal, containing 1.72 per cent sulphur, distributed as shown in Table 101.   This coal was first coked at 1000°C. for 2 hours until no more sulphur was removed by carbonization, at which time the residuum contained 1.90 per cent sulphur, or 1.14 per cent referred to the raw coal.   Pure hydrogen was then passed through the furnace for one hour, after which the coke sulphur was reduced to 1.55 per cent, or 0.93 per cent referred to the raw coal. A second experiment was made with the same coal by introducing the hydrogen from the beginning of carbonization.   In this test the coal was heated at 500°C. for 2 hours and then at 1000°C. for 2 hours with the result that the sulphur of the coke was reduced to 0.86 per cent, or 0.52 per cent referred to the coal.

The Upper Freeport coal of Table 101, containing 1.21 per cent sulphur, was also treated.   When this coal was treated with hydrogen for 2 hours at 500°C., it was found that the coal pyrite was completely decomposed, whereas only about half had been destroyed without hydrogen, according to Table 101.   The speed of pyrite decomposition depends, not only upon the temperature, but upon the partial pressure of sulphur over it, so that, when the presence of hydrogen reduces this partial pressure, the decomposition becomes more rapid. As Table 101 shows that the pyritic sulphur would be destroyed in any event by thermal decomposition, the presence of hydrogen does not effect removal of this constituent from the coke, but merely permits its transformation to become complete at a lower temperature.   When the Upper Freeport coal was treated at 500°C. for one hour and then at 1000°C. for one hour with slightly moist hydrogen, it was found that the coke contained 0.82 per cent of the original sulphur after the 500°C. stage and only 0.07 per cent after the 1000°C. stage.   The distribution of sulphur after the 500°C. stage was 0.01 per cent pyritic, 0.01 per cent sulphate, 0.63 per cent organic, 0.17 per cent sulphide, 0.36 per cent evolved as hydrogen sulphide, and 0.03 per cent in the tar.   These data should be compared with those in Table 101, which gives the sulphur distribution at the same temperature for the same coal when hydrogen was not used.   Although the sulphur reduction at 1000°C. amounted to over 90 per cent, the passage of hydrogen produced no effect on the character of the coke, which was of a rather fragile nature to begin with. The desulphurizing action of hydrogen is due to its conversion of the organic sulphur compounds to sulphuretted hydrogen, which action is more vigorous at the higher temperatures. Monkhouse and Cobb (221), however, claim that when the pyritic sulphur is reduced

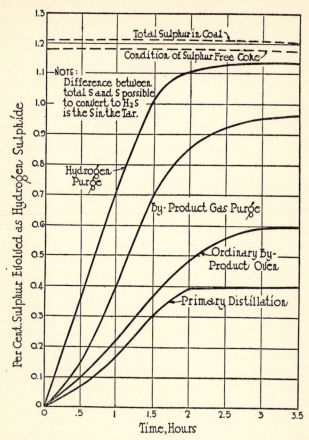

FIG. 52. EVOLUTION OF HYDROGEN SULPHIDE FROM COKE BY PURGING AS A FUNCTION OF TIME

by heat to ferrous sulphide, it is not further necessary for the sulphur to form a carbon compound, but that it can be decomposed freely at 1000°C. by hydrogen, the statement of Roscoe and Schorlemmer (231), as quoted by Powell (229), to the contrary notwithstanding.

Fig. 52 shows the amount of sulphur removed from Upper Freeport coal, as a function of the time, as determined by Powell (229).   The illustration shows the results of purging with pure hydrogen gas, as well as with a by-product coal gas which was rich in hydrogen. For comparison, curves showing the elimination of sulphur as it ordinarily occurs during coking in by-product ovens and in primary distillation are given.   Three hours of purging with by-product gas reduced the coke sulphur from 1.21 per cent to 0.34 per cent.   When the Joliet coking coal mixture, already discussed in this chapter under the subject of temperature effect, was simultaneously coked and purged with hydrogen for 3 hours the coke residuum contained but 0.29 per cent sulphur, as compared with 0.75 per cent sulphur when hydrogen was not used.

Monkhouse and Cobb (221), while studying the liberation of nitrogen as ammonia from coal and coke, also determined the liberation of sulphur as hydrogen sulphide.   Analyses of the coke ash has already been given under the discussion of the effect of nitrogenous and hydrogenous atmospheres on the oxidation and dissociation of ammonia.   Analyses of the raw coal and the 500°C., 800°C., and 1100°C. cokes which were tested were also given in Table 93, from which it is seen that the higher the temperature of carbonization, the less the percentage of initial sulphur that remains in the coke. Taking the sulphur in the coal as 100 per cent, that in the 500°C. coke and in the 800°C. coke was 56.4 per cent and 50.1 per cent respectively.

Fig. 53 shows the result of treating 500°C. low temperature coke successively with nitrogen, hydrogen, and steam at 800°C.   Comparison of this illustration with that of Fig. 49, for the same set of experiments in the removal of nitrogen, shows a great similarity. In an atmosphere of nitrogen, the removal of sulphur is practically negligible, but in atmospheres of hydrogen and of steam the reaction of the sulphur to form hydrogen sulphide is far more sensitive than that of the nitrogen to form ammonia.   The use of nitrogen removed one per cent of the coke sulphur and the hydrogen removed about 51.8 per cent of the coke sulphur, whereas treatment with steam to complete gasification removed an additional 40.2 per cent of the total sulphur in the coke, amounting in all to 93.0 per cent, with the rest remaining in the ash and unaccounted for.   When the experiment was repeated with omission of the hydrogen stage, only 53.7 per cent

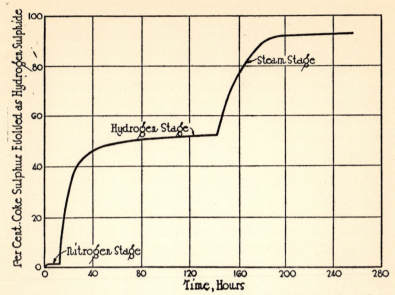

FIG. 53. EVOLUTION OF HYDROGEN SULPHIDE FROM LOW TEMPERATURE COKE
HEATED SUCCESSIVELY AT 800°C. IN VARIOUS ATMOSPHERES

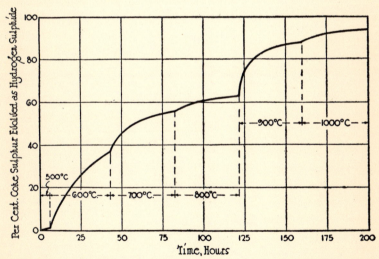

FIG. 54. EVOLUTION OF HYDROGEN SULPHIDE FROM LOW TEMPERATURE COKE
IN AN HYDROGENOUS ATMOSPHERE AT VARIOUS TEMPERATURES

of the coke sulphur was removed as hydrogen sulphide. When the hydrogen stage was omitted, apparently quite a portion of the coke sulphur was oxidized, the hydrogen sulphide and sulphur dioxide later reacting to precipitate sulphur as a white milk in the gas washers.

Fig. 54 shows the result of heating the 500°C. low temperature coke to various temperatures in an atmosphere of hydrogen. A similar experiment up to 800°C. in an atmosphere of nitrogen resulted in only 0.8 per cent of the sulphur of the coke being liberated as

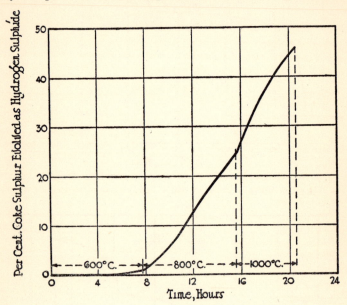

FIG. 55. EVOLUTION OF HYDROGEN SULPHIDE FROM GAS COKE IN AN
HYDROGENOUS ATMOSPHERE AT VARIOUS TEMPERATURES

sulphuretted hydrogen. Up to 800°C., the evolution of hydrogen sulphide from the low temperature coke in an hydrogenous atmosphere was fairly steady, but at 800°C. it fell off rapidly. At 900°C., however, there was a rapid hydrogenation of the sulphur which fell off after about 20 hours treatment and could not be materially increased by raising the temperature to even 1000°C. Treatment in stages of 100°C., up to 800°C., removed 63.4 per cent of the coke sulphur as hydrogen sulphide in an atmosphere of hydrogen, as compared with only 52.8 per cent when it was heated to 800°C. final temperature in a single heating stage, as seen from Fig. 53. After 200 hours of treatment and 1000°C. final temperature, 93.8 per cent of the sulphur was removed from the coke as sulphuretted hydrogen. When next an atmosphere of steam was used in multi-stage heating of the 500°C. coke, only 66.4 per cent of the sulphur was finally obtained as hydrogen sulphide and only traces of sulphur were left in the ash, the remaining sulphur being unaccounted for. When the 1100°C. coke was heated up to 1000°C. in nitrogen and steam, only 60.6 per cent of the sulphur was evolved as hydrogen sulphide, although all was driven from the coke, two-fifths of that

TABLE 102

Sulphur balance for reheating 800°C. coke to 1000°C.

ITEM	ATMOSPHERE	
	Hydrogen	Nitrogen
Calculated to coke:	per cent	per cent
Sulphur evolved as hydrogen sulphide...........	46.2	0.5
Sulphur left in coke............................	53.2	97.6
Sulphur unaccounted for.......................	0.6	1.9
Calculated to coal:	per cent	per cent
Sulphur removed in coking.....................	49.9	49.9
Sulphur removed on reheating..................	23.1	0.3
Sulphur left in coke...........................	26.7	48.9
Sulphur unaccounted for.......................	0.3	0.9

evolved appearing up to 800°C., three-fifths at 900°C., and only a fraction of one per cent at 1000°C.

The result of heating the 800°C. coke up to 1000°C. in stages with an atmosphere of hydrogen is shown in Fig. 55 and Table 102 gives a sulphur balance for these conditions, as well as for an atmosphere of nitrogen. From the sulphur balance and the illustration, it is patent that in a nitrogenous atmosphere very little sulphur in any form was eliminated from the coke. At 600°C. in an atmosphere of hydrogen very little sulphuretted hydrogen was removed from the 800°C. coke, but, at reheat temperatures of 800°C. and 1000°C., hydrogen sulphide was evolved at a fairly uniform rate for 8-hour periods of heating.

When coke, which was produced at 1000°C., was heated through these temperature stages in an hydrogenous atmosphere, the results noted in Fig. 56 were obtained. Only 25.3 per cent of the sulphur in the coke appeared as hydrogen sulphide when heated for over 16 hours to a final temperature of 1000°C., about 76 per cent remaining in the coke. However, when steam was mixed with the hydrogen and passed over the coke, decidedly different results were obtained, as shown in Fig. 56. With the moist hydrogen atmosphere, very

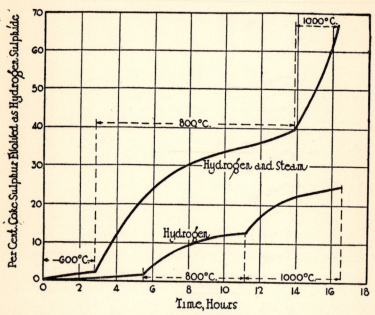

FIG. 56. EVOLUTION OF HYDROGEN SULPHIDE FROM HIGH TEMPERATURE COKE IN AN ATMOSPHERE OF HYDROGEN AND STEAM

little hydrogen sulphide was produced at 600°C., as before, but when the temperature was raised to 800°C., the evolution became rapid, decreasing after about 5 hours, but hydrogen sulphide was evolved in quantities, even beyond 12 hours of heating. Finally, when the temperature was increased to 1000°C., the evolution of hydrogen sulphide became voluminous, the elimination of sulphur being at the rate of about 11 per cent of that in the coke per hour of treatment.

Monkhouse and Cobb (220) (221) noted two important differences in the liberation of ammonia and of hydrogen sulphide from coke by hydrogen. In the first place, there was no loss of sulphuretted hydrogen by thermal dissociation, as in the case of ammonia, and in the second place, hydrogen at 800°C. attacked the sulphur compounds in 1100°C. hard coke, but not the nitrogen compounds. The first of these differences is explained by the fact that the dissociation equilibrium of hydrogen sulphide is only 5.5 per cent dissociated at 750°C.; 15.6 per cent dissociated at 945°C.; and 30.7 per cent dissociated at 1132°C.

CHAPTER VI

Processes of Low Temperature Carbonization

Adaptability of Processes. As may be expected in any new industry, and particularly in one where the public imagination has been fired by the potentialities of by-product recovery in a field where tremendous quantities of raw material are consumed annually, a number of the processes that have been proposed in the past for low temperature carbonization have been *prima facie* promotion enterprises. Most of the processes, however, which have been developed to effect primary distillation are creditable attempts to solve the problem, both technically and commercially. A number of the retorts, so designed, have failed for lack of adequate technical knowledge of the conditions underlying the art of low temperature carbonization. The absence of strong financial backing, an item of paramount importance in the inauguration of new industrial departures, where markets are unreceptive and where profits accrue largely from full-scale operation, has also been a contributory factor in the failure of a number of other processes.

Aside from laboratory experimental apparatus, with daily throughputs of several hundred pounds of coal, many retorts have been built which are capable of handling from 5 tons to 25 tons of coal per day. Several plants have been erected with a daily capacity of over 100 tons of raw material. In one case, a low temperature carbonization plant with a throughput of 500 tons of coal per 24 hours was erected and several of about this same capacity are now (1928) under consideration.

In all, the author has investigated over one hundred and seventy-five different processes for the low temperature carbonization of carbonaceous materials and Brownlie (233) states that there are at least seventy-five more, of which he has selected fifty as typical of the application of low temperature methods to the processing of bituminous coal. The literature, past and present, abounds with methods for the treatment of brown coal, lignite, peat, shale, oil sands, wood, and other materials, rich in distillable hydrocarbons, for the recovery of oils, gas, or carbonaceous residuum, as well as for the coking of coal.

No process of low temperature carbonization is applicable to all raw fuels, both with regard to type and to physical condition. Some retorts are operative with non-coking materials, but not with coking materials; some will function with low grade materials, such as shales and lignites; while others are restricted to particular coals or to blended charges. As regards physical condition, some processes require a pulverized raw material, some use briquets, and some merely crush the coal to suitable size. There is a corresponding variation in the physical condition of the carbonization residuum, as delivered from the low temperature retort, but this, of course, is a function of three variables, the initial physical condition of the charge, the fuel type, and the manner of distillation. Some processes deliver a semi-coke which is suitable only for pulverization as a power char or for briquetting; others give a material fitted for a variety of purposes after sizing, including a domestic size which is adapted to household fuel.

Finally, no method of low temperature carbonization is adapted to give maximum yields of all the products of distillation. This same statement applies also to the quality of the products. Some retorts are particularly adapted to the production of a high calorific coal gas; others are suitable for the recovery of oils; some strive for domestic fuels and artificial anthracites; and, finally, there are those which propose to extract the valuable by-products in the preparation of boiler fuel. In every case, therefore, it is seen that the selection of a process of low temperature carbonization, or the design of a retort to attain that end, is not a matter of simple consideration, but one which, at best, is a compromise and requires considerable prior knowledge.

Classification of Processes. The simple classification of low temperature carbonization processes is a difficult matter, because of the numerous processes and their complex nature. Simple comparisons could be made with regard to motion, in which the retorts are found to be static or dynamic; in relation to position, in which they may be horizontal, vertical, or inclined; in regard to method of heating, in which the charge may receive its heat internally or externally; upon the subdivision of the charge, in which the processes may involve pulverization, crushing, or briquetting; upon operational procedure, in which the retorts may be single or multi-stage processes; upon the bases of heat transfer, involving the principles of carbonization in thin layers by heat conduction, or by convection; and, finally, upon any generalized point of difference of sufficient import to become the basis of classification. Hardly any low temperature process can fall in only one of these simple categories, so that more than one point of difference must be considered in any attempt to reach a satisfactory classification.

Possibly the best classification of low temperature carbonization processes has been given by Fieldner (233) and is reproduced herewith:

Classification of Low Temperature Carbonization Systems

A. Externally heated retorts. Coal in thin layers, not stirred.
    1. Vertical layers of coal in narrow retorts.
    2. Horizontal thin layers of coal.
B. Externally heated retorts. Coal stirred in contact with heated surfaces.
    1. Vertical retorts.
    2. Horizontal retorts.
        a. Stationary retorts with internal stirrers.
        b. Rotating cylinders.
    3. Retorts with coal stirred on a flat heated surface.
C. Internally heated retorts. Coal in direct contact with hot fluids.
    1. Hot gases generated by air or steam blown into the retort.
        a. Coal charged in lumps or briquets.
        b. Coal charged in pulverized form.
        c. Complete gasification.
    2. Hot gases or vapors generated outside the retort.
        a. Combustion products.
        b. Producer gas.
        c. Water gas.
        d. Coal gas.
        e. Superheated steam.
        f. Combinations of the foregoing.
    3. Melted lead in contact with coal.
D. Two-stage carbonization to control the sticking properties of coal.

This classification, however, is not the last word in the matter, for, obviously, no provision is made for processes involving the carbonization of pulverized coal by radiant heat; multi-stage processes may include either or both internal and external heating; and no distinction is made between intermittent and continuous operation, as well as in regard to other distinctive points of difference.

In the final analysis, every low temperature carbonization process has its points of novelty, is gifted with certain advantages, and is confronted with its own peculiar operating difficulties. It is beyond the scope of this book to enter into a comprehensive exposition on the numerous low temperature retorts, but certain processes which are considered representative of an outstanding type and which have been fully tested in operation will be discussed.

Carbocoal-McIntire Processes. The Carbocoal process was based upon the patents granted to Smith and was developed by the International Coal Products Company. Under the financial support of the United States Government in 1918, a large plant, with a daily capacity of 575 tons of raw coal, was erected at Clinchfield, Va., by the Clinchfield Carbocoal Company. The data necessary for the design of this plant were secured from the operation of a semi-commercial plant at Irvington, N. J., from as early as 1915. Operating difficulties, however, together with changing economic conditions, culminated in discontinuance of the Clinchfield plant in the latter part of 1922. The patent rights were acquired by the Consolidated Coal Products Company, who erected a large-scale experimental plant at Fairmont, W. Va., where the Carbocoal process has been further developed and greatly improved by McIntire.

The Carbocoal (189) process is a multi-stage system, involving primary carbonization in externally heated horizontal retorts in which the coal is stirred by paddles; briquetting of the primary char; and secondary carbonization of the briquets in an externally heated inclined retort. The Clinchfield plant consisted of a total of twenty-four primary retorts grouped into four batteries, as shown in the frontispiece, and thirty secondary ovens arranged in ten benches. One point of novelty to be noted in this system is that it combines the methods of both low and high temperature carbonization to obtain a high yield of oil from the former and to produce an anthracised briquet from the latter. A very good description of the Carbocoal process, its development and operating difficulties, has been given by Curtis (213) and his associates.

The primary Carbocoal retort, used at Clinchfield, is shown in Fig. 57. A screw conveyor fed the crushed raw coal to the carbonization chamber, which was of cardiodal cross-section and built of carborundum shapes which were supported on fireclay saddles. A combustion flue surrounded the muffle and two rows of ten burners heated the flue from below. The entire retort rested upon two heat

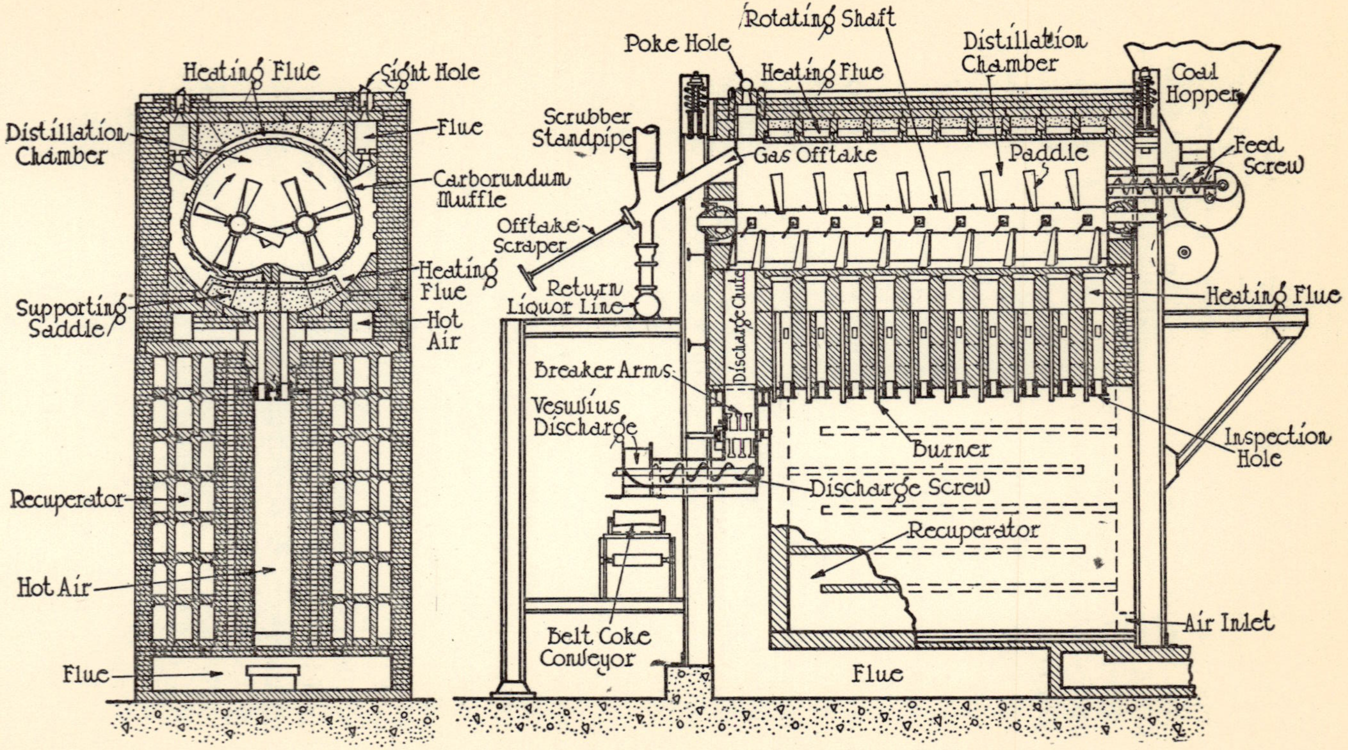

FIG. 57. CARBOCOAL PRIMARY RETORT

210

recuperators in which the combustion air was preheated before being introduced to the burners. Two cast steel shafts, equipped with revolving paddles set at an angle, served to transport the charge to the delivery end and to stir the coal during coking, thus bringing fresh material in contact with the hot sole of the muffle and allowing volatile matter, entrapped within the mass, to escape. When primary carbonization was complete, the semi-coke was pushed into a discharge chute, at the bottom of which it was crushed by breaker arms, and finally delivered by means of a spiral extractor through a water seal to a continuous conveyor. The volatile products driven off during distillation collected in the crown of the muffle and were removed from the carbonization chamber through a gas offtake and scrubber standpipe at the discharge end. The muffle end plates were suspended by springs from the top to provide for heat expansion. The muffle of this retort was about 7.3 feet in maximum width and 16 feet long, while the over-all dimensions were roughly 27 feet high, 12 feet wide, and 37 feet long, including machinery, recuperators, *etc.* The primary retorts were operated at a temperature of about 760°C. and about 3.5 hours were required for carbonization, giving a normal capacity of about 20 tons per 24 hours per retort.

The semi-coke was received from the primary retort in the form of black, friable, irregular lumps which were prepared for briquetting by crushing to $\frac{1}{8}$ inch mesh while hot. The briquets were formed in a roll press, using hot pitch, obtained from fractionation of the low temperature tar. This stage yielded a hard dense briquet, suitable for a fuel, but it was not smokeless because of the tar which was introduced for binding purposes. Accordingly, the raw briquets were delivered to the secondary retort for further treatment.

The secondary Carbocoal retort is illustrated in Fig. 58. The selection of an inclined oven for this purpose depended upon its ease of charge and discharge, together with reduction of excessive breakage by elimination of the weight of thick layers of the briquets themselves. The secondary retort was charged with raw briquets at the upper end and, after carbonization, the finished briquets were discharged into a quenching car at the lower end. An inclined horizontal partition divided the retort into two carbonization chambers in order to reduce the crushing pressure until the briquets had been thoroughly hardened by heat. The distillation gases were removed from the crown of the oven at the lower end by a standpipe connected with the hydraulic main.   The oven was heated externally on each side by vertical flues, fired from burners located in the crown.   The combustion gases passed downward through a heat recuperator, which supported the carbonization chamber and in which the combustion

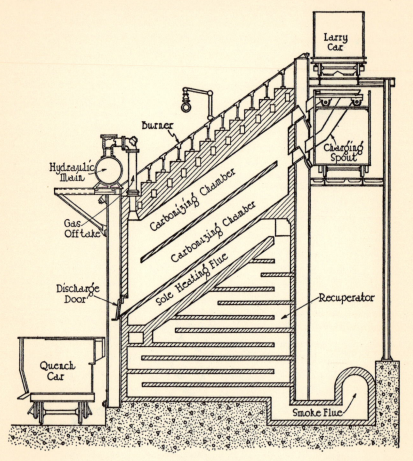

FIG. 58. CARBOCOAL SECONDARY RETORT

air was preheated.   Each of the two carbonization chambers was approximately 14 inches wide, 4 feet high, and 25 feet long.   The secondary retort was built of silica brick and measured about 45 feet high, 4 feet wide, and 40 feet long in over-all dimensions.   The secondary retort operated at about 980°C. and approximately 8 hours were required for distillation. The finished briquets were delivered as a hard silvery product, being reduced in size about 25 per cent through shrinkage.

The additional equipment at Clinchfield consisted of a very extensive by-product recovery plant for extraction of light oil and ammonia from the gas and for the condensation of primary tar. There was also provided a complete tar distillery for fractionating the low temperature tar.

A very great number of different coals, from all over the world, were tested in the Carbocoal process. Table 103 gives the ultimate

TABLE 103

Proximate analyses of raw coal and Carbocoal briquets

CONSTITUENT	HIGH VOLATILE COAL	EEDIUM VOLATILE COAL
Analysis of coal:	*per cent*	*per cent*
Moisture..	4.5	2.3
Volatile matter................................	37.4	24.6
Fixed carbon...................................	47.4	55.8
Ash..	10.7	17.3
B.t.u. per pound (dry).........................	13,483	12,462
Analysis of Carbocoal briquet:	*per cent*	*per cent*
Volatile matter................................	4.4	4.5
Fixed carbon...................................	77.7	72.2
Ash..	17.9	23.3
B.t.u. per pound (dry).........................	11,551	11,358

analyses of two coals which were carbonized by this method, as well as the analyses of the corresponding Carbocoal briquets. The high volatile sample of bituminous coal was from Ohio, while the medium volatile specimen, with high ash, was from England. Analysis of another sample of Carbocoal has already been given in Table 78. These analyses should be compared with those of Table 1 to see how nearly the raw bituminous coal was converted to a fuel resembling anthracite. Reference has been made in Chapter IV, under the subject of power char, to tests made on the use of these briquets as a fuel for locomotives and for marine boilers.

The primary and secondary yields from carbonization of the coals given in Table 103 are tabulated in Table 104, where it is to be observed, as expected, that the high volatile coal was the richest in by-products. Space does not permit a detailed discussion of the character of the products, but certain particulars in this connection have been presented heretofore. In Table 62, the fractionation of a tar from the Carbocoal process has been given; in Table 72, the yield of crude light oil has been reported; and, in Table 50, the distribution of various tar acids, as determined by Morgan and Soule (48), has been reproduced. A distillation analysis of Carbocoal tar was given in Fig. 24, while the phenolic content of the various tar

TABLE 104

Primary and secondary yields from Carbocoal process

PRODUCT	HIGH VOLATILE COAL	MEDIUM VOLATILE COAL
Primary yield per net ton coal:		
Pounds semi-coke..............................	1,234	1,396
Gallons dry tar.................................	33.4	16.3
Pounds ammonium sulphate.....................	10.2	5.1
Cubic feet gas..................................	3,622	2,552
B.t.u. per cubic foot............................	893	851
Secondary yield per net ton coal:		
Pounds Carbocoal briquets......................	1,223	1,505
Gallons dry tar.................................	5.4	7.5
Pounds ammonium sulphate.....................	9.9	10.1
Cubic feet gas..................................	3,690	5,019
B.t.u. per cubic foot...........................	379	348

fractions was shown in Fig. 22, to which reference should now be made.

It has been mentioned, that the Carbocoal retort was subsequently improved by McIntire (234) at Fairmont, W. Va. The McIntire primary low temperature retort is shown in Fig. 59. It will be noted, that there are two distinct departures in this retort from the older design, apart from many minor improvements relating to accessibility of parts, method of heating, etc. In the first place, the costly carborundum shapes were replaced by a corrugated metal semi-cylindrical muffle floor, which is more durable, and gives better heat transmission. And, in the second place, the rotating paddles were replaced by an oscillating shaft whose paddles sweep back and forward through the grooves in the muffle floor. The corrugations are cast in sections and are held together by tension produced with springs, so that there is the utmost freedom for expansion, no bolts being used to hold the sections together. The floor of the retort is operated at 650°C., but the maximum temperature of the charge is about 455°C., while the temperature of the gas in the roof of the retort never exceeds 345°C. This retort is said to operate satisfactorily and, up to 1926, some 22,000 tons of coal had been successfully carbonized in it.

Test results in this retort indicate that one net ton of Pennsylvania coal, from the Pittsburgh seam, containing 36 per cent volatile matter, yields 1,480 pounds of semi-coke, 31 gallons of tar, 2 gallons of light oil, about 10 pounds of ammonium sulphate and approximately 3,000 cubic feet of gas, with a calorific value of 950 B.t.u. per cubic foot. The semi-coke contains 10 per cent to 14 per cent volatile. An analysis of the gas which is evolved from the McIntire retort, as determined by Fieldner (36), has been given in Table 6.

McIntire has conducted a number of experiments with a view of developing a satisfactory oven for the secondary carbonization of briquets, manufactured from the semi-coke discharged by the primary retort. A tunnel kiln and several internally heated retorts were built and abandoned. The carbonizer finally adopted consists of five superimposed horizontal retorts into which the briquets are charged on trays by special machinery. The briquets are heated for 30 minutes, at a temperature of about 650°C., by radiation from the crown and sole of the retort. By this means, breakage is reduced to a minimum and carbonization is said to be complete. The carbonized briquets contain more volatile than the old Carbocoal briquets, 8 per cent to 10 per cent volatile matter being allowed to remain.

Coalite Processes. We have already seen in Chapter I that the Coalite process is based upon patents issued to Parker (28) (29), one of the pioneers in low temperature carbonization. Some of these patents were granted as early as 1890, but real progress was not made until 1906, when he introduced the principal of carbonization with superheated steam. The processes are controlled by Low Temperature Carbonization, Ltd., the successor to several other companies engaged in its development. The Coalite retorts are all

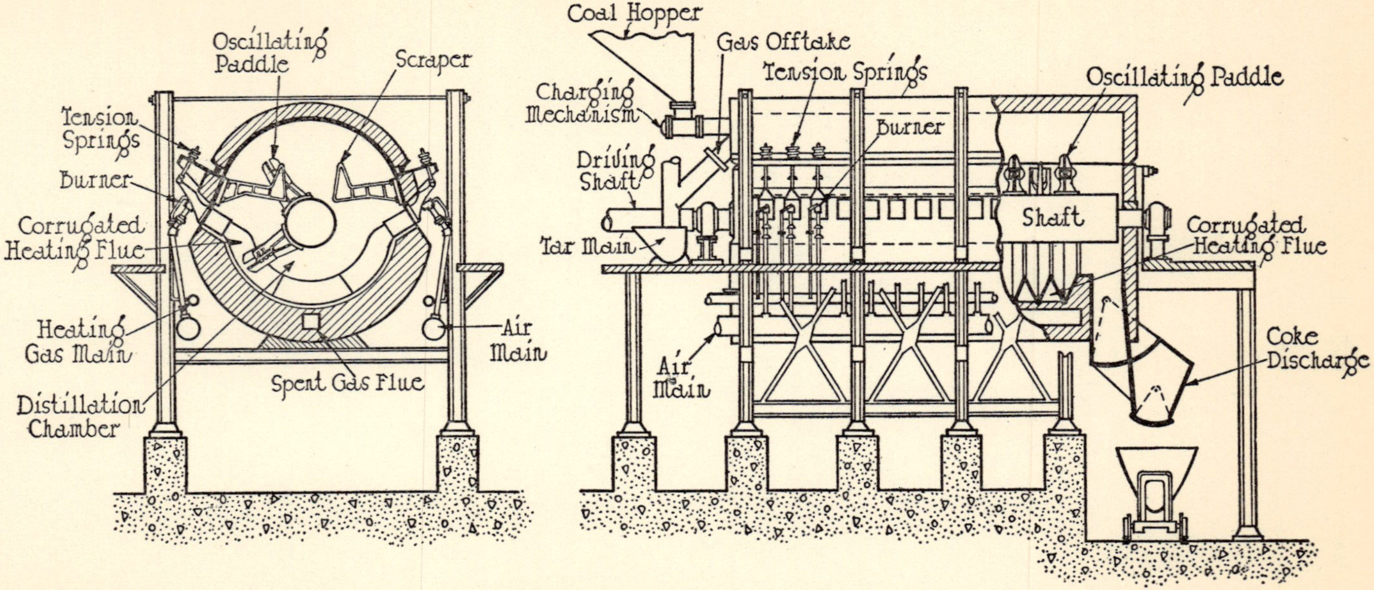

FIG. 59. McINTIRE PRIMARY RETORT

Labels in top diagram:
Oscillating Paddle
Corrugated Heating Flue
Coke Discharge
Shaft
Gas Offtake
Burner
Tension Springs
Coal Hopper
Charging Mechanism
Driving Shaft
Tar Main
Air Main

Labels in bottom diagram:
Scraper
Oscillating Paddle
Air Main
Spent Gas Flue
Tension Springs
Burner
Corrugated Heating Flue
Heating Gas Main
Distillation Chamber

static, externally heated processes, involving carbonization in thin layers.

After Parker's initial experiments, The Eticoal Syndicate erected a plant at Barugh, near Barnsley, England, with a daily capacity of about 50 gross tons of coal. The installation consists of thirty-two retorts, each composed of a single iron casting, containing 12 vertical tubes in a nest of two rows. The tubes are 9 feet long and taper from 4.5 inches in diameter at the top to 5.5 inches at the bottom. The casting is mounted in a firebrick flue and supported over a discharge chamber, provided beneath for each two retorts. During distillation, the charge is retained within the tubes by top and bottom covers. The temperature of the retorts is maintained at about 650°C., for approximately 4.5 hours, to carbonize the coal completely. The semi-coke is finally rammed from the carbonizing tubes and allowed to cool in the closed chamber beneath the retort until the next charge is ready for removal.

A test of the Coalite retorts at Barugh was conducted by the Fuel Research Board (235) and the yields obtained from the carbonization of Dalton Main, a medium caking coal, are given in Table 105, along with the yields indicated from an assay of the same fuel in the Gray and King assay apparatus, described under the subject of coal assay in Chapter I. The factors given in the table are the proportionality constants that must be applied to yields obtained in the standard laboratory assay apparatus in order to convert them to those expected with the same fuel from the Coalite retorts.

The low temperature gas from the test had a calorific value of 765 B.t.u. per cubic foot, before scrubbing, and 705 B.t.u. per cubic foot, after washing to remove 2.13 gallons of light oil per gross ton of coal. The yield of ammonium sulphate agrees with that reported by Armstrong (212) in Table 88. Tests by Brittain, Rowe, and Sinnatt (125), on the distribution of phenols in Coalite tar, have been given in Table 50, while the percentage of bases in the various tar fractions was reported in Table 53 and the sulphur distribution in Table 54.

In 1911, The British Coalite Company erected a plant of different design at Barking, near London. This plant consisted of twenty retorts with a daily throughput of 32 gross tons of raw coal. This is a wide narrow oven built of fireclay. It is 11.5 feet high, about 6 inches wide, and is tapered in length from 2.5 feet at the top to 3.0 feet at the bottom. A sliding door at the bottom and a hinged lid at the top keep the retort closed during coking. After about 7 hours of distillation, the coke is dumped into a triangular shaped cooling chamber beneath the setting, where it remains until the temperature is reduced below the ignition point, so that the semi-coke can be removed without combustion.

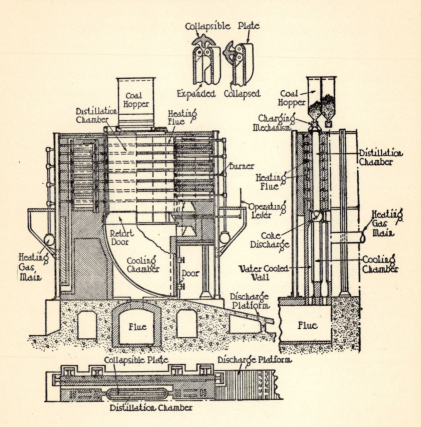

FIG. 60. DAVIDSON MODIFICATION OF COALITE RETORT

The most recent design of the Coalite retort is a modification by Davidson (187) of the retorts at Barking, described above.   Brownlie (236) has described a setting of 20 retorts of this description at Barugh, where the other setting of tubular retorts, previously described, is erected.   With an operating temperature of about 650°C.

and a carbonizing period of about 8 hours, the maximum throughput of this setting is approximately 36 tons of coal per 24 hours. Fig. 60 illustrates the Coalite retort, as modified by Davidson. It is built of firebrick with dimensions of 9.5 feet high, 7.5 feet long at the base, and 11 inches wide. The crushed raw coal is charged from twin hoppers at the top through a rotary valve. Just beneath the retort is a cooling chamber, shaped as a right angular sector and built of steel plate, provided with a water-jacket for cooling the coke. A cast-iron rocking cylindrical valve closes the bottom of the carbonizing chamber and supports the charge during carbonization. Firebrick combustion flues and heat recuperators are placed in the bench between adjacent retorts.

The most unique feature of this modification of the Coalite process is the mechanical device which facilitates escape of the gas during

TABLE 105

Test yields from Coalite retorts at Barugh

PRODUCT PER GROSS TON	DRY COAL	DRY ASSAY	FACTOR
Pounds coke............................	1,615	1,635	0.99
Cubic feet gas.........................	5,930	4,105	1.44
Gallons tar............................	22.9	33.5	0.68
Pounds ammonium sulphate..........	14.3	8.7	1.64

coking and final discharge of the semi-coke. Two perforated cast-iron plates are connected by linkage and suspended within the carbonization chamber in a parallel position, so that the charge is separated into two thin layers, about 3.5 inches thick, against each side wall of the retort. The center of the retort is thus segregated into a gas-collecting chamber, about 4 inches wide, by the two perforated plates. As the plastic layer of the charge moves to the center during coking, the low temperature gas finds an easy path through the cooler layers of the charge into the space between the plates, from which it is withdrawn at the top. When coking is complete, the linkage mechanism permits the plates to be collapsed so that, even though the charge may have swelled considerably during coking, it can be removed easily and dropped into the cooling chamber.

It is said, that an average coal, containing 25 per cent to 35 per cent volatile matter, when distilled in the Davidson modified Coalite retort at 550°C., yields per gross ton approximately 6,000 cubic feet to 6,500 cubic feet of 700 B.t.u. to 750 B.t.u. per cubic foot gas, without deduction for heating the retorts; about 24 gallons of oil, fractionating to 3.6 gallons of light oil, 9.6 gallons of Diesel oil, and 9.6 gallons of lubricating oil; 15 pounds of ammonium sulphate; and 1,568 pounds of semi-coke smokeless fuel, containing 8 per cent to 10 per cent volatile matter.   A proximate analysis of the semi-coke has already been given in Table 78.

Freeman Process.   This process bears the name of its inventor, Freeman, and is controlled by the British Oil and Fuel Conservation, Ltd.   The Freeman retort belongs to the general class known as multiple retorts.   It is an externally heated vertical carbonizing machine, in which the raw material is progressively distilled in thin layers upon rotating horizontal plates.   This type of retort is suitable for non-coking and weakly coking coals, shales, etc., but soon plugs in operation with untreated sticky materials.

According to Tupholme (237), the Freeman retort which was installed at Willesden, London, but now dismantled, was 27 feet high, about 5 feet in diameter, and consisted of six stages, as shown in Fig. 61.   A central shaft carried a series of rotating disks, one to each distillation stage.   The cast-iron shell of the retort formed alternate carbonization and combustion chambers, in such a way that the floor of each distillation zone was heated by gas burners from below. A small, annular, gas-collecting chamber was formed above each carbonization chamber and connected with it through perforations, so that the volatile products from each stage could be separately removed and condensed to effect partial fractionation of the oils.

It will be seen from Fig. 61, that the crushed raw fuel is fed by a sprocket valve into the top of the retort, where it falls upon the first rotating disk.   A set of stationary scrapers, not shown in the illustration, is fitted to the top of each carbonization chamber and a second set of moving plows, also omitted in the illustration, is fastened to the bottom of each rotating platform.   The charge is thus raked from the center of each disk to the periphery, where it falls to the floor of the carbonization chamber.   It is then carried back to the center of the retort by the rotating plows to be dropped, finally, through an annular passage onto the second rotating disk of the next distillation chamber.   The material thus zig-zags its passage during coking from the top to the bottom of the retort.   The semi-coke is

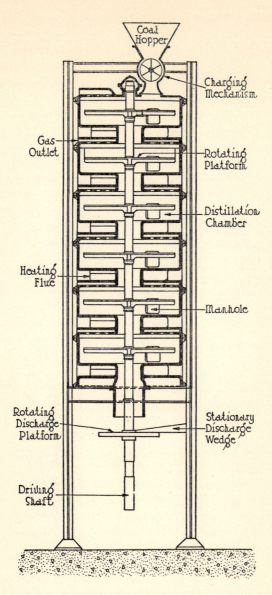

Fig. 61. Freeman Retort

finally ejected in pulverulent form from the last chamber to a discharge table.

The Freeman multiple retort at Willesden was tested by the Fuel Research Board (23), before being dismantled to make room for further experiments.   The average temperatures, maintained in the various chambers during the tests, were approximately as follows: 105°C. in the first chamber, 215°C. in the second chamber, 330°C. in the third chamber, 420°C. in the fourth chamber, 460°C. in the fifth chamber, and 500°C. in the sixth chamber.   The first distillation chamber serves merely to preheat and dry the coal, while the last chamber may be used, either as a heating or cooling stage, as desired.

TABLE 106

Analyses of coal and semi-coke from test of Freeman retort

CONSTITUENT	KIRBY COAL	BRYNNA COAL
Coal analysis:	per cent	per cent
Moisture	9.4	3.9
Volatile matter	32.1	32.2
Fixed carbon	51.6	59.4
Ash	6.9	4.5
Nitrogen	1.36	1.07
Semi-coke analysis:		
Moisture	3.7	1.8
Volatile matter	10.6	14.2
Fixed carbon	76.1	79.2
Ash	9.6	4.8

Proximate analyses of two coals and the semi-coke produced therefrom are given in Table 106.

The Kirby coal given in Table 106 was typical of non-caking slack, while the Brynna gas coal was indifferently caking.   The maximum temperature of carbonization was 500°C. in each case.   The products yielded in the carbonization of these two fuels are given in Table 107. The coke was not incandescent when discharged, but it readily ignited, due to its extreme combustibility.   It was too small for use as a domestic fuel, but was an excellent material for briquetting or pulverizing.   It is interesting to note the low yield of ammonium sulphate, although Table 106 shows the coals to have contained sufficient quantities of elementary nitrogen to give a fair yield, provided the temperature of carbonization was sufficiently high. This was apparently not the case, or else, such ammonia as was evolved, was rapidly decomposed.

The figures given in Table 107 are based upon a gross ton of raw fuel as charged, which included 13.7 per cent moisture in the Kirby coal and 5.6 per cent in the Brynna coal. The gas from Kirby slack contained 10.9 per cent hydrogen and had a gross calorific value of 895 B.t.u. per cubic foot, while that from the Brynna gas coal contained 12.6 per cent hydrogen and had a gross thermal value of 978 B.t.u. per cubic foot. Comparison of the yields with those obtained from the Gray and King assay apparatus at the somewhat higher temperature of 600°C. showed the following conversion factors for Kirby slack: 0.89 for semi-coke; 0.51 for gas; 0.81 for tar; and 0.24 for ammonium sulphate. The conversion factors for the Brynna gas

TABLE 107

Yield of products in test of Freeman retort

PRODUCT PER GROSS TON	KIRBY COAL	BRYNNA COAL
Pounds semi-coke..................................	1,700	1,715
Cubic feet gas....................................	1,990	1,830
Gallons tar.......................................	24.7	23.8
Gallons crude light spirit........................	1.03	1.24
Pounds ammonium sulphate......................	3.6	1.8

coal were: 0.95 for semi-coke; 0.53 for gas; 0.74 for tar; and 0.20 for ammonium sulphate.

Fuel Research Board Processes. In 1917, the British Government provided for the organization of the Fuel Research Board, as a branch of the Department of Scientific and Industrial Research, and the establishment of a Fuel Research Station at Greenwich, London. This station, which was initially under the directorate of Beilby and later of Lander, was charged with the task, among other duties, of conducting experiments on the low temperature carbonization of coal and of testing such private plants as requested this service. A number of tests conducted under this latter function have been referred to under the discussion of individual processes, so that now only the experiments carried on for the purpose of developing operative retorts will be dealt with.

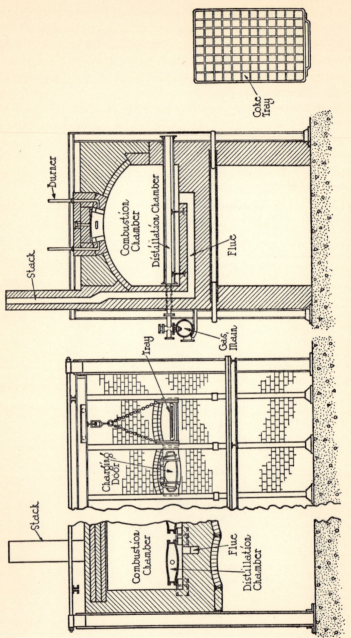

FIG. 62. FUEL RESEARCH BOARD HORIZONTAL RETORT

The Fuel Research Board (114) inaugurated its work with the erection of a battery of nine horizontal retorts of the type shown in Fig. 62. After six years of satisfactory operation, all but two of these have now been dismantled to provide room for further experiments. The retorts were built of mild steel convex plates, riveted to two steel channels, which formed the sides. They were 9 feet long, 2.5 feet wide, and 5 inches to 7 inches deep. The gas offtake connected with the rear wall, while the front was closed by a self-sealing door. The crushed coal was placed in thin layers upon shallow metal trays, two of which were charged at a time to each retort. The trays were formed into a grid of 96 cells by vertical partitions, so that the coke was formed into briquets of convenient domestic size. All the retorts were set in a single heating flue and they were charged and discharged

TABLE 108

Yields from test of Fuel Research Board horizontal retorts

PRODUCT PER GROSS TON	LANGLEY BRIGHTS COAL	DALTON MAIN COAL
Pounds semi-coke..............................	1,625	1,635
Gallons tar...	19.8	20.4
Cubic feet gas	3,600	3,770
Pounds ammonium sulphate.....................		3.6

in an order which minimized the cooling effect produced by these operations.

In these retorts, the maximum temperature was not allowed to exceed 600°C., under which condition from 3 hours to 4 hours were required for carbonization. The yield of products, obtained from carbonizing two coals, which yielded semi-coke of satisfactory coherency when distilled in the Fuel Research Board horizontal retorts, is given in Table 108. The factors for conversion of yields from the Gray and King assay apparatus to the yields from full-scale horizontal retorts were found to be 1.00 for coke, 0.57 for tar, and 0.97 for gas. Fig. 17 showed the rate of gas evolution and the calorific value of the gas obtained from these retorts, as a function of the time of carbonization, while Table 26 showed the composition of the low temperature gas. A proximate analysis of the semi-coke was given in Table 78, while fractionations of the low temperature tar were reported in Table 62, Table 63, Table 64, and Table 72.

The Fuel Research Board (239) attempted to effect low temperature carbonization in a battery of standard Glover-West continuous vertical retorts by the simple procedure of lowering the flue temperature. It was not expected, however, that any economical operation could be obtained from such a retort built to function at high temperatures. The retorts were built of oval silica brick shapes. They were 21 feet high and 33 inches by 10 inches in cross-section. Their normal capacity was 2.5 gross tons of coal per day, but when the carbonizing temperature was reduced to an average of 780°C., the daily throughput fell to 1.8 gross tons per 24 hours. A short spiral extractor continuously removed the carbonized charge from

TABLE 109

Proximate analyses of coal and semi-coke from test of Glover-West retorts

CONSTITUENT	TEST NUMBER 1	TEST NUMBER 2	TEST NUMBER 3	TEST NUMBER 4
	per cent	per cent	per cent	per cent
Coal analysis:				
Moisture..........................	6.5	5.5	5.7	6.2
Volatile matter.....................	31.7	32.7	32.2	32.4
Fixed carbon.......................	51.8	53.5	53.2	52.4
Ash..............................	10.0	8.3	8.9	9.0
Semi-coke analysis:				
Moisture..........................	0.6	1.4	1.7	1.5
Volatile matter.....................	7.0	6.8	7.2	6.3
Fixed carbon.......................	79.0	81.1	78.9	80.1
Ash..............................	13.4	10.7	12.2	12.1

the retort and delivered it to a cast-iron cooling chamber, from which it was removed intermittently. Four such retorts were placed in a common setting, separated into pairs by a vertical partition, and heated by seven separately fired horizontal flues. Provision was made for the introduction of steam during carbonization and the beneficial results of this on the distribution of heat through the retort has been shown in Fig. 9.

Table 109 gives analyses of the coal and semi-coke which was obtained in four tests of the Glover-West retorts by the Fuel Research Board, the mean temperature in the combustion chambers being approximately 770°C. in each case. The charge consisted of a mixture of 60 per cent Mitchell Main gas nuts and 40 per cent Ellistown

Main breeze.   Test No. 1 was conducted in the absence of steam; 7.24 per cent steam was admitted in Test No. 2; 13.47 per cent in Test No. 3; and 20.0 per cent in Test No. 4.   The products yielded from each of these tests are tabulated in Table 110.   The composition of the low temperature gas from these tests has already been given in Table 43.   It is interesting to note, that increasing percentages of steam give increasing yields of tar.

The effect of various percentages of steam on the composition of the gas from high temperature carbonization in Glover-West retorts has been noted from tests by the Fuel Research Board (115) given in Table 41.   A number of experiments on the carbonization of peat in Glover-West retorts were also carried out by the Fuel Research Board (106) and these have previously been referred to in Table 27, where the yields and gas composition were given; in Table 60, where a

TABLE 110

Yield of products obtained in test of Glover-West retorts

PRODUCT PER GROSS TON	TEST NUMBER 1	TEST NUMBER 2	TEST NUMBER 3	TEST NUMBER 4
Pounds of semi-coke.................	1,556	1,595	1,572	1,577
Gallons tar...........................	15.3	17.0	18.3	19.9
Cubic feet gas......................	7,190	6,700	7,350	7,750
Pounds ammonium sulphate...........	21.4	20.6	18.1	28.2

fractionation of the peat tar was recorded; and in Table 77, where ultimate and proximate analyses of the carbonization residuum were reported.

A second battery of four externally heated vertical retorts were tested by the Fuel Research Board (240).   These retorts consisted of a standard Glover-West spiral extractor connected by a special iron casting with three upper cast-iron sections.   The retorts were of rectangular cross-section 15 feet high, tapering from 28 inches by 9 inches at the top to 33 inches by 15 inches at the bottom.   All four retorts were mounted in a common firebrick setting.   With flue temperatures of 650°C., a throughput was attained of 6 tons of briquets and about 5 tons of crushed coal per day.   After a good deal of difficulty with the formation of breeze by the extraction mechanism and with bridging of the charge, due both to design and to heat distortion, these retorts were finally dismantled and the information gained from their operation used to improve the retort construction.

The Fuel Research Board finally erected a battery of four narrow cast-iron continuous vertical retorts of the design shown in Fig. 63.

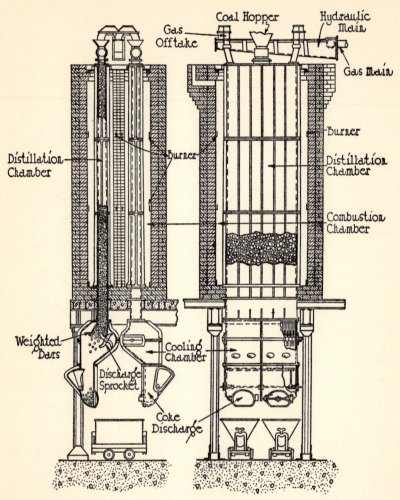

FIG. 63. FUEL RESEARCH BOARD VERTICAL RETORT

These retorts are 21 feet high and taper in length from 6.5 feet at the top to 6.92 feet at the base. Two of these, designated as "D" retorts, taper in width from 4 inches at the top to 8 inches at the bottom, while two, designated as "E" retorts, tapered in width from 7 inches at the top to 11 inches at the bottom.   In all other respects, the two modifications of the narrow vertical retorts are identical.   The retorts are built in three sections of good gray cast-iron one inch thick. A modified Woodall-Duckham extractor, consisting of a curved comb, which sustains the charge, and a toothed wheel, which slowly rotates between the prongs, is used.   An outrush of coke from the side of the extractor is prevented by the pressure of weighted hinged rods.   A number of vertical ribs were cast onto the outside of the retorts in an attempt to prevent warping.   The combustion chamber consists of a plain firebrick setting surrounding each pair of retorts and heated by 48 gas burners arranged in three stages of 16 each.   Care is taken to place the burners close to the flue wall, in order to prevent the flame from impinging directly upon the retort castings.   Two standpipes

TABLE 111

Yields in test of Fuel Research Board narrow vertical retorts

PRODUCT PER GROSS TON	COAL BRIQUETS	DALTON MAIN COAL	MITCHELL MAIN COAL
Pounds semi-coke....................	1,706	1,665	1,747
Gallons tar.........................	16.7	20.7	16.2
Cubic feet gas......................	5,160	5,190	4,460

at the top of each retort remove the volatile products and deliver them to an hydraulic main.

These retorts have been operated by the Fuel Research Board (241) for over a year at flue temperatures up to 625°C.   The thinner "D" retorts were badly distorted by growth of the cast-iron, after prolonged operation at 650°C.   After carbonization of over 1,350 tons of raw coal, of various types, in the model "E" retorts, they have been declared successful and arrangements have been completed to give them a commercial trial by the erection, at London, of a battery of these retorts, with a daily capacity of 100 tons, by the Fuel Production Company, Ltd., organized under the joint auspices of the British Government and the Gas Light and Coke Company.

Tests demonstrated that, with carbonization temperatures ranging from 605°C. to 625°C., the throughput per day of each "E" retort varied from 4.1 gross tons to 2.7 gross tons of coal, depending on the fuel used.   A number of different coals, both coking and non-coking,

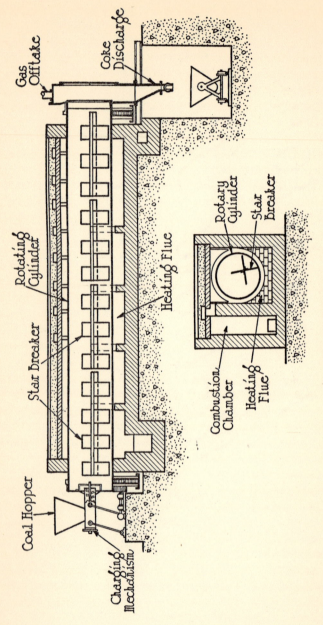

Fig. 64. Fusion Retort

as well as blended and briquetted fuels, have been successfully distilled. The yields obtained from three different materials are given in Table 111. The briquets consisted of a mixture of 74 per cent Durham coal, 20 per cent semi-coke breeze, and 6 per cent pitch. Instead of working the retorts continuously, it was found more satisfactory to work them intermittently, fresh charges being introduced every hour, in the case of Dalton Main, and at 2-hour intervals in the case of the other two fuels.

Fusion Process. The Fusion low temperature retort is the invention of Hutchins and is controlled by the Fusion Corporation, Ltd. Much of the developed was carried out in a 5 gross ton per day unit, installed at the works of the Electro-Bleach By-Products, Ltd., Cledford, England. This system belongs to the type of externally heated rotary kilns which contain an internal device for agitating the charge. According to Tupholme (242), two types of retorts have been designed, the single and the double-tube type

The single-tube Fusion retort is shown in Fig. 64. It consists of a mild steel cylinder which is mounted horizontally upon rollers at the ends. The crushed fuel in introduced at one end of the rotating tube by an automatic feeding device and the coal is transported through the kiln by the combined action of rotation and the head of raw material which is built up by fresh coal at the charging end. At the discharge end of the retort, there is a stationary chamber, into the bottom of which the semi-coke falls to await delivery, while the gas is removed by an offtake and conducted successively to a dust-catcher, condenser, scrubber, and, finally, to the gas-holder. A star-shaped breaker is placed within the cylinder, but in no way connected with it, so that rotation of the retort causes the breaker to tumble over and over, stirring the charge and chipping off the hard crust, which tends to form on the inner wall when carbonizing sticky fuels. The retort is surrounded by a firebrick flue, containing on one side a combustion chamber from which the hot products of combusted producer gas are extracted by heating flues and circulated around the rotating cylinder.

The double-tube Fusion retort operates on essentially the same principle as the single-tube design. In this modification, two cylinders are mounted concentrically. The inner and smaller cylinder contains the breaker. This construction has two advantages. In the first place, it permits charging and discharging at one end, thus eliminating one gas-tight gland between the rotating and stationary parts. In the second place, the coal is preheated in the inner tube before actual carbonization in the outer cylinder. It has already been demonstrated in Chapter IV, under the subject of preheating and oxidation of the charge, that this thermal pretreatment destroys the coking power of the coal to prevent adhesion of the plastic material to the retort walls, as often occurs in kilns of this design. Ordinarily, if some means is not provided to prevent the formation of this crust, when dealing with sticky materials, it becomes so thick that sufficient heat cannot be conducted through the refractory material to carbonize the charge without raising the flue temperature to regions which endanger the retort shell.

A test of the semi-commercial single-tube Fusion retort at Cledford was made by the Fuel Research Board (243). The tube of the retort is 25 feet long, 2.5 feet in diameter, and contains five breakers, 20 inches in diameter, placed end to end. The temperature of carbonization ranged from a minimum of 325°C., in the flue, to a maximum of nearly 625°C., just past the middle of the retort. Under these conditions, the daily throughput was nominally 5 tons, depending on the character of the fuel treated. The Welback Cannel, used in the test by the Fuel Research Board, contained 1.8 per cent moisture, 46.6 per cent volatile matter, 36.8 per cent fixed carbon, and 14.8 per cent ash. The carbonaceous residuum from distillation contained 9.7 per cent volatile matter, 64.8 per cent fixed carbon and 25.5 per cent ash. The products yielded by carbonization, per gross ton of raw fuel, consisted of 1,196 pounds of semi-coke, 60.2 gallons of oil, 2,740 cubic feet of gas, 4.5 gallons of light oil scrubbed from the gas, and only about 3 pounds of ammonium sulphate. It is said that about 65 gallons of tar per gross ton of coal could be obtained by rearranging the discharge chamber. The above yields gave the following conversion factors for yields, as determined in the Gray and King assay apparatus: 0.98 for semi-coke; 0.73 for tar; and 0.86 for gas. The gross calorific value of the gas was estimated at 1,305 B.t.u. per cubic foot, before scrubbing, and was determined as 1,110 B.t.u. per cubic foot, after scrubbing. The solid residuum was discharged in small pieces of about the size it was introduced into the retort and was, therefore, suitable for briquetting and pulverization.

Greene-Laucks Process. This retort bears the name of its two inventors, Greene and Laucks, but is controlled by the Old Ben Coal Corporation, Chicago. The experimental work was carried out by the Denver Coal By-Products Company at Denver, Colo., but subsequently a semi-commercial plant was built at Waukegan, Ill., according to Greene (244). The Greene-Laucks process belongs to the general class of vertical externally heated retorts with an internal spiral conveyor. It is operated primarily to produce a domestic fuel from low grade bituminous coal screenings.

This retort has undergone a number of modifications with respect to minor details, but it remains essentially the same in principle of design. Fig. 65 shows two of the battery of four retorts erected at Denver. These retorts consist of a cast-iron shell about 12 inches in diameter and 18 feet long. Mounted centrally within this casing is a hollow shaft, 8.5 inches in diameter, which has a 1.5 inch spiral web cast on its exterior. Each pair of retorts is fed from a common hopper by a screw conveyor, which introduces the raw coal at the bottom of the retort. The central core is mounted upon a thrust bearing at the bottom and is geared to rotate slowly, so that the charge is forced upward by the motion and discharged at the top after carbonization. The speed of rotation varies from 1 r.p.m. to 3 r.p.m., depending upon the material being processed and upon the percentage volatile matter which is permitted to remain in the coke. Each retort is mounted in a firebrick setting, leaving a 4 inch heating flue surrounding the metal shell. Sticking of the charge to the rotor is prevented by heating the interior walls of the shaft by a gas burner, consisting of a perforated gas pipe. The height of this retort was subsequently reduced to 12 feet, while the Waukegan modification was again increased to 18 feet high and enlarged to 3 feet in diameter.

With a shell temperature of about 450°C., extensive tests on bituminous coals showed a yield of low temperature tar amounting to 0.876 gallons per one per cent of volatile matter in the raw fuel. The average yield of products per net ton from bituminous coal was 1,400 pound of semi-coke, 35 gallons tar, 4,000 cubic feet of gas, and 12 pounds of ammonium sulphate. About half of the gas, which had a calorific value of approximately 700 B.t.u. per cubic foot, was required for heating the retort. A low grade Colorado shale, containing 28 per cent volatile matter and 30 per cent ash, yielded upon carbonization 1,500 pounds of solid residuum, 30, gallons of tar, 4,000

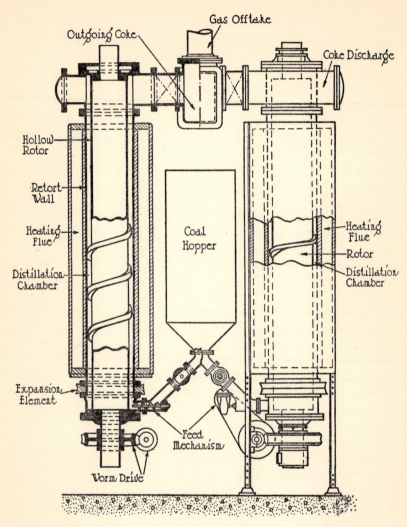

Fig. 65.   Greene-Laucks Retort

cubic feet gross of 793 B.t.u. per cubic foot gas, and 15 pounds of ammonium sulphate.

K. S. G. Process. The Kohlenscheidungs Gesellschaft, Essen, Germany, is responsible for this process, which was invented by Cantieny (245). The development work was carried out at the Mathias Stinnes Colliery at Karnap. A plant of this type, with a large daily capacity, is now (1928) under erection at New Brunswick, N. J., by the International Coal Carbonization Company, a subsidiary of the International Combustion Engineering Company, who have acquired the process. The K. S. G. process belongs to the general type of externally heated rotary kiln retorts in which the coal is preheated before actual distillation.

As shown in Fig. 66, the K. S. G. retort consists of two coaxial cylinders securely fastened together and mounted at an inclination upon rollers, so that they rotate as a unit. The entire weight of the retort is carried by the cooler inner cylinder, which, according to Mueller (246), is an important advantage, in that the supporting structure never exceeds 300°C., and sagging of the retort, caused by reduction of tensile strength through heating of the steel shell, is avoided.

The K. S. G. kiln, which is installed at Karnap, is 76 feet long. Its inner cylinder is 5.75 feet in diameter, while its outer shell is 10 feet in diameter. The charge requires about 2.5 hours to pass through the retort when the speed of revolution is approximately once in 1.5 minutes. A retort of this size has a daily throughput ranging from 60 tons to 80 tons. It will be seen from Fig. 66, that the crushed raw fuel is introduced by a special screw conveyor, which projects well into the lower end of the inner or preheating cylinder. Spiral flights, fastened to the inner wall of the smaller cylinder, convey the coal to the upper end of the retort, where it falls through discharge ports into the outer or carbonizing cylinder. It is claimed that this pretreatment sufficiently removes the sticking quality of the fuel, so that it does not stick to the walls of the outer chamber. The retort is mounted in an ordinary firebrick combustion chamber, in such a way that the hottest zone of the retort is at the point where the pretreated coal falls into the carbonizing cylinder. By this procedure, the pretreated coal is rapidly brought through the plastic stage long before the semi-coke is discharged, thus giving the material sufficient time to cement the coal particles together and harden, with the result that breeze is reduced to a minimum. The pretreated charge, having been deposited at the upper end of the outer chamber,

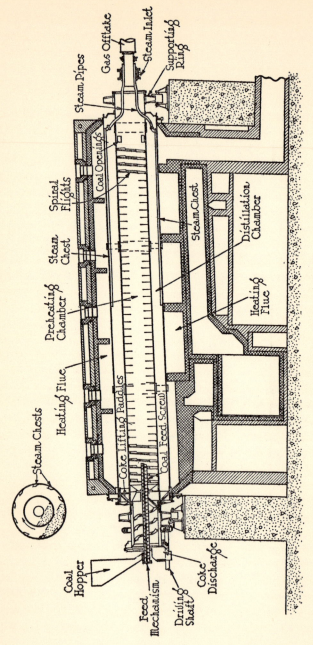

Fig. 66. K. S. G. Retort

descends to the charging end under the combined action of gravity and rotation. At the bottom end of the retort, the finished semi-coke is elevated by a plow into a short extremity of the inner cylinder, where reverse spiral flanges transport the material to the discharge exit. The volatile products are withdrawn through a hollow shaft at the upper end of the retort. Provision is made for introducing steam to the carbonizing cylinder through twelve longitudinal steam chests which are arranged around the periphery of the outer cylinder and connected with a rotating valve so that steam is introduced only while coal is above the steam chests. The temperature of pre-heating ranges from 200°C. to 300°C., while that of carbonization ranges from 600°C. to 700°C. The superheated steam is introduced at a pressure of about 7.5 pounds per square inch and at a total temperature of approximately 450°C.

Using a weakly coking German coal, containing 25 per cent volatile matter, 57 per cent fixed carbon, about 15 per cent ash, and 3 per cent moisture, the average yield was 1,837 pounds of semi-coke; 11.3 gallons of dry tar; 2,420 cubic feet of low temperature gas; and slightly over one gallon of light oil scrubbed from the gas. The thermalvalue of the low temperature gas ranged from 750 B.t.u. to 830 B.t.u. per cubic foot. About 85 per cent of the semi-coke was in lumps, ranging in size from 0.5 inch to 4.0 inches, and proximate analysis showed it to contain 9.3 per cent volatile matter and 18.6 per cent ash. When coals containing a higher percentage of volatile matter were used, a greater yield of tar was obtained, but the through-put of the retort was correspondingly reduced.

Maclaurin Process. The patents on this process are controlled by Maclaurin Carbonization, Ltd. The Maclaurin (188) retort is an internally heated process of the partial gasification type. It combines both the principles of low temperature carbonization and of the manufacture of producer gas.

After his initial small-scale experiments, Maclaurin (247) erected a semi-commercial plant with a daily capacity of 20 gross tons at the Port Dundas plant of the Glasgow Corporation, Scotland. The Port Dundas retort consisted of a gas producer and a carbonizing shaft built into a single setting with a connecting conduit, so that the hot producer gas could be led directly from the top of the gasification chamber into the bottom of the carbonizing shaft. The hot producer gas, rising up through the layers of fresh coal, distilled it with its sensible heat. The semi-coke was extracted at intervals from the bottom of the carbonizing shaft and partly charged to the combustion chamber for complete gasification. The top of the retort was built of steel, as an inverted cone, and the volatile products were led over the top of the funnel to a gas-collecting chamber, from which it was

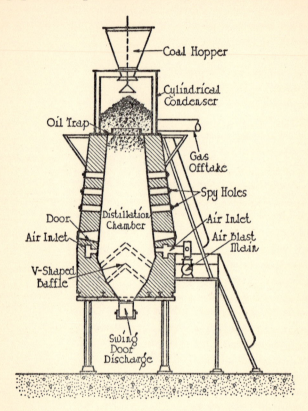

FIG. 67. MACLAURIN RETORT

withdrawn to the condensers. The gasification and carbonization chambers were segregated in the Port Dundas retort to reduce the ash that would appear in the semi-coke, were both operations carried out in a single chamber. It was subsequently discovered, however, that the ash from partial gasification can be very easily separated from the semi-coke, so that segregation of the gasification chamber from the distillation shaft was entirely unnecessary. An analysis of the semi-coke obtained from this retort has been given in Table 78.

Following the experience gained at Port Dundas, a retort of the design shown in Fig. 67 was erected and tested at Grangemouth, Scotland, and the results are said to have been sufficiently satisfactory to warrant the installation of a battery of five Maclaurin low temperature retorts at the Dalmarnock Gasworks of the Glasgow Corporation for the production of smokeless fuel.

The Grangemouth retort, which somewhat resembles a blast furnace in shape, has a daily capacity of 20 tons. It is square in cross-section and stands about 45 feet over all. Externally, the retort tapers from about 8 feet at the top to about 13 feet at the bottom, but internally the maximum width of 8 feet occurs about 7 feet from the base. Air is blown into the retort at the point of its maximum internal width, so that this section of the retort constitutes the partial gasification zone, while the superincumbent layers of fuel constitute the carbonizing shaft. The top of the firebrick shaft is surmounted by a double-walled metal cylinder, into which the raw coal is introduced from a charging hopper immediately above. Any oils, which are distilled from the coal and condense on the cold metal walls, are collected by a trough at the top of the refractory shaft, thus preventing the low temperature oil from trickling down the walls to the hot gasification zone where they would be cracked. A V-shape dividing wall extends across the retort just below the combustion zone and seems to divide the charge so that it can be withdrawn from two discharge doors at the bottom of the retort. The mixture of producer and low temperature gas is withdrawn at the top of the retort, the metal cylinder being built with hollow walls to form an annular gas-collecting chamber. The temperature in the retort ranges from about 900°C., in the combustion zone, to about 70°C., at the top of the retort, the bulk of the volatile products, however, being removed at temperatures from 300°C. to 500°C.

A test on bituminous coal at Grangemouth showed a yield, per gross ton of coal, amounting to 1,096 pounds of semi-coke, 18.7 gallons of oil, 27,731 cubic feet of gas, and 14.5 pounds of ammonium sulphate. About 74 per cent of coke was larger than one inch lumps. The composition of the gas, which had a gross heating value of 247 B.t.u. per cubic foot, has already been given in Table 26. The original coal contained 30.5 per cent volatile, 53.7 per cent fixed carbon, 8.1 per cent ash, and 1.3 per cent moisture, whereas proximate analysis of the large lumps of the residuum showed 3.0 per cent volatile matter, 81.2 per cent fixed carbon, 13.5 per cent ash, and 2.3 per cent moisture. Most of the ash from combustion was concentrated in the breeze, which contained from 20 per cent to 35 per cent ash.

Tupholme (248) reports some yields when the Grangemouth retort was used to completely gasify the coal for the purpose of recovering the low temperature oil, ammonia, and gas, without the production of coke. The fact that the solid fuel is completely gasified, of course, has very little bearing on the characteristics of the tar produced, as long as the tar is distilled out by the sensible heat of the gas before the coke reaches the combustion zone. Table 112 gives the proximate

TABLE 112

Analyses of fuels tested and yields from complete gasification in Maclaurin retort

CONSTITUENT	POOR CANNEL COAL	BITUMINOUS REFUSE	ANTHRACITE REFUSE
Coal analysis:	*per cent*	*per cent*	*per cent*
Moisture...........................	0.7	2.2	1.2
Volatile matter.....................	26.0	19.0	7.7
Fixed carbon.......................	23.5	26.5	36.5
Ash................................	49.7	52.3	55.6
Yield per gross ton:			
Cubic feet gas......................	46,767	69,240	60,800
Gallons oil.........................	31.0	8.1	2.4
Pounds ammonium sulphate........	8.5	17.0	10.3

analyses of three low grade fuels completely gasified in the Maclaurin retort, without the production of smokeless fuel. The thermal efficiency of complete gasification was 81 per cent, for the cannel coal, 88 per cent, for the bituminous refuse, and 72 per cent, for the anthracite refuse.

McEwen-Runge Process. This process, which is based upon the invention of McEwen, is controlled by the International Combustion Engineering Corporation and was largely developed by Runge (249) at the Lakeside Station of the Milwaukee Electric Railway and Light Company. The McEwen-Runge process is an internally heated static vertical retort for the treatment of pulverized coal.

McEwen's initial attempt at the low temperature carbonization of powdered coal was made in a closed circuit of cast-iron pipe 6 inches in diameter and approximately 70 feet in length. In this apparatus the pulverized coal was held in suspension by the rapidly moving superheated gas, which acted both as the carbonizing medium and as the means of transport for the fuel. The completely carbonized particles were finally separated from the heating medium by a cyclone dust-catcher. The original scheme was eventually aban-

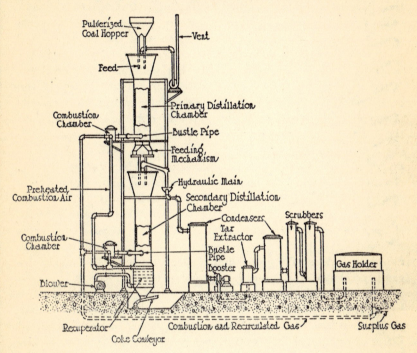

FIG. 68. McEWEN-RUNGE PROCESS

doned, when it was found impossible to maintain the dust in suspension at the temperature required for carbonization without maintaining excessive gas velocities, which would necessitate an undue length for the carbonizing circuit.

The Milwaukee development unit, shown schematically in Fig. 68, consists of two superimposed steel cylinders, each about 30 feet in length and 6 feet internal diameter. The cylinders are lined with refractory to protect them from the heat. The upper cylinder constitutes the primary retort, where the coal is treated by preheating or partial oxidation to destroy its coking property, while the lower cylinder forms the secondary retort, where the coal is carbonized. The pulverized coal is introduced at the top of the primary retort through four feed pipes which project about 8 feet into the cylinder and which are fed by screw conveyors. The raw pulverized coal then falls freely to the bottom of the primary retort against a current of hot air, or products of combustion, introduced by means of a bustle pipe at the bottom of the chamber. By the time the pretreated coal collects in the bottom of the primary retort its agglomerating power has been entirely destroyed and the hot material is fed by screw conveyors through four additional feed pipes into the top of the secondary retort, where it again falls counter-current to a current of ascending hot inert heating gas introduced in the same manner at the bottom of the cylinder. Two combustion chambers are provided, one for the primary and one for the secondary retort. A certain proportion of the coal gas is combusted in the primary heating chamber and the hot flue gas is used to raise the temperature of the primary retort to approximately 320°C. It is found that, if a certain amount of excess air is present, the treatment is far more effective than if preheating alone is used. Very little volatile matter is removed in the primary retort, so that the gas is vented to the atmosphere. A certain proportion of the scrubbed low temperature gas is preheated in the secondary combustion chamber to bring the temperature of the secondary retort to approximately 570°C. The hot semi-coke, which is pulverulent in form, collects in the cooling chamber at the bottom and may be fed hot to a pulverized coal boiler or reduced in temperature below its ignition point by a heat exchanger before being discharged by a spiral extractor. The volatile products are removed at the top of the retort by two gas offtakes which connect with an hydraulic main. Both the primary and secondary retorts are expanded to a diameter of about 13 feet at the top, to reduce the velocity of the gas to such an extent that none of the pulverized material is carried through the gas offtake. The capacity of the Milwaukee installation exceeds 200 tons of raw coal per day.

Using a high volatile Youghiogheny coal, containing 34.6 per cent volatile, 57.6 per cent fixed carbon, and 7.8 per cent ash on a dry basis, the yield per net ton in extensive tests was approximately 1,400 pounds of semi-coke, 25 gallons of tar, 3 gallons of light oil scrubbed from the gas, and about 4,000 cubic feet of surplus gas, with a calorific value of approximately 540 B.t.u. per cubic foot.   When the raw coal was pulverized, so that 60 per cent passed 200 mesh, 85 per cent passed 100 mesh, and 100 per cent passed 40 mesh screens, the resultant semi-coke showed that 7 per cent passed 200 mesh, 22 per cent passed 100 mesh, and 100 per cent passed 10 mesh screens.

Nielsen Process.   The low temperature retort designed by Nielsen (91) (250) is a horizontal rotary kiln, internally heated by the sensible heat of hot gas.   The process, originally controlled by Messrs. Laing, Marshall, and Nielsen, is now owned by the Sensible Heat Distillation, Ltd., London.   A plant of this type, with a daily capacity of 100 gross tons per day, has been erected in India by the Carbon Products Company.   While the general scheme of internal heating is always adhered to in this system, there are a number of variations in the method of applying it.   Thus, distillation may be effected by the sensible heat of unignited producer or water gas, by combusted gas, by recirculated and superheated coal gas, and by combusted powdered coal.

The Nielsen process, outlined diagrammatically in Fig. 69, is arranged for the use of superheated producer gas, mixed with superheated steam, as the heating medium.   A portion of the producer gas is combusted in a gas fired superheater to raise the temperature of the rest of the producer gas to the required degree.   A waste-heat boiler, surmounting the superheater, serves to generate steam for mixing with the heating gas.   Once the process is started, a part of the low temperature gas can be drawn from the system and recirculated to replace the lower calorific producer gas, giving a final product of superior heating quality.

Tupholme (252) gives the dimensions of the unit, which was erected in India with 100 gross tons daily capacity, as 90 feet long, 7 feet in diameter, for the first half of its length near the charging end, and nearly 9 feet in diameter, for the remainder of its length.   Near the discharge end, there is an annular cooling chamber 8 feet long and 14 feet in diameter.   A hand-operated sliding valve connects the discharge chamber with the retort, the end of the kiln stopping abruptly in a bulkhead.   A second sliding door permits the cooled semi-coke to be extracted from the apparatus.   The kiln is mounted upon

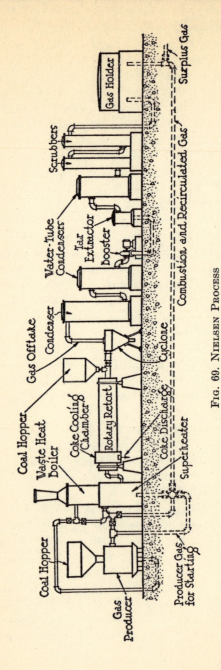

FIG. 69. NIELSEN PROCESS

rollers at each end and in the center, being tilted at a slight angle so that the combined action of rotation and the inclination causes the charge to travel through the retort.   The kiln is built of plate steel sheets and is lined with refractory to protect the metal from the influence of hot heating gas, introduced at the lower end of the cylinder to secure the benefit of counter-current heating.   The installation of the Carbon Products Company is of the simple hot producer gas type.

The average temperature of the heating gas as it enters the Nielsen retort is 750°C. and it emerges at a temperature ranging from 120°C. to 245°C.   The refractory lining, which is of double thickness over the length of the kiln that is especially large in diameter, prevents the

TABLE 113

Analyses of coals tested and cokes yielded in Nielsen retort

CONSTITUENT	BARNSLEY COKING COAL	CANNEL COAL	BROWN COAL
Coal analysis:	per cent	per cent	per cent
Moisture...........................	4.33	6.01	45.53
Volatile matter.....................	32.77	40.69	37.06
Fixed carbon.......................	55.78	47.12	11.66
Ash...............................	7.12	6.18	5.75
Semi-coke analysis:			
Volatile matter.....................	10.15	13.49	20.86
Fixed carbon.......................	80.95	79.03	53.73
Ash...............................	8.90	7.48	25.41

metal shell from exceeding 45°C.   About 2.5 hours are required for the charge to pass through the kiln.   A part of the semi-coke is used to fire the gas producer.

Tests on the Nielsen retort, with a bituminous slack as the raw fuel and producer gas as the heating medium, showed a gross tonnage yield of 21.6 gallons of oil, 44,000 cubic feet of gas, and 15.2 pounds of ammonium sulphate.   In addition there was a gross production of 1,475 pounds of semi-coke, of which 620 pounds were consumed in the gas producer, giving a net yield of 855 pounds.   The gas from the process consisted of a mixture of about 5,000 cubic feet of true low temperature coal gas, with a calorific value of about 735 B.t.u. per cubic foot, and approximately 39,000 cubic feet of producer gas, with a thermal value of about 140 B.t.u. per cubic foot.   Thus the mixture amounted to 44,000 cubic feet, with a heating value of 230 B.t.u. per cubic foot.   Analysis of the mixed gas showed it to contain: 5.6 per cent carbon dioxide, 22.7 per cent carbon monoxide, 10.5 per cent methane, 14.1 per cent hydrogen, 45.6 per cent nitrogen, and about 1.6 per cent hydrocarbons and free oxygen.   A fractionation of the low temperature tar from the Nielsen process has been given in Table 62 and a proximate analysis of the semi-coke is reported in Table 78.   The proximate analyses of several other fuels tested in the Nielsen retort, together with analyses of the semi-coke, are tabulated in Table 113.   The Barnsley coal, given in Table 113, was a coking slack, which yielded a fairly soft coke; the cannel coal was a coking fuel; and the brown coal was a sample from Germany, which yielded a semi-powdery solid residuum.

Piron-Caracristi Process.   This process bears the name of its two inventors, Piron (252) and Caracristi (253).   The Piron-Caracristi process belongs to the class of internally heated retorts in which carbonization is effected by means of molten lead.   It consists essentially of a long horizontal tunnel kiln, through which the fuel is transported in thin layers by means of an endless conveyor.   Two units of this design, each with a daily throughput of approximately 50 tons of raw coal, were erected by the Ford Motor Company, one at their River Rouge, Detroit, plant and one in Canada at their Walkerville, Ontario, plant.   Both of these installations, however, were dismantled because of operating difficulties, which are now said to have been overcome.

A Piron-Caracristi retort, designed for a daily capacity of about 50 tons of fuel, is illustrated by longtidudinal and cross-sectional views in Fig. 70.   Its over-all dimensions are approximately 47 feet long, 33 feet high, and 22 feet, wide.   The distillation chamber consists of an arched brick tunnel about 14 feet wide and 6.5 feet high.   The floor of the distillation chamber is formed by molten lead, which is maintained in the liquid state by a number of transverse U-shaped cast-iron flues of rectangular cross-section, which are placed side by side beneath the lead.   The cast-iron flues are fastened down to prevent them from floating on the molten lead.   The heating flues, which are gas fired, are built into the firebrick setting alongside the distillation chamber, so that the hot combusted gases can be drawn through the transverse cast-iron flues to maintain the lead at the required temperature. An endless conveyor, built of hinged plates, passes over sprocket wheels at each end of the tunnel, the upper part of the conveyor floating on the surface of the molten lead and the lower part passing through a conveyor tunnel built immediately below the distillation chamber. This serves to transport the charge through the retort. A second apron conveyor is placed in the lower tunnel to receive the finished semi-coke at the opposite end of the retort from which it is charged and return it to the charging end for delivery, after it has cooled sufficiently to prevent its ignition. A regenerator or recuperator is placed on top of the setting to preheat the combustion gas by extracting heat from the spent flue gas.

The crushed raw coal is fed in thin layers to the apron conveyor and carbonized in about 5 minutes, during which time it passes through the distillation chamber. The entire heat for distillation is transmitted by metallic conduction from the molten lead, maintained at about 650°C., through the plates of the apron conveyor and into the thin layer of raw fuel. At the far end, the semi-coke falls in slabs upon the return conveyor on which it is cooled, during the return passage through the lower tunnel, before discharge.

Among all molten metals available as a heating agent, lead has a number of advantages which render it particularly suitable. In the first place, it is not attacked by sulphur in the coal gas, except at temperatures considerably higher than those prevailing in the distillation chamber. Furthermore, it has a low melting point and a high boiling point, which prevents freezing and loss of vapor respectively, thereby eliminating the necessity of close temperature regulation. Experience has shown that practically no lead is lost by oxidation and no difficulty is experienced in retaining the molten metal within a refractory structure. The lead losses consist almost entirely of small quantities of metal lifted out of the bath by the conveyor at the discharge end of the retort and most of this can be recovered later.

A test in the Piron-Caracristi process installed at Walkerville, Ontario, using a bituminous coal containing approximately 38 per cent volatile matter, 5.4 per cent moisture, and 4 per cent ash, yielded a semi-coke containing an average of 9.7 per cent volatile matter. The products obtained per net ton of coal amounted to 26 gallons of tar, 3,973 cubic feet of gas, and 1,425 pounds of semi-coke. The low temperature gas had a calorific value of about 793 B.t.u.

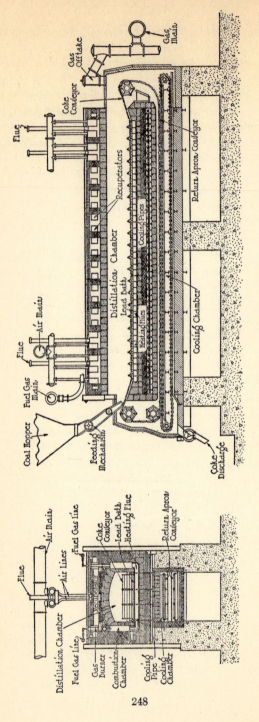

Coal Hopper

Feeding Mechanism

Flue

Air Main

Fuel Gas Main

Coke Discharge

Flue

Distillation Chamber

Lead Bath

Heating Flues

Cooling Pipes

Cooling Chamber

Return Apron Conveyor

Recuperators

Coke Conveyor

Gas Offtake

Gas Main

Distillation Chamber

Air Main

Flue

Air Lines

Fuel Gas Line

Fuel Gas Line

Gas Burner

Combustion Chamber

Coke Conveyor

Lead Bath Heating Flue

Return Apron Conveyor

Cooling Pipe

Cooling Chamber

Fig. 70. Piron-Caracristi Retort

per cubic foot. The semi-coke was pulverized and used as a fuel for firing steam boilers.

Sutcliffe-Evans Process. This process for the low temperature carbonization of coal is frequently referred to as the Pure Coal Briquet process, as well as by name of its inventors, Sutcliffe and Evans (254). It was developed by Pure Coal Briquets, Ltd., at

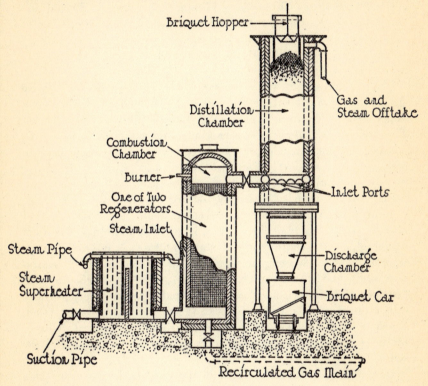

FIG. 71. SUTCLIFFE-EVANS RETORT

Leigh, England. The Sutcliffe-Evans process is an internally heated continuous vertical retort, whose chief novelty resides in preliminary preparation of the coal, particularly in super-pressure briquetting before carbonization.

This process depends largely for success upon the washing, grinding, and blending of the raw fuel. The crushed coal is usually washed, so that its ash content does not exceed 6 per cent, dried to less than

3 per cent moisture, and then ground to a size determined by the quality of fuel desired.   Ordinarily the coal is prepared to pass a 30 mesh screen, which gives satisfactory results without excessive grinding cost.   Non-coking coal or coke breeze is next mixed with the charge in suitable proportions to prevent swelling of the briquets during carbonization.   Most British coals give best results with about 22 per cent coke breeze.   Finally the mixture is formed into briquets, without the use of a binder, under the extreme pressure of approximately 20,000 pounds per square inch.   A special rotary briquetting press, designed by Sutcliffe and Speakman, Ltd., is used in this stage of the process.

The Sutcliffe-Evans retort, shown in Fig. 71, consists of a vertical steel cylinder lined with refractory and provided with a charging hopper and a discharge chamber at top and bottom, respectively. The raw briquets descend the carbonization shaft under their own weight.   Two vertical checkerwork regenerators are used in connection with the retort.   Part of the low temperature gas is burned in the combustion chamber of one regenerator, the hot spent gas being drawn through the brickwork and finally through a steam superheater.   Meanwhile the superheated steam, mixed with another portion of the low temperature gas, is circulated through the other regenerator until the mixture of steam and gas is intensely superheated.   The hot heating gas is then led to the base of the carbonization shaft and introduced to the retort, where it carbonizes the briquets with its sensible heat.   As rapidly as one regenerator is cooled down, circulation of the heating gas is diverted to the other, which has meanwhile been reheated.   The mixture of volatile products and steam is removed by a gas offtake at the top of the retort.

In a test with Lancashire coal in the Sutcliffe-Evans retort at a temperature of approximately 400°C., there was obtained per gross ton of briquets, 1,400 pounds of semi-coke briquets, 53 pounds of ammonium sulphate, 18 gallons of tar, 4.8 gallons of light oil, and about 17,000 cubic feet of gas.   The gas had a calorific value of 437 B.t.u. per cubic foot and approximately 9,000 cubic feet of the gross yield was required for heating the regenerators.   The high yield of ammonium sulphate is remarkable.   The carbonized briquets contained approximately 5 per cent volatile matter, whereas the raw coal contained 35 per cent.   The percentage volatile matter remaining

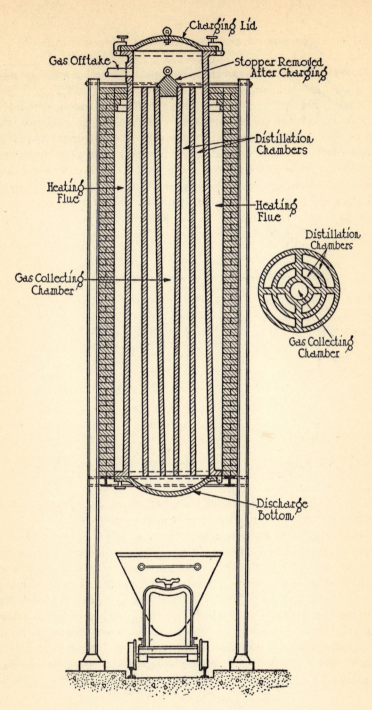

Charging Lid

Gas Offtake

Stopper Removed
After Charging

Distillation
Chambers

Heating
Flue

Heating
Flue

Distillation
Chambers

Gas Collecting
Chamber

Gas Collecting
Chamber

Discharge
Bottom

FIG. 72. TOZER RETORT

251

in the carbonized briquets can be reduced to as little as 1.5 per cent by raising the temperature of the heating gas to 1000°C.

Tozer Process. The Tarless Fuel Syndicate, London, developed and control the process invented by Tozer (190). In principle, the Tozer system is an intermittent static vertical cast-iron retort. It is externally heated and depends upon the method of thin layers and upon heat conduction by metal walls to effect carbonization at low temperatures. Beginning as early as 1909, a number of different retorts were designed, culminating with that shown in Fig. 72.

A battery of Tozer retorts, of the design shown in Fig. 72, with a daily capacity of 25 tons, was erected at Battersea, London, and

TABLE 114

Analyses of fuels and semi-cokes in tests of Tozer retort

CONSTITUENT	BITUMINOUS COAL	CANNEL COAL	LIGNITE
Coal analysis:	*per cent*	*per cent*	*per cent*
Moisture..........................	0.0	1.64	5.24
Volatile matter.....................	32.85	57.82	35.74
Fixed carbon.......................	58.31	36.61	49.03
Ash................................	8.84	3.93	9.99
Semi-coke analysis:			
Moisture..........................	0.0	2.25	
Volatile matter.....................	7.71	7.96	12.50
Fixed carbon.......................	82.3	82.77	75.60
Ash................................	9.99	7.02	

tested on many different carbonaceous materials. This retort is built of silicon cast-iron, which was found to stand up well after eight years of service at temperatures as high as 650°C. The casting is about 10 feet high and consists of three coaxial cylinders held together by four radial fins. The inner chamber is kept empty during charging of the retort by means of a removable stopper, thus providing a gas-collecting passage. Two quartered annular cells constitute the distillation chambers, into which the coal is delivered. The retort tapers slightly from top to bottom to facilitate discharge. The cast-iron cylinder is provided with a hinged bottom to support the charge and to provide a communicating passage between the carbonization chamber and the gas-collecting zone. A removable lid permits charging at the top and maintains the system gas-tight. The casting is surrounded by a refractory setting, which provides an external heating flue adjacent to the retort. Even though the coal may be as far as 10 inches from a heating surface at certain points in the retort, sufficient heat is conducted by the metal walls and fins to completely carbonize the charge in layers approximately 5 inches thick. When the temperature of carbonization is maintained at 540°C., about 4.5 hours are required to complete the distillation.

Marshall (255) has reported the yields obtained from a number of different fuels in the Tozer retort, as well as the composition of the residual coke. These data are reproduced in Table 115 and Table 114, respectively. The bituminous coal referred to in these tables was a Silkstone slack, the cannel was from Wigan, and the lignite and shale

TABLE 115
Yield of products in tests of Tozer retort

PRODUCT PER GROSS TON	BITUMI-NOUS COAL	CANNEL COAL	LIGNITE	SHALE
Pounds semi-coke...................	1,700	880	1,200	Waste
Gallons tar.........................	23.8	102.1	27.2	36.1
Pounds ammonium sulphate........	12.1	22.0	18.5	19.1

were from Spain. The temperature of carbonization was approximately 650°C. in each case. An analysis of another sample of semi-coke, manufactured in the Tozer retort from a strongly caking coal, was given in Table 78.

In addition to the yields per gross ton of raw fuel tabulated in Table 115, the Tozer process gives approximately 4,500 cubic feet of 450 B.t.u. stripped gas, from 2 gallons to 4 gallons of light oil being removed in the scrubbing process. A distillation analysis of a low temperature tar, obtained in the carbonization of an ordinary bituminous coal, has been given in Table 62. One point of particular interest in Table 115 is the notably high yield of tar obtained from Wigan cannel. The semi-coke from the Tozer process is said to be suitable for domestic uses and tests have demonstrated its value as a fuel for complete gasification.

CHAPTER VII

Operation, Design, and Materials of Construction

General. Lander conceives the successful development of a commercial carbonization process as passing through four distinct stages: first, laboratory investigation of the method under close control and with accurate measurement; second, work on an intermediate scale in a plant able to deal with several hundred pounds of raw material daily; third, erection of a full-scale unit with a daily capacity of not less than five tons, which will allow multiplication in number; and fourth a commercial battery which consists of a number of full-scale units erected in a locality which will test its economic possibilities.

In the foregoing chapters, we have dealt at length with the phenomena accompanying the transition of coal under application of heat, so that the principles to be noted during the first and second stages of development have been laid down. The successful solution of any low temperature process depends upon the utmost attention to and the thoughtful working out of details. While a knowledge of the physico-chemical reactions accompanying the thermal breaking down of the coal conglomerate is the *sine quo non* of any successful process, of quite as much importance is a knowledge of the properties of the materials of construction, of the difficulties of operation, of the principles of design, and of the economies which justify its existence. It is the purpose of this and the next chapter to consider these phases of the subject which are of particular interest during the third and fourth stages of commercial development.

Operation of Retorts. Caracristi (256) has given a very frank discussion of the operating difficulties of low temperature carbonization, as has Curtis (213) and his associates. To preserve the primary character of the low temperature products, it is necessary to avoid localized heating, which causes decomposition of the hydrocarbons and adversely affects the process, both by virtue of loss of valuable products and by the deposition of amorphous carbon, which is detrimental to continuous operation of the plant. The deposition of amorphous carbon, sufficiently hard to disrupt the driving mechanism,

254

was experienced in the Carbocoal primary retort, resulting in the adaption of a cutting blade to the paddles, as illustrated in the McIntire modification.

Temperature regulation is of great importance for a number of different reasons, principally among which is the sensitivity of the quality of the low temperature products to the temperature of distillation and the danger of exceeding a temperature which will injure the retort, if it be constructed of metal. Of course, the lower the temperature consistent with complete carbonization, the greater is the thermal efficiency of the process. Great care must be taken to prevent infiltration of air, either to the combustion chamber or to the carbonization chamber, in order to maintain close temperature regulation, in the first case, and to prevent destruction of the hydrocarbons, in the second.

Tempering of the semi-coke to prevent spontaneous combustion is a serious matter. Of course, this can be effected by water quenching the material, as is done in some instances, but this is not good practice, for it breaks up the lumps, producing excess breeze, and lowers the net heating value of the fuel by virtue of its moisture content. Furthermore, it is desirable to recover the sensible heat of the coke, as far as is possible, in order to increase the thermal efficiency of the process. This can be accomplished by means of heat recuperators or by dry quenching. The spontaneous combustion of semi-coke can be prevented easily by crushing and pulverizing it, provided it can be used in this form, for the finely divided material permits the absorption of sufficient oxygen to prevent further spontaneous oxidation.

It is common experience for low temperature processes to encounter the building up of a thick layer of carbon on the inner wall of the retort shell, due partly to cracking of hydrocarbons and partly to the sticking of fusing coals. This is a serious condition, to be avoided in all events, for, aside from its interference with the operation of moving parts, it greatly reduces heat transfer, because of its thermal insulating character, and increases the likelihood of injuring a metallic retort through over-heating in an effort to attain the necessary heat transfer to carbonize properly the coal. The carbon layer bakes harder with age and is difficult to remove.

It seems that a great deal of trouble has been found in handling fusing coals in a rotary retort, because they stick to the walls and build up a thick heat-insulating layer. To avoid this difficulty, recourse has been had to various mechanical and chemical devices. Thus, Hutchins introduced a star-shaped breaker into his Fusion process to chip the coke from the inner walls, while the K. S. G. process destroys the sticking quality by preheating the coal before carbonization. No serious mechanical difficulties are encountered in carbonizing non-coking materials when in motion, but, because of the absence of binding resins, the residuum after distillation is pulverulent in nature and of little value as a fuel, unless further processed by briquetting or by pulverization.

Another source of trouble in practice is the clogging of the raw coal feed pipes. This arises from the condensation of hydrocarbons or water vapor on the cool incoming coal to form a sticky paste. The Piron-Caracristi process partially remedied this difficulty by admission of steam with the coal, but finally completely avoided it by projecting the feed pipe into the hot oven. This expedient was adopted also in the McEwen-Runge process, where the pulverized coal is introduced through pipes extending several feet into the carbonization shaft.

In those processes in which molten lead is used as the heating medium, Caracristi (256) reports that there is no difficulty in holding the bath of lead in a refractory structure. Except for mechanical defects, such as cracks, bricks, which had been in use over a period of several months, showed no indication of lead infiltration upon examination. Furthermore, the loss of lead may be effectively prevented by a judicious location of traps and cooling pipes.

Moving metallic parts, especially those made of cast-iron, which are subjected to high temperature, such as chain conveyors, are subject to growth. This subject will be treated more fully later, but it should be pointed out that some provision must be made for taking up the slack or bringing the moving parts into register.

McEwen and Runge depend upon convection to transfer the heat from their recirculated hot gas to the pulverized coal particle. Gentry (208) has pointed out that the transfer of heat by convection in such circumstances is a function of a power of the relative velocity of the fluid and the particle. The laws of falling bodies in non-vortical fluids are well known and it is safe to conclude from them, even for a case of turbulent flow, that there are certain definite limits to heat transfer between a particle and a gaseous fluid in motion at certain gas velocities, due to the reduction to zero of the relative velocity of particle and fluid.   This sets a maximum limiting velocity of gas circulation, which depends, among other things, on the size of the particles, density of the gas, *etc.*, beyond which the efficiency of heat transfer is reduced and beyond which difficulties will be encountered with the gas carrying the pulverized coal out of the retort.   One very important aspect of low temerature carbonization in pulverized form is found in the fact that, both by convection and radiation, heat transfer depends directly upon the area of the absorbing body.   Consequently, carbonization of small particles should and does effect an enormous reduction in the time of distillation.

In the early days of low temperature carbonization, the first attempts to develop a continuous process naturally led to an internal spiral conveyer.   Most of these efforts utterly failed, because the inventors could not prevent the charge from plugging in the retort. The Greene-Laucks process seems to have successfully surmounted this difficulty, and probably the provision for heating the inner surface of the screw has a great deal to do with elimination of this trouble. In the Marshall-Easton process, which also uses internal spiral conveyors, the problem has been solved in an ingenious mechanical way by providing a nest of interlocking spirals, so that no rotary motion whatever is imparted to the charge, which moves only vertically through the retort.

Rotary retorts have received a good deal of attention in Germany, where several large-scale plants have been in operation for a number of years.   Rotary retorts, heated externally or internally, have certain well known advantages.   In the first place, they are continuous processes and avoid high maintenance, inevitably associated with a discontinuous process, where the retort is periodically heated and cooled.   Furthermore, the rotary retort permits bulk treatment of the charge, which requires less handling and correspondingly lowers the cost of processing per unit of throughput.   The constant tumbling of the charge during carbonization assists heat transfer enormously by presenting fresh surfaces to the hot wall, in the case of external heating, and to the hot gas, in the case of internal heating.   As a consequence of this stirring up of the coke, heating is very uniform and likewise the volatile content of the semi-coke.   On the other hand, there is a great diversity in the size of the lumps of semi-coke produced.   Some pieces are very large and must be broken, others are just right for domestic use, and there is a relatively large amount of breeze, which must be briquetted for the market.   Many experimenters with rotary retorts, however, have had a good deal of trouble with dust raised in the retort by the tumbling charge and carried over into the tar main by the gas.   This reduces greatly the value of the tar and causes much trouble in the by-product plant.   In certain instances, even after the installation of special dust-catchers, 2 per cent dust was carried over into the tar.

Design of Retorts.   Despite the basic simplicity of the low temperature carbonization process, reduction to practice in commercial installations introduces a number of complications of a serious nature.   Caracristi (256) summarizes them as follows:

(1) The necessity for large tonnage throughput, per unit of time and cost.

(2) Low heat conductivity of coal in mass.

(3) The difficulty of constructing an apparatus in which heat losses are minimized to a point where heat input in not prohibitive.

(4) The formation of gases which condense even at relatively high temperatures into sticky resins or tars.

The use of any structures similar in design to those employed in high temperature distillation is entirely precluded in primary carbonization by the first two difficulties listed above.   It is necessary to design the structure in such a manner that the evolved gases pass from their point of origin to a region no higher in temperature than that at which the gases were evolved, in order to prevent cracking them.   At the same time, it is equally important to prevent their passage into regions which are cool enough to cause their condensation, a condition which injures the oils through redistillation, as they trickle again into the hot zones, and a condition which tends to block the operation of the retort by formation of a pasty mass.

Caracristi (256) apparently believes that the third factor listed above is the dominating problem in low temperature carbonization. Unless due effort is made to reduce heat losses, their cost may reach a value which will entirely outweigh the gain in value of the recovered by-products.   Reduction of heat loss can be accomplished by proper thermal insulation or by an increase in plant throughput at a given temperature.   The only effective heat is that which goes into the charge and a large part of this is carried away as sensible heat of the products.

The fourth consideration, that of the formation of sticky resins, creates an operating situation which is difficult to overcome in commercial practice. The sticky property of coals, of course, disappears with the volatile content, so that the trouble from this source decreases in a given coal as coking proceeds.

We have witnessed in Chapter VI the variety of structures of widely different design in which low temperature carbonization has been effected. These structural differences arise from an understanding of the fundamentals of the coking process and from ingenious solutions of its various problems, particularly those of dealing with fusing coals, of securing the necessary heat transfer, and of obtaining a high throughput. The first of these problems has been discussed already under the subject of operation of retorts. The question of heat transfer has more or less resolved itself into the principle of external heating in thin layers, the principle of internal heating, or the principle of stirring the charge. These problems have been discussed at various times, particularly under the subjects of heat transfer and of internal and external heating in Chapter I. The retort throughput obviously depends upon the method of heating and resolves itself into multiplication of small units, in the case of heating externally by the principle of carbonization in thin layers, or mass distillation, in the case of internally heated or of rotary retorts.

Mass throughput requires continuous operation. As pointed out before, so long as the fuel is shale or other non-coking material, no trouble is experienced with moving parts, but the swelling and sticking of caking fuels renders the retort inoperative and is a difficult property of coal to surmount. Since the production of a domestic fuel requires the manufacture of a coherent product, this type of fuel is the class most usually met in practice. According to Simpkin (257), continuity of operation has been effected in low temperature carbonization processes in the following manners:

(1) Retorts constructed upon the principle of the tunnel kiln with provision to transport the coal through the carbonization chamber in suitable containers.

(2) The vertical shaft retort in which the charge is transported through the carbonization chamber under its own weight.

(3) Retorts in which the charge is transported by rotation of the structure itself.

(4) Retorts in which the fuel is transported by agitation from internal mechanical devices.

Intermittent working is severe on metal retorts, which grow hot when empty and thereafter cool rapidly when filled by the incoming charge. A semi-intermittent operation, accomplished by dropping the charge of vertical retorts a few feet at a time, such as was adopted in the Fuel Research Board narrow vertical retorts, apparently provides a satisfactory compromise.

It has been observed that much enterprise and ingenuity has been expended by those responsible for the development of the various low temperature processes and naturally the question arises as to which method is the most satisfactory. Due consideration must be given to a number of factors in reaching such a decision, as outlined by Simpkin (257):

(1) The character of the material to be processed.

(2) The relative importance attached to the products of carbonization.

(3) Efficiency, reliability, and simplicity of the method.

(4) The initial and operating costs per unit of throughput

In consideration of the potential fuel resources residing in the great variety of carbonaceous materials, ranging all the way from mine refuse and shales to high grade bituminous coal, designers of low temperature plants have been justified in constructing certain retorts with the intent of treating only one variety of material. At the same time others have set for themselves the more ambitious task of designing a retort of greater flexibility in the type of materials which it can treat.

The solid residuum from the distillation of shales is practically worthless, while that from colliery refuse is of doubtful value. In certain circumstances the residuum from carbonization of the latter might be used as a producer fuel. With such materials as these, the best process is one which gives special attention to the production of tar and gas. On the other hand, when the object in view is to process better grades of fuel to extract their by-products or to modify the nature of the solid material, the selection of the best process would rest upon the special character ascribed to the various products, means at hand for their disposition, and finally the market condition for by-products in that locality. Obviously, if the primary object is the production of a domestic fuel, no process can be considered which delivers the semi-coke for the most part in a finely divided form.   On the other hand, if the purpose of carbonization is the production of a power char, less discrimination can be made in the selection of the raw fuel for distillation and the delivery of the finished product in a finely divided state may be more of an asset than a deterrent to the process.   If the solid product is desired in a firm or lumpy condition, there is little doubt that the oven type of retort is the best, but, if throughput of material is the first consideration, without regard to the conditions of the semi-coke, either the vertical shaft or rotary retort should be given preference.   It has already been pointed out in Chapter VI, under the subject of adaptability of processes, that no single retort will yield a maximum of even two of the most important products.   The production of large yields of oil is ordinarily accompanied by a friable coke, and likewise, if a large volume of gas is wanted, the coke is somewhat less desirable and the oils are low both in quantity and quality.

The economic efficiency of a retort resides not alone in its thermal efficiency.   The most desirable process for the treatment of a given fuel to yield predetermined products of known relative importance is that which delivers the semi-coke, tar, and gas at the minimum cost per unit.   Thermal efficiency is, of course, a factor in the attainment of this end, but of even greater importance is the reduction of overhead and operating costs.   Simplicity of design will usually contribute not only to a minimum initial expenditure, but to reduction of operating expense, through elimination of maintenance and attention that is required in more complicated operations.   On the other hand, the extra capital requirements to effect continuity and automatization will often be more than offset by savings in the cost of labor.

Evans (84) conducted a comprehensive series of experiments to determine the nature of the carbonization of coal at high temperatures in vertical retorts.   His work is of equal interest in low temperature carbonization, because particular attention was given to the inward movement of the plastic layer and its effect on the path of travel of the gases.   We have already seen in Chapter I, under the subject of plastic layer, that coking coals fuse somewhere in the vicinity of 400°C. and form a plastic zone which progresses towards the center of the retort as coking proceeds.   It was demonstrated that this plastic layer was approximately one inch thick and that its resistance to the flow of gas was of an order several thousand times that of raw crushed coal and several hundred times that of medium temperature coke. Evans found that the maximum pressure developed shortly after the passage of the plastic layer, at a temperature of roughly 425°C., and that the coke solidified shortly thereafter at approximately 440°C.

According to Evans (84), the difference in pressure across the plastic layer is dependent upon the percentage of voids in the charge and, therefore, upon the size to which the coal is crushed. Thus, he found a difference in pressure equal to 60 inches of water, when using an unscreened coal with a small percentage of voids, and a pressure difference of about 20 inches of water, when a screened lump coal, containing a large percentage of voids, was used. He made the remarkable observation that the resistance of gas flow was dependent upon its direction. Thus the pressure difference between two points about 5 inches apart was 30 inches of water, when the gas flowed across the plastic zone towards the core of the retort, and 40 inches of water, when the direction of flow was towards the retort wall. This shows that the plastic layer is more resistant to gas flow when backed by coke than when backed by green coal.

While in the past there has been a good deal of difference of opinion as to the relative quantities of the volatile products which pass upward inside and outside of the fusion zone, this question seems to have been pretty well established by Evans' experiments (84). Since it is evident that the flow of gas will follow the path of least resistance, due consideration must be given to the character of the original coal in determining whether the gas passes through the cold core of green coal or through the hot ring of semi-coke. Obviously, the coarser the raw coal and the greater the voids, the greater will be the proportion of the volatile products which pass upward through the core. In high temperature carbonization Evans estimates that roughly 90 per cent of the gas is evolved after passage of the plastic condition. In low temperature carbonization, probably 25 per cent of the gas is evolved inside of the plastic envelope and 75 per cent outside. In addition to the amount of gas liberated in the respective regions, the quantity which is removed by the different passages depends upon their relative resistance. At the beginning of distillation, the area within the plastic envelope is large and the area of the annular passage through the semi-coke is small, so that the resistance to gas flow is roughly inversely proportional to the area of the passages. Consequently, some of the gas liberated outside the plastic envelope breaks through the fusion zone and escapes through the core. As carbonization progresses, the inner passage becomes smaller and the outer passage correspondingly larger, so that a smaller and smaller percentage of the gas flows thorugh the plastic zone and out through the core passage. During the first 3 hours of high temperature carbonization, Evans (84) found that approximately equal quantities of the volatile products passed outward through the raw coal and outward through the coke, but, after that period, flow through the interior practically ceased. In low temperature externally heated vertical retorts, it is estimated that approximately half of the gas takes each passage. As the fused layer migrates inward, the region of maximum pressure, which is always outside of the plastic envelope, follows, but the distance between the two regions constantly becomes smaller. In general, the maximum pressure decreases in value as it moves towards the core and finally drops rapidly when the plastic envelope reaches the center and disappears.

In vertical retorts, a certain taper is necessary to facilitate discharge of the coke. Evans (84) has pointed out the very interesting fact that, for a retort of given area and given taper, there is a given rate of heating which will permit the plastic layer to reach the center of the retort at the bottom before it does so at the top. If this rate of heating be exceeded, the fusion layer will close first at the top of the retort and trap all volatile products inside of the plastic envelope at the bottom. This causes enough pressure to build up to force the gas through the fusion zone into the free passage outward through the hot coke. It might also be pointed out, that the resistance to flow of gas along the retort walls, as compared to that through the core, is greater at the bottom of a vertical retort than at the top. As a consequence, a larger percentage of the volatile products which are evolved at the bottom of the retort will flow through the core, than is the case for those evolved at the top.

In the design of low temperature retorts, it is well to bear in mind the various stages in which carbonization proceeds. These have been outlined by Fulweiler (258) as follows:

(1) A preliminary decomposition which begins as soon as the coal has acquired a certain fairly definite temperature. As this stage is quite strongly endothermic and approaches a fusion, the temperature remains fairly constant until completion.

(2) The products from the first stage, consisting principally of higher members of the aliphatic hydrocarbons, suffer considerable molecular rearrangement. In general, compounds containing less than three atoms of carbon are formed. This stage may be regarded as a continuation of the simplification in which every distillation results.

(3) The gaseous vapors, resulting from the second stage, when evolved from the protecting influence of the actual coal particles, are acted upon by the conducted and radiant heat of the more highly heated portions of the charge proper, of the sides of the retort, and of the superheated regions above the coal.

The first two stages take place more or less simultaneously within the charge itself. The reactions which take place in the third stage are very complicated, depending, as they do, upon the time of exposure and upon the temperature. We have seen in the foregoing chapters, that the mechanism of the third stage consists of the splitting up and breaking down of the aliphatic hydrocarbons and their reunion into complex carbo-cyclic compounds. The benzene hydrocarbons may be further decomposed with the liberation of hydrogen and carbon and the formation of still higher cyclic derivatives. It is the third stage of distillation that is tremendously affected by the method of carbonization and, therefore by the conditions under which it occurs.

Fulweiler (258) has also listed the six factors which influence carbonization. These general conditions are as follows:

(1) Size of the coal particles.
(2) Moisture content of the coal.
(3) Temperature of carbonization.
(4) Volume ratio of charge to retort.
(5) Time of carbonization.
(6) Pressure permitted during carbonization.

All of these conditions can be simplified into the three effects of time, temperature, and pressure by tracing them back to their origin. In the foregoing chapters, each of these factors has been treated at length, as have others indirectly derived from them.

Materials of Construction. It is of historic interest to note, that the gas industry was born in a metallic retort, for Murdock's first efforts were confined to the use of a cylindrical iron pipe. Since gas was the primary product in the early days of the carbonization industry, progress in the art naturally led to higher and higher temperatures, until the shortcomings of metallic retorts became so conspicuous that they were entirely superceded by those made of refractory materials. As regards the preferability of refractory or of cast-iron retorts, Lander and McKay (186) see no basis of superiority of one above the other, all things being taken into consideration. However, two particular advantages can be associated with a metallic retort: first, its excellent heat conductivity and high thermal diffusivity, thus giving better thermal efficiency to the process and reducing the period of carbonization by virtue of the high rate of heat transfer; and, second, the facility with which the system can be kept gas-tight. Its one drawback is the ease with which a metallic retort can be injured by overheating. The advent of low temperature carbonization again made their use a possibility and brought into prominence the great advantages of metallic retorts, as compared with those built of refractory. Of course, this applies only to externally heated processes and it cannot be said for internally heated processes that metal has any superiority over refractory as a material for the construction of carbonization chambers, aside from the consideration of leakage.

As a criterion by which to judge the speed of heat transfer through the retort, the thermal diffusivity is more important than the thermal conductivity in low temperature carbonization, where the periods of heating are relatively short. This is especially true in the case of intermittent processes. The truth of this fact can be made clear by the following considerations. The general case of simple linear propogation of a thermal disturbance is represented by Fourier's law of linear diffusion:

$$\frac{dT}{dt} = \kappa \, \frac{d^2 T_2}{dx} \qquad [26]$$

where κ is the diffusivity of the substance; T, the temperature; t, the time; and x, the distance within the material. In general, this equation cannot be solved for any but the simplest cases, so that the solution for such a complex shape as a retort is quite beyond possibility for practical application. Fourier's law of diffusion is worthy of consideration, however, from the standpoint of heat transfer, because it demonstrates that the diffusivity of the material is the physical constant which is of importance during the process of heating up the retort, rather than the thermal conductivity, which is the limiting factor only after the steady state of heat transfer has been attained. Of course, the diffusivity is itself related to the thermal conductivity in the following way:

$$\kappa = \frac{k}{c\,\rho} \qquad [27]$$

where k is the thermal conductivity; c is the specific heat of the material; and ρ is its density. When, however, the steady state of heat transmission has been reached, then $\frac{dT}{dt} = 0$, which is to say, that the temperature gradient within the retort wall is uniform. Under this condition, Fourier's diffusion equation can be solved to give the well known equation for the quantity of heat, Q, flowing between two parallel isothermals at temperatures, T_1 and T_2, respectively:

$$Q = \frac{k\,(T_2 - T_1)\,A\,t}{x} \qquad [28]$$

where A is the area considered perpendicular to the direction of heat flow, and x is the distance between the two isothermals. It will be recognized that this is the integrated form of Newton's law given in Chapter I, Equation [11], under the subject of heat transfer.

We can now summarize with the statement, that, in the transient thermal condition, the greater the diffusivity of the material, the faster is the propagation of temperature by conduction, and, in the steady state, the greater is the thermal conductivity of the material, the higher is the heat transfer. The diffusivity of cast-iron is roughly forty times greater than that of fireclay. The thermal conductivity and, hence, the diffusivity is constant only in a limited sense. It has long been known that both of these properties are functions of the temperature, as will be shown later.

Aside from such materials as carborundum, which is occasionally employed for special purposes in the construction of carbonization plants, the refractories ordinarily used fall into three classes: fireclay brick, which contains not more than 75 per cent silica; siliceous brick, which contains 80 per cent to 92 per cent silica; and silica brick, which contains over 92 per cent silica. Their respective properties differ materially. The fireclay or aluminous retorts are usually made from a mixture of plastic fireclay, flint fireclay, and "bats," while siliceous retorts are composed of a ganister with clay as a binding agent. All refractories should be fired at a temperature higher than will be reached in practice, so that there will not be excessive shrinkage or expansion with use. This is a point which requires little attention in low temperature carbonization, so long as the bricks are well fired for high temperature work.

Refractory retorts may be of several types: the one-piece hand-molded, machine-molded or cast retorts, and segmented retorts. The molded retorts are usually built of fireclay, while the segmental retorts may be built of shapes made of aluminous fireclay, of siliceous, or of silica material. Their thickness varies generally from 2.5 inches to 4 inches. They should be able to withstand abrasion, as the deposits of carbon and ash which accumulate are usually removed by scraping and scurfing the refractory. Fireclay has the disadvantage, compared to the other materials, of being especially susceptible to the corrosive action of salt in the coal.

According to Cole (259), molded retorts tend to crack after they have been in use a short time, due to the absence of joints to relieve heat strains which have been set up. On the other hand, the joints which are provided in segmental retorts permit full adjustment to the temperature conditions and prevent distortion. If the shapes are properly jointed and cemented, it cannot be said that the segmental retorts are subject to any greater leakage than moulded retorts. The gas-tightness of the joint is further improved by the deposition of carbon by cracked hydrocarbons. The segmental shapes should also be designed to give maximum strength to the wall structure. Porter (260) has noted that joints in the retort wall offer a relatively high resistance to heat transfer, to such an extent that considerations of thermal conductivity of different retort materials become of lesser importance when joints are present.

The requirements for a refractory cement, as established by Gill (261), are that it must be highly refractory, non-contracting, chemically inert at the working temperature, and must be capable of maintaining gas-tight joints. In addition to these qualities, it should have good adhesive and plastic properties. Generally, the more nearly alike are the brick and the cement, with respect to both their chemical and physical properties, the more satisfactory will be the result.

American silica bricks contain as much as 98 per cent silica, which is somewhat higher than that found in European samples. Silica brick has a considerably higher thermal conductivity and diffusivity than most other refractory materials, as will be shown later, although this question has been one subject to controversy in the past. It is usual to attribute the greater average coking rate and throughput per oven in American high temperature practice to this property of silica refractories, which are so extensively used in the United States. However, Porter (260) feels that this is due more to the low degree of distortion and thermal expansion of this material, which allows the ovens to be operated at a higher temperature, than to the higher rate at which it transmits heat. As far as low temperature carbonization is concerned, it will be presently seen that the high diffusivity of silica brick gives it a great advantage over most other refractories and its comparatively great strength gives an additional advantage in permitting the use of thinner walls. These advantages, however, are in part offset by the tendency of this material to spall when subjected to frequent temperature changes, especially those at low temperatures.

Cole (259) points out that, when steam is introduced into vertical retorts, erosion occurs in both fireclay and quartzite or siliceous retorts, but not in those constructed of silica material. The action is similar to spalling, which is generally considered to be the cause of the failure, although some authorities attribute it to a chemical reaction.

In addition to their use in the retort proper, refractories play an important part in thermally insulating the retort setting to prevent heat losses. The heating gas, consumed in carbonization, is conserved in proportion as the losses by radiation and convection are reduced. Aside from the increased thermal efficiency gained thereby, working conditions are made more comfortable for the men employed in operating the plant. Brick of a porous non-conducting nature, or diatomaceous earth, either in the form of bricks or powder, are usually employed for purposes for insulation. The use of refractories is also extensive in the construction of regenerators, combustion chambers, and other elements of the heating system, but this subject will be treated later under the discussion of heating of retorts.

Refractory Retorts. Chief among the characteristics of refractories, which are used in the construction of ovens, should be immunity to injury from sudden fluctuations in temperature and freedom from volumetric changes. For general construction purposes, grog bricks, composed of a mixture of fireclay and grog, or silica bricks of moderate porosity and high refractoriness, which have been well burnt to prevent excessive expansion when in use, are perhaps the most suitable. Siliceous refractories have an advantage over fire-clay material for combustion chamber construction, in that higher temperatures can be used. With bricks of this type, temperatures of 1350°C. can be worked continuously. With few exceptions, fire-bricks will show signs of squatting at 1325°C. and siliceous bricks at 1400°C., when loaded to 50 pounds per square inch. In actual prac-tice, however, the load on the refractory will seldom exceed 30 pounds per square inch. Silica bricks can be used continuously at 1450°C., or even higher. As far as internally heated low temperature carbon-ization processes are concerned, these are considerations of great im-

TABLE 116

Physical properties of common refractories

PROPERTY	MATERIAL		
	Fireclay	Siliceous	Silica
Refractoriness (no load)............	1650°–1670°C.	1650°C.	1670°–1690°C.
Refractoriness (load = 50 pounds per square inch).................	1325°C.	1400°C.	1600°C.
Porosity...........................	18–30%	34–37%	25–35%
True specific gravity...............	2.6–2.7	2.45–2.55	2.33–2.40
Apparent specific gravity...........	1.9–2.1	1.6–1.63	1.6–1.7
Linear expansion (15° to 1000°C.)...	0.5–0.6%	0.7–0.8%	1.0–1.25%

portance, but the temperatures are so low in externally heated retorts that no particular weight need be attached to questions of re-fractoriness, except in certain parts of the combustion chamber which are likely to become excessively heated.

Some of the physical properties of the refractories which are com-monly used in the construction of coke ovens are summarized in Table 116, after Gardner (262). Except in the instance of silica brick, it should be observed that the difference in refractoriness of the various bricks under their own weight and under a load of 50 pounds per square inch is very great, approaching as much as 300°C. Con-sequently, the test of a material for refractoriness, unless it be made under loaded conditions, is of little value when used for purposes of design. The high rigidity of silica is due in part, at least, to the purity of the rock used in its manufacture.

Searle (263) admits that it is controversial whether fireclay or silica materials are to be preferred in the construction of coke ovens. Their relative advantages and disadvantages are numerous. Unless exceedingly well burnt, fireclay refractories contract in use and are liable to crack, while silica refractories, on the contrary, tend to expend and must be very carefully heated during the initial stages of starting up, as well as during any subsequent temperature fluctuations below 600°C. On the other hand, silica materials are less likely to fail from overheating than those of fireclay, because they do not soften until very near the fusion point. In addition, the former are less subject to the corrosive action of salt and ash in the coal. In the past, there has been some question as to whether silica refractories have better thermal properties than those of fireclay. Later, it will be shown that, while at low temperatures there is in reality not a great difference, at higher temperatures the thermal conductivity and diffusivity of silica brick are considerably greater.

Gardner (262) states that aluminous, siliceous, and silica refractories are all capable of withstanding the rapid fluctuations in temperature which are occasioned by the introduction of wet coal into a hot retort. In silica materials, there is a certain range of temperature, whose upper critical point is in the vicinity of 600°C., where there is a great expansion for a relatively small increase in temperature. Below this critical point, which is well within the limits of low temperature carbonization by external heating, silica refractories are liable to suffer severely from spalling. For that reason they are not recommended for use in retorts operated intermittently at temperatures below 600°C. When the temperature is maintained as high as 1000°C., however, sufficient heat is stored in the material to prevent its temperature falling to the critical contraction point when the retort is charged. In any event, the material should be well burnt and its porosity should be such as to give good mechanical strength. Silica brick, which are soft-burnt and which contain a high percentage of quartz and a poorly developed bond, spall less readily than hard-burnt bricks. When used at high temperatures, however, or when accidentally overheated, soft-burnt silica bricks expand greatly and distort the structure. For that reason, it is better to use a well burnt refractory and choose a material less subject to spalling.

Harvey and McGee (264) investigated the problem of abrasion in silica brick. Where the product of only one manufacturer was concerned, they found that the resistance to abrasion was inversely related to the porosity of the sample. However, for silica brick in general, they were able to find no particular connection between any characteristic property of the brick and its resistance to abrasion, but they concluded that it was influenced by any, or all, of the following factors: porosity, degree of burn, quality of ganister used as a raw material, percentage of lime used as a bond, and workmanship.

The action of salt is commonly regarded as one of the causes of trouble with refractories. This is not of importance in low temperature carbonization, when externally heated retorts are used, because the sodium chloride present in coals, often to the extent of 0.5 per cent, does not begin to volatilize until about 800°C. is reached. However, in internally heated processes by the method of partial gasification, as in the Maclaurin process, where the coal passes through an incandescent zone, this may be a matter of consequence.

An explanation of salt erosion, as given by Gardner (262), is that the volatilized sodium chloride mixes with the gas in the retort and is further decomposed, at least partially, into sodium carbonate and hydrochloric acid by reaction with carbon dioxide and water vapor. This reaction has already been discussed in Chapter V, under the subject of rate of ammonia decomposition. These vapors do not attack the surface of the brick, but penetrate the material to some extent and the corrosive vapors are deposited in the pores. The depth at which the reaction takes place depends upon the temperature within the refractory. The sodium carbonate fumes react with the alumina and silica to form sodium aliminum silicate. This compound has a low melting point and tends to convert the refractory to a porous and friable mass, which disintegrates rapidly if the salt action is serious. In turn, the hydrochloric acid reacts with iron in the coal ash to form ferric chloride, which also penetrates the refractory, and decomposes to deposit iron oxide within the pores. The iron oxide tends to increase the fluxing action by combining with the sodium aluminum silicate. In the case of operation at low temperatures, the alkali fumes cause the refractory surfaces to become crazed after several years of working, but this action rarely interferes with the operation of the retort until disintegration begins to occur.

A large amount of finely divided ash is carried over into the combustion chamber from the gas producer which is used to furnish gas for heating the retort. This hot ash exhibits a high affinity for refractories which contain more than a small percentage of alumina. At high temperature, this causes rapid slagging, especially if the material is one of a porous nature. As far as the retort itself is concerned, this slagging action of molten ash is not of great importance in low temperature plants, because the temperatures are kept at a minimum. In certain parts of the combustion chamber, however, the refractories are exposed to injury from this source. This is also true, in particular, for those low temperature processes in which heating by partial gasification is adopted, for here the fine particles of hot ash come in direct contact with the brick lining of the carbonization shaft. The extent to which ash slagging of the refractory takes place depends greatly upon the nature and composition of the material. In this respect, silica bricks seem to stand up better than other types of refractories. Apparently, the absence of alumina, iron, and alkalies in this material, together with the large size of the silica grains, renders the attack of the ash much less severe.

Quite a lot has been published on the disintegrating effect of carbon monoxide on brick containing iron oxide. This is of particular importance in low temperature processes involving partial gasification. Booze (265) has pointed out two obvious solutions of this problem: first, the use of brick free from iron oxide and, second, the use of refractory which has been sufficiently hard-burnt to effect the union of iron with the slag to form silicate. It has been demonstrated, in the latter case, that disintegration does not take place, due either to the fact that the bricks are structurally stronger and able to withstand the disintegrating action or to the fact that iron in the form of a silicate is no longer able to function as a catalyst for the action of the carbon monoxide. While it has been objected that refractories, which are burnt sufficiently to effect formation of iron silicate, are so brittle that they spall readily, it has also been maintained that this is not necessarily the case and, even if they do spall, the injury is not so serious as the disintegrating effect of carbon monoxide.

Aside from aluminous, siliceous, and silica materials, there are many other refractories which are available for retort and setting construction, but their cost or other peculiarities usually eliminate them from consideration. Carborundum bricks or shapes have many special advantages, particularly in the form of high thermal diffusivity and mechanical strength, but their initial cost is many times above that of fireclay products. Magnesite bricks, although highly desirable from the standpoint of their thermal properties, have not been satisfactory in coke ovens because of their tendency to spall. The practical question of cost is also a deterrent to the use of refractories made of this and such other materials as chromite and zircon.

It is not good practice to use a single refractory throughout in setting construction, or even in the retort itself. By a prudent selection of materials, the contraction of one can be matched against the expansion of another, which, with proper arrangement of expansion joints, will prevent thermal distortion of the structure. It is best to segregate various sections of the structure and consider the requirements for the refractory in each location with respect to temperature, load, heat transfer, expansion and contraction, abrasion, spalling, and salt and ash erosion.

Leakage in refractory retorts is far more serious in low temperature than in high temperature carbonization practice for two reasons: first, because the temperature control is more important in the former and high calorific gas, permeating into the combustion chamber, will render proper temperature regulation impossible, and, second, because of the relatively small gas yield in primary distillation, escaping gas represents a far greater percentage loss. The size of the pores greatly affects the permeability of gas through refractories. There is a double advantage, therefore, in selecting material with fine pores, for not only does such a refractory have the minimum gas leakage, but also the maximum structural strength.

Properties of Refractories. Data on the thermal conductivity of refractories and, therefore, on their thermal diffusivity are very scarce and, such as are available, are in great disagreement among the authorities. Wologdine (266) made some measurements which are often quoted, but they were not for a range of specific temperatures and were made on under-burnt refractories. For these reasons, they are open to such criticism that they will not be repeated here. Not only with regard to the absolute values of thermal conductivity is there great uncertainty, but much confusion also exists as to the relative heat conductivity of fireclay, of siliceous, and of silica refractories. Summarizing the situation, Gardner (262) concluded that, at moderate temperatures, there was probably very little difference between any of them, but, at high temperatures, silica was undoubtedly superior to either fireclay or siliceous bricks. He attributes the high thermal conductivity of silica to a property of the material itself, though probably assisted by radiant heat transmission through the relatively numerous and large pores of that material.

The measurements by Dudley (267), as well as those by Dougill, Hodsman, and Cobb (268), apparently sustain the view taken by Gardner (262) that the thermal conductivity of silica is greater at high temperatures than that of other common refractories. In C. G. S. units, Dudley reported the following conductivities at 100°C.: fireclay 0.0016, quartzite 0.0020, and silica 0.0022; which increased at 1000°C. to: fireclay 0.0034, quartzite 0.0034, and silica 0.0043. He also gave the mean thermal conductivity of magnesite, between 445°C. and 830°C., as 0.013. Analysis of the fireclay showed it to contain 52.9 per cent silica and 42.7 per cent alumina. The quartzite brick analyzed 73.9 per cent silica and 22.9 per cent alumina. Formerly, this brick was frequently used in by-product oven construction. The silica brick, which contained 95.9 per cent silica, is extensively used in by-product oven construction. The magnesite brick was a dead-burnt material, containing 86.5 per cent magnesite and 7.0 per cent ferric oxide.

Hersey and Butzler (269) examined a Georgia fireclay brick and reported a true thermal conductivity of 0.00187 at 370°C. and 0.00263 at 910°C. Dougill, Hodsman, and Cobb (268) measured the mean specific conductivity of a number of materials over the range extending approximately from 350°C. to 1350°C. The average of their results gave 0.0034 for fireclay, 0.0025 for siliceous, 0.0036 for silica, and 0.0124 for magnesite brick. They reported the true thermal conductivity of magnesite to be 0.0194 at 250°C., 0.0138 at 500°C., 0.0107 at 750°C., and 0.0092 at 1000°C., thus showing a decrease in conductivity for this material as the temperature rises. The same authors found the true thermal conductivity for fireclay to be 0.0020 at 250°C., extending linearly to 0.0040 at 1000°C. Dougill, Hodsman, and Cobb quote some data by Heyn and Bauer, which are approximately in agreement with their measurements. These determinations at 500°C. were: 0.0028 for fireclay, 0.0024 for silica, and 0.014 for magnesite; and at 1000°C. they were: 0.0040 for fireclay, 0.0046 for silica, and 0.0085 for magnesite.

The disagreement of the measurements by Dudley (267), by Dougill Hodsman, and Cobb (268), by Heyn and Bauer, and by Hersey and Butzler (269) may not be looked upon as serious, considering the difficult nature of the experiments, but the results of this group of experimenters depart so much from the measurements obtained by Wologdine (266) and by Green, as hereafter described, that all data on the thermal conductivity and duffusivity of refractories at high temperatures must be accepted with caution.

By far the most extensive data on thermal conductivity have been gathered by Green (270) (271) (272) (273). The curves in Fig. 73 have been plotted from his figures, which should be used with care, since they are lower than those quoted above by other authorities. As the thermal conductivity depends greatly upon the texture of the material, a short description of each sample will be given. Sample 1 and Sample 2 were magnesite bricks of very close texture. Sample 1 had an apparent specific gravity of 2.56 and a true specific gravity of 3.38, while those of Sample 2 was 2.63 and 3.29, respectively. Sample 3 and Sample 4 were of fireclay retort material. Sample 3 had a very close texture and evenly graded grog. Its apparent specific gravity was 1.91 and its true specific gravity 2.54. Sample 4 had a very open texture and unevenly graded grog. It contained an abundance of small fissures. The apparent specific gravity was 1.85 and the true specific gravity 2.45. Sample 5 and Sample 6 were of fireclay brick. Sample 5 had a close structure with very few fissures and evenly graded silica grains. Its apparent specific gravity was 2.03 and the true specific gravity 2.46. Sample 6 had a very open texture and poorly adhering unevenly graded grog. Its apparent specific gravity was 1.92 and its true specific gravity 2.46. Sample 7 and Sample 8 were of silica brick. Sample 7 had a uniform close fine-grained texture, but it was quite porous and friable. The apparent specific gravity was 1.51 and the true specific gravity 2.20. Sample 8 had a very open texture with abundant large fissures. Its apparent specific gravity was 1.77 and its true specific gravity 2.31. Sample 9 and Sample 10 were from the same batch of siliceous brick. Sample 10 had seen long use in a coke oven, while Sample 9 was unused. The texture of the unused material was very close.

The thermal diffusivities for the same materials as illustrated in Fig. 73 are shown in Fig. 74, from the measurements by Green (270) (272). The C. G. S. unit used to measure thermal diffusivity is the rise in temperature in one cubic centimeter of material by one calorie in one second through one square centimeter of a layer one centimeter thick by a temperature difference of one degree Centigrade. It will be observed that the relative thermal diffusivities of the various materials have only slight similarity to their relative conductivities.

The silica brick, used by Green (270), was of very poor quality, when judged from the standpoint of American practice. Silica bricks used in the United States contain a larger percentage of silica, are denser, and not nearly so porous. This undoubtedly accounts for the unusually low thermal values given for silica in Fig. 73 and

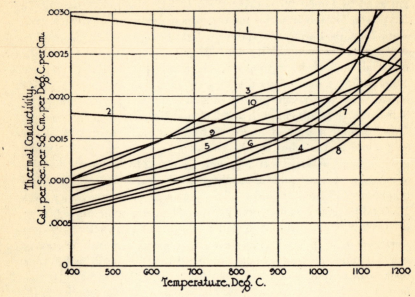

FIG. 73. THERMAL CONDUCTIVITY OF REFRACTORIES AS A FUNCTION OF TEMPERATURE

1 = Magnesite: 87.9 per cent MgO; 24.5 per cent porosity. 2 = Magnesite: 81.8 per cent MgO; 20.0 per cent porosity. 3 = Fireclay retort: 72.5 per cent SiO_2; 24.5 per cent porosity. 4 = Fireclay retort: 67.1 per cent SiO_2; 24.5 per cent porosity. 5 = Fireclay brick: 68.4 per cent SiO_2; 17.3 per cent porosity. 6 = Fireclay brick: 67.5 per cent SiO_2; 24.6 per cent porosity. 7 = Silica: 94.0 per cent SiO_2; 31.3 per cent porosity. 8 = Silica: 95.4 per cent SiO_2; 23.2 per cent porosity. 9 = Siliceous (unused): 81.1 per cent SiO_2; 32.3 per cent porosity. 10 = Siliceous (used): 81.1 per cent SiO_2; 26.5 per cent porosity.

Fig. 74. That the thermal properties of refractories depend greatly upon the temperature at which they were fired has been observed by Wologdine (266) and has been confirmed by others. This is especially true of silica brick, which has a remarkably low thermal conductivity when poorly fired. Green (271) concluded, regarding the relative thermal qualities of fireclay and silica products, that superior well-fired silica bricks are better heat conductors than those of fireclay below 800°C. and that most silica bricks, except those that have been ineffectively fired, are better conductors than fireclay at high temperatures. However, many silica bricks and firebricks have

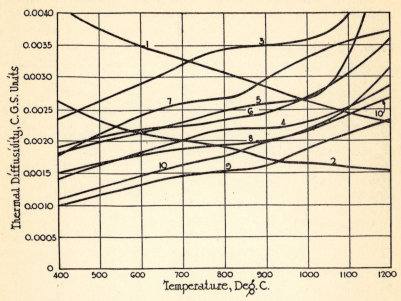

FIG. 74. THERMAL DIFFUSIVITY OF REFRACTORIES AS A FUNCTION
OF TEMPERATURE

1 = Magnesite: 87.9 per cent MgO; 24.5 per cent porosity. 2 = Magnesite: 81.8 per cent MgO; 20.0 per cent porosity. 3 = Fireclay retort: 72.5 per cent SiO_2; 24.5 per cent porosity. 4 = Fireclay retort: 67.1 per cent SiO_2; 24.5 per cent porosity. 5 = Fireclay brick: 68.4 per cent SiO_2; 17.3 per cent porosity. 6 = Fireclay brick: 67.5 per cent SiO_2; 24.6 per cent porosity. 7 = Silica: 94.0 per cent SiO_2; 31.3 per cent porosity. 8 = Silica: 95.4 per cent SiO_2; 23.2 per cent porosity. 9 = Siliceous (unused): 81.1 per cent SiO_2; 32.3 per cent porosity. 10 = Siliceous (used): 81.1 per cent SiO_2; 26.5 per cent porosity.

equal conductivities at low temperatures. Even though magnesite has a high conductivity, its high specific heat and high density reduce its diffusivity and, in fact, make it notably less than that of other materials at high temperatures. The thermal conductivity of used siliceous brick is from 10 per cent higher at 500°C. to 22 per cent higher at 1300°C. than that of the unused material. Although little change was observed in the specific gravity, Green (272) attributes this increase with use to alterations in the texture of the material by changes in its constitution and porosity. The thermal conductivity of most all refractories, except that of magnesite, which is a particularly dense material, rises rapidly above 1000°C., probably because the transmission of heat by radiation across the pores of the material becomes sensibly appreciable, as compared with the heat transmission through the material by pure conduction.

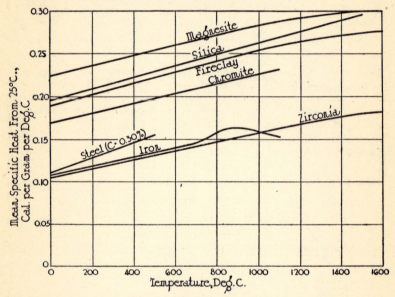

Fig. 75. Mean Specific Heat of Refractory and Ferrous Materials as a Function of Temperature

The mean specific heat of refractories is a function of the temperature, as may be seen in Fig. 75. The curves have been plotted from data determined principally by Wilson, Holdcroft, and Mellor (274), by Bradshaw and Emery (276), and by Dudley (267), supplemented by the data collected by Wilkes (15). It is interesting to note the small difference between the mean specific heats of silica and fireclay refractories. In all of the common refractory materials, the mean specific heat increases practically linearly up to 1000°C., after which there is an apparent falling off. Very few determinations seem to have been published on the specific heat of carborundum, but Wilkes (15) reports a mean specific heat of 0.201 at 100°C. and 0.187 at 1000°C. for this material, which seems to indicate that its heat capacity decreases with the temperature, as contrasted with the increase observed in other materials.

Heretofore, the author has made frequent reference to the spalling of refractories, particularly of silica brick, without any consideration being given to the cause of this phenomenon. According to Searle (263), spalling is the tendency of refractories to flake caused by the appearance of numerous fine cracks when the material is subjected to frequent sudden heating. It naturally results in a reduction of strength of the material and finally is responsible for its complete failure by disintegration. The cause of these cracks is attributed to the sudden transformation of quartz into tridymite or cristobalite, due to its incomplete conversion during burning. This situation is particularly liable to occur when a flame plays directly on the refractory. It can be avoided by carefully heating the material gradually so that the conversion of the quartz to its other allotropic forms may occur slowly. Repeated heating of silica brick to 800°C. at a slow rate will reduce the tendency of the material to spall. Tridymite bricks are well known to spall less than those of quartz or of cristobalite, and this procedure favors the formation of tridymite. The average loss by spalling of a brick is about 30 per cent, but it varies directly with the fineness of the material. Consequently, a coarse-grained brick should be used where it is desirable to reduce spalling to a minimum, unless other properties possessed by such a material make its selection unwise. If properly manufactured, machine-made bricks spall no more than the hand-made ones.

An example of the effect of rate of heating below 700°C. on the spalling of silica brick has been furnished by Ross (276), who found that the specimen invariably spalled when heated at the rate of 270°C. in 20 minutes, 520°C. in 40 minutes, and 690°C. in 60 minutes. When, however, the rate of heating was reduced to 50°C. in 15 minutes, up to 500°C., and 100°C. in 15 minutes, above that temperature, spalling seldom occurred. He concluded, therefore, that the changes in the brick structure which caused spalling took place below 500°C.

The composition of all refractories consists largely of a mass of crystals which may have several allotropic forms, each of which is stable only over a limited range of temperature. A large change in volume usually accompanies the inversion of one allotropic form into another and these changes are sharply defined on the expansion curve for the material. In this respect, silica is the chief constituent of refractories to be reckoned with. The curves in Fig. 76 give the linear thermal expansion of some common refractories, as determined by Norton (277). These data agree with the less precise measurements of Bogitch (278) for magnesite up to 1400°C. and for chromite up to 900°C.

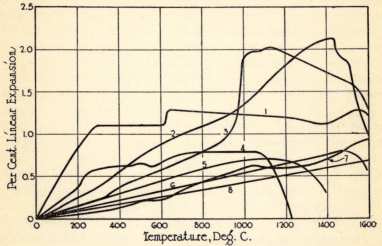

Fig. 76. Linear Expansion of Refractories as a Funtion of Temperature

1 = Silica. 2 = Magnesite. 3 = Chromite. 4 = Diatomaceous. 5 = Fireclay. 6 = Kaolin. 7 = Zirconia. 8 = Carborundum.

The silica sample was cut from an ordinary commercial brick, containing about 97 per cent silica. Its thermal expansion rose rapidly to 1.09 per cent at 260°C., at which volume it remained constant until 620°C. was reached. The length of the sample then suddenly increased to 1.29 per cent. Since only about 5 per cent tridymite was present, there is no indication of inversion of that allotropic form of silica at 110°C. At 260°C., the conversion of α-cristobalite to β-cristobalite, together present to the extent of about 70 per cent, is clearly defined. Quartz was present in an amount approaching 25 per cent and its inversion, at 610°C., is very sharp. Beyond 620°C., the brick contracted uniformly to about 1400°C. and then expanded rapidly to a maximum at 1525°C., due to the conversion of quartz to cristobalite. At about 1525°C., the brick again began to shrink and started to soften at 1700°C.

The composite curve for kaolin is plotted from three samples fired at different temperatures, ranging from 1430°C. to 1620°C., and represents approximately the characteristic of a sample burnt at 1500°C. The expansion of a kaolin brick, fired at 1430°C., is about 21 per cent above the composite curve and that for a sample fired at 1620°C. is approximately 21 per cent less than the composite curve. Kaolin brick expands more or less uniformly up to about 1400°C., beyond which a permanent shrinkage takes place. In general, it may be said that permanent contraction begins to appear just below the temperature at which the brick was burnt. There are slight irregularities in the expansion curve for kaolin, not shown in the composite curve, but these are unimportant and occur principally from inversions of small amounts of silica present as a bond or as an impurity.

The composite curve for fireclay is constructed from four samples of brick from Missouri, Pennsylvania, Colorado, and Maryland. The specimen from Missouri contained 53.1 per cent silica, that from Pennsylvania 54.2 per cent, that from Colorado 62.6 per cent, and that from Maryland 62.3 per cent. Each individual sample departed more or less from the composite curve to the extent of perhaps 20 per cent, at points, due to silica inversions. On the whole, however, the increase in linear expansion for fireclay can be considered approximately uniform up to about 1000°C., beyond which there was a contraction in every case, except that of the Pennsylvania sample, which began to increase rapidly in length at 1250°C., finally reaching 4.8 per cent expansion at 1600°C. The Maryland brick began to contract rapidly at 1000°C. and continued to do so until it fell to a total expansion of only about 0.11 per cent at 1400°C., beyond which it again increased in a manner similar to the specimen from Pennsylvania, reaching finally 2.2 per cent at 1600°C.

The expansion of carborundum was almost linear, was less than that of the other refractories, and showed no sign of contraction up to 1700°C. The zirconia brick contained 27.3 per cent silica, which accounts for the fluctuations in its expansion curve. It will be observed that these variations are closely related to those in the curve for silica brick. The general trend in expansion of the magnesite brick was a uniform increase up to 1440°C., after which an irreversible shrinkage occurred, due probably to inversion of periclase. Except for small irregularities, due no doubt to a small amount of free silica, the chromite brick expanded uniformly to about 900°C., beyond which there was a tremendous change in size up to 1000°C. Thereafter, there was a slow contraction up to 1500°C., after which a rapid contraction developed. The similarity of the diatomaceous earth insulating brick expansion curve with that of silica shows the former to be composed largely of that material. The insulating brick shrank rapidly beyond 1100°C.

Silica bricks expand as much as 20 per cent of their original size when fired and this is accompanied by a reduction in specific gravity from about 2.60 to about 2.30. In fact, the specific gravity furnishes a good indication of the extent to which the brick has been burnt. This expansion is due to a conversion of quartz, whose specific gravity is 2.65, to the allotropic modifications of crystobalite and tridymite with specific gravities of 2.33 and 2.27, respectively. However, since the conversion is never complete, even though the brick be twice burnt, there is always a further permanent expansion which takes place during use and must be allowed for by providing expansion joints or openings at intervals in the brickwork. In practice, approximately 0.25 inches per linear feet is allowed for this purpose.

Norton (279) considers the tendency of a brick to spall as being directly proportional to its coefficient of linear expansion, other things being equal. Since this coefficient varies with the temperature, it is necessary to pick out the temperature at which spalling occurs. This has been determined as between 300°C. and 700°C. In the light of this theory, the curves in Fig. 76 fully account for the observation that silica and chromite spall very easily.

The crushing strength of a refractory depends upon the amount of cementing material which has been fused during burning to bind the particles of the material together. The strength, consequently, is contingent upon the temperature and duration of the burn. When the refractory is subsequently heated intensely, a part of this cementing material fuses and lessens the strength of the brick, so that it deforms easily under load. We have already seen in Table 116 an illustration of the way the squatting temperature is reduced under load. Another example has been reported by Mellor (280), who examined a number of British fireclays. In a number of samples, whose unloaded melting point average 1640°C., with a range extending from 1580°C. to 1690°C., the average melting point under a load of 54 pounds per square inch was 1415°C., with a range of 1380°C. to 1435°C. When the load was increased to 72 pounds per square inch, the average fusion point was 1395°C., with a range of 1350°C. to 1395°C. Mellor has suggested that the relationship between the

TABLE 117

Crushing strength of refractories

	POUNDS PER SQUARE INCH				
MATERIAL	Temperature				
	20°C.	800°C.	1000°C.	1300°C.	1500°C.
Bauxite 1	9,430	5,080	10,150	784	
Bauxite 2	5,660	3,770	9,720	1,350	218
Fireclay 1	2,770	1,775	1,490	10,500	568
Fireclay 2	13,050	7,880	8,160	5,110	923
Fireclay 3	15,750	6,880	10,720	1,634	284
Silica 1	3,410	1,775	2,630	2,270	1,420
Silica 2	2,560	1,277	1,136	852	568
Silica 3	2,415	1,977	1,575	936	618
Carborundum	5,900	6,020	8,310	2,130	995
Chromite	6,390	6,390	6,030	3,050	1,065
Magnesite	6,390	2,910	2,700	2,200	426
Zirconia	5,610	3,910	4,900	1,280	145

bending temperature, T, and the pressure applied may be represented by the formula:

$$T = T_0 \, \epsilon^{-CW} \qquad [29]$$

where T_0 is the bending temperature without load; W is the pressure in pounds per square inch; and C is a numerical constant depending upon the clay, mode of manufacture, *etc.*

There is much discrepancy between the crushing strengths of different samples of the same refractory, tested at various temperatures, as will be observed from Table 117. The data in this table are all taken from the measurements by Bodin (281), except those for the third sample of silica brick, which are by Le Chatelier (282). The variation between respective samples of a given material arise from such factors of manufacture as the kind and quantity of bond used, firing temperature of the kiln, duration of burn, pressure used in molding, etc. Thus Sample 1 of bauxite was fired at 1500°C. and Sample 2 at 1300°C. The figures of Bodin are probably somewhat high for commercial bricks, as they were made on small test specimens. The crushing strength of common refractories decreases with rise in temperature up to about 800°C. Strange as it may seem, Bodin (281) found that thereafter the strength increases rapidly until approximately 1000°C. is reached, due probably to a transition in the structure of the material. Thereafter, the crushing strength falls rapidly with rise in temperature. Magnesite and chromite refractories were exceptional, in that no increase in strength was observed between 800°C. and 1000°C.

Metallic Retorts. In the past, cast-iron retorts were used extensively in gasworks, as we have seen, but they were later supplanted by refractory retorts for a number of reasons. For high or moderate temperature carbonization, the refractory retorts had the advantage of being cheaper, more durable, and more refractory, which is to say, that they were capable of operating without injury at a higher temperature. On the other hand, for such operating temperatures, clay retorts have one serious disadvantage, as compared to those of cast-iron, that is, they do not stand cooling down, invariably contracting and consequently cracking. But neither is cast-iron perfect in this respect, as we shall see later, for it is subject to growth upon repeated heatings. As far as low temperature carbonization is concerned, there are two big advantages to metallic retorts, such that, if other difficulties can be surmounted, they are vastly superior to refractories. As already pointed out, these advantages are principally; first, the highly desirable thermal properties of metals, and, second, the absence of gas leakage. Of somewhat minor importance is the lesser retort breakage and the adaptability of metal retorts to the use of moving parts which may be used to effect the transportation and discharge of the material that is being carbonized.

Case-iron retorts have certain advantages over other types of metallic retorts. In the first place, it is the cheapest metal, second, it is almost as strong as ordinary cast steel, within the temperature range of low temperature carbonization, third, it has excellent corrosion-resisting qualities, and, fourth, it lends itself to cheap quantity production. However, the designer of a cast-iron retort is con-

fronted with a number of difficult problems.   In addition to the usual
expansion, which can be provided for when designing the retort setting,
and the problem of warping, which can be taken care of by strengthening the retort with carefully placed ribbing and proper design of the
setting to prevent local overheating, there is the question of the
growth in cast-iron after repeated heatings, especially when superheated steam is present.

Carpenter (283) has demonstrated, as we shall see later, that cast-
iron growth is greatest in castings of high silicon content and least in
castings of low silicon.   He attributes this to the fact that the silicon
is present in the iron as iron silicide, which reacts with the graphite
present to form oxidizing gases, which in turn attack the iron chemically.   Without the presence of graphite the silicon has no effect.
Carpenter (284) fully recognized that, while there is little difficulty
in getting suitable cast-iron to stand temperatures up to 625°C., it
was another matter, and a very difficult one at that, to get a casting
which would withstand use at 650°C.   He suggested that the use of
chromium as an alloy, in preference to manganese, was good practice
in many such cases.

The Fuel Research Board has had a rather successful experience in
the use of mild steel retorts in their horizontal setting.   Mild steel
does not suffer from growth like cast-iron, but it is easily overheated
to produce softening slightly above 600°C.   Moreover, mild steel
has a low elastic limit, within the temperature range used for primary
distillation, and suffers a creep, after a time, at loads below the elastic
limit.   This creep has been particularly noted in low temperature
rotary retorts, which have been supported on trunnions only at the
ends of the heated cylinder.   In such cases, there has been a creep,
sometimes mistaken for growth similar to cast-iron, of sufficient
magnitude as to cause the retort to become inoperative.   This difficulty has been ingeniously overcome in the K. S. G. retort by supporting the entire load from an inner cooler cylinder, as has been
pointed out already in Chapter VI.

Efforts have been made to discover ferrous and other alloys which
would withstand usage at high temperatures and these investigations
have in part been successful.   There are a number of metals of various
compositions which have the desired properties at elevated temperatures for primary carbonization retorts.   Unfortunately, however,
these alloys are all so expensive, at the present time, as to render
their use entirely prohibitive from a commercial standpoint.

Properties of Cast-Iron. Principal among the properties of cast-iron is its tensile strength and the manner in which this characteristic varies with the temperature. One of the features to be observed in this metal is the fact that the change in tensile strength of cast-iron up to 850°F. is comparatively small. There are some indications of a maximum between 650°F. and 900°F. Above the

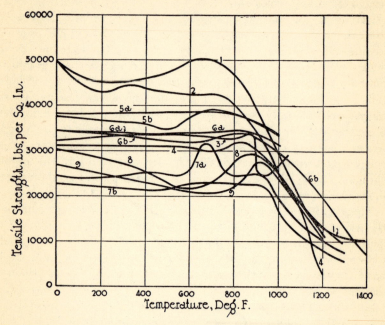

Fig. 77. Tensile Strength of Malleable Iron, Semi-Steel, and Cast-Iron as a Function of Temperature

1 = Malleable iron. 2 = Malleable iron. 3 = Semi-steel. 4 = Semi-steel. 5 = Semi-steel. 6 = Semi-steel. 7 = Cast-iron. 8 = Cast-iron. 9 = Cast-iron. a = Annealed. b = As cast.

latter temperature the metal softens rapidly and the tensile strength accordingly drops sharply.

The curves in Fig. 77 give the tensile strength of cast-irons, as a function of the temperature, for a variety of different alloys from measurements by a number of authorities. Specimen 1, after Schwartz (285), was a malleable cast-iron containing from 2.8 per cent to 3.5 per cent carbon and 1.1 per cent to 2.0 per cent silicon. Specimen 2 was also a malleable cast-iron from another source (286) and of unknown composition. Specimen 3 was a semi-steel of unknown composition (286). Specimen 4 was a semi-steel, as measured by Harper and MacPherran (287). It contained 1.84 per cent silicon, 0.106 per cent sulphur, 0.52 per cent phosphorous, and 0.64 per cent manganese. Specimens 5 to 7, inclusive, are after Campion and Donaldson (288). Specimen 5 was a semi-steel which contained 2.8 per cent total carbon, of which 1.6 per cent to 2.0 per cent was graphite, and 1.1 per cent to 1.4 per cent silicon. Specimen 6, also a semi-steel, contained 3.1 per cent total carbon, of which 2.1 per cent to 2.4 per cent was graphite, and 1.3 per cent to 2.0 per cent silicon. Specimen 7 was a cast-iron which contained 3.0 per cent to 3.3 per cent total carbon, of which 2.7 per cent was graphite, and 1.1 per cent to 2.0 per cent silicon. Specimens 5a, 6a, and 7a, were all annealed, while specimens 5b, 6b, and 7b were all as cast. Specimens 8 and 9 are for cast-irons from the results obtained by Smalley (289). Specimen 8 analyzed 3.3 per cent total carbon, of which 2.8 per cent was graphite, and 2.2 per cent to 2.7 per cent silicon, while Specimen 9 showed 3.7 per cent total carbon, with 3.5 per cent graphite, and 2.9 per cent silicon. From these curves, the difficulty of working cast-iron, or indeed any other metal, continuously over a temperature range from 1000°F. to 1200°F. may easily be appreciated. But we shall see later that the whole trouble does not stop there, in the case of cast-iron, which has the unfortunate habit of growth with time and temperature.

Kennedy and Oswald (290) studied the effects of various percentages of silicon, nickel, and chromium on the strength and other properties of cast-iron. With about 1.40 per cent silicon and no chromium present, the tensile strength reached a maximum increase of 52 per cent, over the base metal, with the addition of 3.88 per cent nickel, 45 per cent of which increase was obtained with 1.23 per cent nickel. With about 1.40 per cent silicon and 0.51 per cent chromium the highest value of 57 per cent increase in tensile strength was obtained with the addition of 1.10 per cent nickel. With higher silicon content, the effect of nickel in increasing the strength of cast-iron was not so noticeable. Silicon apparently destroys the effectiveness of nickel in strengthening iron, unless means are taken to counteract it, as by the addition of chromium. Thus, with the presence of about 2.60 per cent silicon and increasing amounts of nickel and chromium, the maximum increase in tensile strength of about 35 per cent, was obtained with the presence of 0.85 per cent nickel and 0.59 per cent chromium.

The specific gravity (291) of wrought iron varies from 7.80 to 7.90, that of white cast-iron extends from 7.58 to 7.73, while gray cast-iron ranges from 7.03 to 7.13 at ordinary temperatures. The mean specific heat of cast-iron, from 20°C. to 100°C., is 0.1189, according to Schmitz (292), but Honda, as quoted by Hatfield, Wollman, and Priest (15), gives, as the mean specific heat from 0°C. to 100°C., the value of 0.131 to 0.142 for the material as cast and 0.116 to 1.139 when the material was annealed. Nichol (293) made some measurements on the mean specific heat of wrought iron over several short temperature ranges. From 15°C. to 100°C. he found it to be 0.1152; at 500°C. he gave it the value 0.176; and from 1000°C. to 1200°C. he measured the mean specific heat of wrought iron as 0.1989. The mean specific heat of a rather pure sample of iron from 0°C. to various temperatures has been accurately determined by Harker (294). His data have been plotted in Fig. 75, along with the mean specific heats of refractories. It will be observed from the illustration, that the results are not greatly different from those for zirconia brick. Schwartz (285) has calculated the true specific heat of malleable cast-iron and found it to be approximately 0.108 at 0°C.; 0.135 at 250°C.; and 0.180 at 500°C.

Very little information is available on the thermal conductivity of cast-iron. Kaye and Laby (295) give 0.149, as the mean conductivity between 0°C. and 100°C. Some data by Jaeger and Diesselhorst (291) give the thermal conductivity of wrought iron as 0.144 at 18°C. and 0.143 at 100°C., with a decrease of 0.00008 for each degree Centigrade increase in temperature. It can be deduced, however, that the thermal conductivity decreases with temperature, for such is the case of electrical conductivity in metals and the two phenomena are closely related. Without an adequate knowledge of the thermal conductivity at high temperatures, it is impossible to calculate the thermal diffusivity, except for ordinary temperatures. Ingersoll and Zobel (296) report the thermal diffusivity of cast-iron at ordinary temperatures as 0.121 and of wrought iron as 0.173, which data are sufficient to indicate that, in order of magnitude, the thermal conductivity and diffusivity are several hundred fold greater than those found in refractories.

Schwartz (285) has measured the thermal expansion of malleable cast-iron up to 1100°F., as shown in Fig. 80.   This is the same sample of material whose tensile strength was reported as Sample 1 in Fig. 77. His results are in agreement with the measurements of Souder and Hidnert (297), who carried their temperatures up to 1650°F., where vast changes in the structure of the material took place.   The sample tested by them contained 3.08 per cent carbon and 1.68 per cent silicon.   Reference to Fig. 80 shows the expansion and contraction which accompanied the heating of this sample of cast-iron.   The linear growth upon cooling amounted to 0.92 per cent for one heating.

The growth of some cast-irons may be tremendous.   Thus, Rugan and Carpenter (298) observed a volume increase of 63 per cent after 32 heatings to 850°C. in a cast-iron containing 3.38 per cent carbon, 6.14 per cent silicon, 0.30 per cent manganese, and negligible quantities of sulphur and phosphorus.   This was, of course, exceptional, but volume increases of half this amount are not extraordinary. Since the volume changes more rapidly than the weight during growth, the specific gravity of cast-iron decreases with repeated heatings and with it there is a decided change in the physical properties of the material.   Its mechanical strength and thermal characteristics suffer accordingly.   The action can proceed so far that a failure in tensile strength may occur, or even advance to a stage where the casting can be crumpled between the fingers.

Outerbridge (299) (300) conducted the first systematic examination of cast-iron growth.   He observed that white cast-irons do not grow to the same extent as gray cast-irons and established that the breaking up of the carbides through the separation of graphitic carbon was insufficient, of itself, to account for the phenomenon.   Rugan and Carpenter (298), however, were the first to demonstrate that the volumetric changes were accompanied by a gravimetric increase, from which they were able to advance a theory for the action which has been accepted rather generally.   They laid particular stress on the influence of silicon, to which exception has been taken by others. While it cannot be denied that the amount of silicon present is of great import, its influence is apparently of an indirect nature, in that it favors the separation of large graphite flakes which make the alloy ductile and assist the premature appearance of cracks.

The effect of temperature, in accelerating the linear growth of cast-iron, is well illustrated in Fig. 78, which is plotted from measurements by Schwinning and Flössner (301). The sample in question was composed of 3.49 per cent carbon, 2.56 per cent silicon, 0.46 per cent manganese, 0.735 per cent phosphorus, and 0.135 per cent sulphur. The growth began slowly at about 450°C. and was strong at 500°C. Miscroscopic examination revealed that the first period of slow growth up to 18 heatings, of 3-hour duration, was accompanied by a slow change of pearlitic structure into a mixture of pearlite and cementite. No decomposition of the carbide was noted until the second stage of growth, after the 18th heating, where the cementite

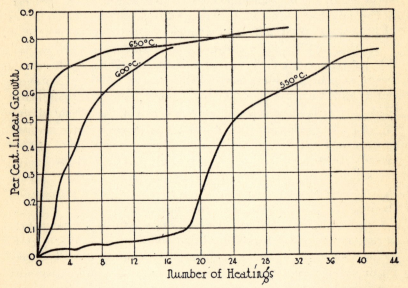

FIG. 78. GROWTH OF CAST-IRON AS A FUNCTION OF TEMPERATURE AND NUMBER OF HEATINGS

was destroyed with the release of graphitic carbon, which set in veins and grew in thickness until all the metal was ferrite. At 650°C. the early stages of growth were entirely eliminated and destruction of the carbide set in at once.

The usefulness of cast-iron in the construction of low temperature retorts, or its appurtenances, has been restricted by the tendency of this material to undergo permanent volume changes, when the castings are repeatedly heated or used continuously in the vicinity of 650°C. or even lower temperatures. This phenomenon depends not only upon the factors of time and temperature, but upon the composition. In general, white cast-irons shrink and gray cast-irons grow, but Rugan and Carpenter (298) observed that white cast-irons, which contain more than 3 per cent carbon, tend to deposit temper carbon upon prolonged heating, which, in turn, contributes to the metal's expansion. They found that white cast-iron, which contained about 3 per cent carbon and negligible amounts of the other constituents, and especially one in which the silicon content did not exceed 0.3 per cent, remained practically constant in volume when heated many times to 900°C.

The effect of the various elements on the growth of cast-iron was studied also by Rugan and Carpenter (298) and later by Carpenter (302). They found that phosphorus tends to reduce growth, to the extent that the presence of 0.3 per cent phophorus lessens the growth about 3 per cent. Manganese retards the rate of growth and in most cases diminishes the absolute amount. The small quantity of sulphur found in commercial cast-iron has only a minor effect and this contributes to the action's retardation. The presence of dissolved gas may cause an expansion of one per cent to 2 per cent when the silicon content is 1.75 per cent to 3.0 per cent, but, with the silicon present exceeding the higher figure, occluded gas has no influence. When the silicon amounts to less than one per cent, dissolved gases may cause a growth to the extent of as much as 10 per cent. Broadly speaking, the percentage volume growth is proportional to the percentage of silicon present, which, according to Carpenter (284) amounts to a 15 per cent volume increase with one per cent silicon, 27 per cent with 2 per cent silicon, and 37 per cent with 3.5 per cent silicon.

Rugan and Carpenter (298), as a result of their investigations, recommended the use of a special semi-steel for high temperature work. Its composition consists of 2.66 per cent total carbon, all of which should be combined, 0.59 per cent silicon, and 1.64 per cent manganese, with 0.01 per cent sulphur and phosphorus. Such a casting showed no growth, but, on the contrary, a slight contraction of 0.13 per cent after 150 heatings to 850°C. This sample had a tensile strength of 50,200 pounds per square inch initially, which increased to 55,300 pounds per square inch after conclusion of the heatings. Analysis showed 2.37 per cent combined carbon and 0.25 per cent temper carbon at the end of the experiment, representing a conversion of only 9.6 per cent.

The mechanism of cast-iron growth is only partially understood. It is generally agreed that the phenomenon is due, in part, to the deposition of carbon, as a result of the breaking down of iron carbide, and, in part, to oxidation of the elements present. While occlusion of gasses in the metal, together with casting stresses, may also be factors contributory to growth, opinions differ widely among the authorities regarding the relative importance of each, and, in fact, even in regard to the sequence of events leading up to expansion. It is generally accepted, however, that the presence of silicon is highly undesirable and that the rate at which the metal deteriorates is roughly proportional to the amount of silicon present.

Carpenter (283) definitely concluded that silicon was chiefly responsible for swelling in the gray cast-irons examined by him, whether the cause of growth be superheated steam above 250°C., hot furnaces gases, hot air, or repeated or prolonged heating at high or low temperatures. According to his view, silicon is present as dissolved iron silicide, but this is absolutely innocuous unless graphite is present, by thermal decomposition of cementite or otherwise, so that the breaking down of iron silicide into silicon and iron oxide permits the penetration of oxidizing gases, which attack the metal chemically. The solution of the problem naturally resides in using an alloy which contains no free carbon and which further does not deposit it upon prolonged or repeated heating. Consequently, Carpenter (283) concluded that no gray cast-iron and only a few white cast-irons were suitable for use under such conditions. The choice of a suitable material thereby leads to a consideration of the many varieties of mild, medium, and hard steels, all of which have no free carbon, do not deposit it upon prolonged or repeated heating, and which are low in silicon content. The presence of manganese retards the deposition of temper carbon and toughens the alloy.

On the other hand, Oberhoffer and Piwowarsky (303), as well as Honegger (304), conclude that the mere presence of silicon does not necessarily cause rapid growth in cast-iron, but that everything depends upon the size and arrangement of the graphite plates. Even if relatively low in silicon, an iron tends to grow rapidly, if, during solidification, it is cooled at such a rate as will cause the production of coarse graphite plates.

Pearson (305) examined the growth of cast-irons of low silicon content, including, among others, two samples made by the hot-mold process. Repeated heating to 900°C., for one-hour periods, showed a constant increase in length at the end of about 40 heatings, the volume increase being about 5.47 per cent, as compared with 16 per cent to 37 per cent observed in ordinary commercial gray cast-irons. The sample in question contained 3.33 per cent carbon and 0.68 per cent silicon. Similar results for hot-molded low silicon cast-iron were obtained by Donaldson (306), except that his tests were carried only up to 550°C. In many instances, where a white cast-iron could be successfully used as a heat-resisting metal, the difficulty of producing the castings without internal strains, liable to cause cracks, is a practical foundry consideration which renders its use impractical. The hot-mold process, however, deserves consideration on this score in that it gives a means, hitherto unavailable, of producing a machinable gray cast-iron from pigs of such low silicon content as would yield a white or mottled iron under ordinary conditions.

Andrew and Hyman (307) made a comprehensive study of the effect of various alloys on cast-iron growth, using a base material containing 3 per cent to 4 per cent carbon, 0.4 per cent to 1.6 per cent silicon, and 0.5 per cent to 1.8 per cent manganese. After 50 heatings to 900°C., the sample containing nickel had increased in length about 9.5 per cent, the sample containing aluminum about 7.0 per cent, and two samples containing chromium about 5.0 per cent and 3.5 per cent, respectively. It appears, therefore that aluminum and nickel have an action similar to silicon in favoring the deposition of temper carbon, which is detrimental to the casting from the standpoint of growth. Kennedy and Oswald (290) investigated the effect of other alloys and confirmed the conclusion of Rugan and Carpenter (298) that high phosphorus has a marked influence in slowing the rate of growth. They also observed that an iron deoxidized with titanium grew much more slowly than one of the same composition with that element absent.

Properties of Steel. The tensile properties of steel depend greatly upon its composition and quite as much upon the treatment which it receives during manufacture. The variations in composition are so infinite and the special treatments by rolling, forging, annealing, and quenching are so numberless that it is quite beyond the scope of this book to undertake a detailed discussion of this subject. It can be said, in general, regarding the tensile strength of carbon steels, that, for temperatures below 850°F., the cast sample has the lowest value, the cast and annealed specimen is somewhat stronger, the rolled sample has even a higher value, and, finally, the rolled and heat-treated specimen has the highest tensile strength of all.   However, above 850°F. and extending to beyond 1400°F., a statistical examination of the determinations by many authorities has convinced the present

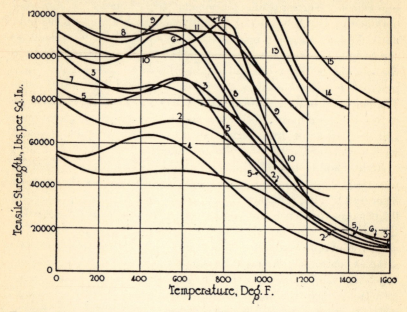

FIG. 79. TENSILE STRENGTH OF CARBON AND ALLOY STEELS AS A FUNCTION OF TEMPERATURE

1 = Cast steel: 0.15 per cent C.   2 = Cast steel: 0.30 per cent C.   3 = Cast steel: 0.55 per cent C.   4 = Rolled steel: 0.15 per cent C.   5 = Rolled steel: 0.35 per cent C.   6 = Rolled steel: 0.60 per cent C.   7 = Nickel steel: 37 per cent Ni.   8 = Cobalt steel: 5 per cent Co.   9 = Chrome-molybdenum steel: 0.41 per cent Mo.; 1 per cent Cr.   10 = Manganese steel: 1 per cent Mn.   11 = Chrome-nickel steel: 7.4 per cent Cr.; 20.8 per cent Ni.   12 = Chrome-molybdenum steel: 0.34 per cent Mo.; 0.86 per cent Cr.   13 = Tungsten steel: 19.3 per cent W; 3.4 per cent Cr.; 0.88 per cent V.   14 = Chrome steel: 13.4 per cent Cr.

author that in this temperature region there is no particular advantage to either heat-treatment or rolling in the average case, as will be observed from Fig. 79.   This statement does not apply to the case of mild steels, with 0.15 per cent and less of carbon, for the results of this study indicate that cast mild steel possibly has a stronger tensile strength between 800°F. and beyond 1400°F. than the rolled variety, so far as conclusions may be drawn with limited data. Neither does the statement apply to high carbon steels, with carbon contents exceeding 0.90 per cent, in which case the difference between the tensile strengths of the rolled and cast samples is quite indistinct over the entire range of temperatures. This generalized conclusion is a statistical statement and hence great departures are found in individual samples.

The data in Fig. 79 are composite curves which represent the average result for carbon steels containing 0.4 per cent to 0.8 per cent manganese, 0.1 per cent to 0.6 per cent silicon, 0.005 per cent to 0.04 per cent phosphorus, and 0.02 per cent to 0.05 per cent sulphur. The ultimate short-time tensile strength, as a function of the temperature, is given for each of three cast steels, of various carbon contents, and also for each of three rolled steels. The measurements for alloy steels are for individual samples. Sample 1 represents a cast steel containing 0.15 per cent carbon. It is plotted principally from the results obtained by Dupuy (308). Sample 2 represents a cast steel containing 0.30 per cent carbon. It is the composite result of measurements by Malcolm (309) and by Dupuy (308), together with another sample of unknown composition (286). Sample 3 represents a cast steel with 0.55 per cent carbon. It is the composite curve from data gathered by Dupuy (308), by Tapsell and Clenshaw (310), and by Malcolm, as he is quoted by French and Tucker (311). Sample 4 is the characteristic curve of a rolled steel containing 0.15 per cent carbon. It is the composite result of measurements by French and Tucker (311) (312), by White and Clark (313), and by Dupuy (308). Sample 5 represents a rolled steel with 0.35 per cent carbon. It is the composite result of determinations by Fahrenwald (314), by Lynch, Mochel, and McVetty (315), by French and Tucker (311) (312), by French (316), by Perrine and Spencer (317), and by Dupuy (308). Sample 3 represents the characteristic of a rolled steel which contains 0.60 per cent carbon. It is plotted from the results obtained by Tapsell and Clenshaw (310), by French and Tucker (311), by Dupuy (308), and by Dickenson (318).

As compared with the cast-irons, semi-steels, and malleable irons illustrated in Fig. 77, it can be said that the maximum allowable tensile stresses above 900°F. of those materials do not differ much from the maximum allowable tensile stresses of the carbon steels illustrated in Fig. 79, considering the tendency of the latter to creep. It has already been pointed out that the main advantage of steel over cast-iron in the construction of low temperature retorts is the absence of growth in the former, but, on the other hand, steel tends to creep under load, at temperatures above 500°F., and this phenomenon generally requires the use of a much lower stress than the ultimate strength of the material would indicate. As a matter of fact, according to Mellanby and Kerr (319), at 1000°F. the creep limit of 0.35 per cent carbon steel is only 20 per cent of its ultimate tensile strength, whereas, with a chrome-nickel alloy steel, the creep limit was approximately 45 per cent of the ultimate strength at that temperature. It can be said, in general, that the higher the temperature, the smaller is the creep limit when computed as a percentage of the tensile strength.

The tensile strength of alloy steels have been pretty well investigated at elevated temperatures, though the measurements have rarely been carried higher than 1100°F. Determinations of the tensile strength of alloy steels have been made by MacPherran (320), who investigated a great variety of alloys, by Bregowsky and Spring (321), by Lynch, Mochel, and McVetty (315), by French and Tucker (312), and by Malcolm and by Welter, as they are quoted by French and Tucker (311). Mockel (322) also examined fifteen samples of high chromium stainless steels. The tensile strength of some of these specimens of ferrous alloys are included in Fig. 79 for purpose of comparison with carbon steels. Samples 7, 10, 11, 12, and 13 are from the measurements of MacPherran (320), Samples 8 and 9, are from the determinations of French and Tucker (312), Sample 14 is the specimen of stainless steel with minimum tensile strength, as examined by Mockel (322), while Sample 15 is a composite curve constructed from ten of Mockel's measurements on stainless steel. Sample 7 contained 37 per cent nickel. Sample 8 contained 5 per cent cobalt. Sample 9 contained 0.41 per cent molybdenum and one per cent chromium. Sample 10 contained one per cent manganese. Sample 11 contained 7.4 per cent chromium and 20.8 per cent. nickel. Sample 12 contained 0.34 per cent molybdenum and 0.86 per cent chromium. Sample 13 contained 19.3 per cent tungsten, 3.4 per cent chromium, and 0.88 per cent vanadium. Sample 14 contained 13.4 per cent chromium.

The properties of alloy steels doubtlessly render them of great value for high temperature use, but their cost is practically prohibitive for the construction of low temperature retorts.   Like carbon steels, alloy steels are also subject to creep.   Malcolm (323) feels perfectly assured that cast chrome-nickel alloy steel will stand

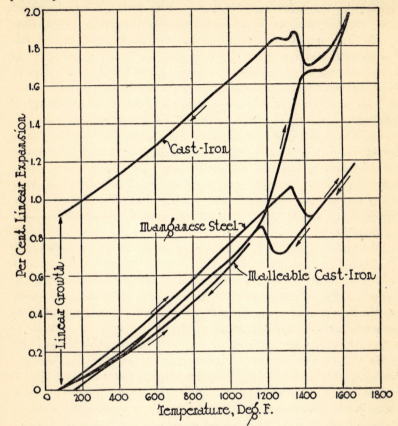

FIG. 80. LINEAR EXPANSION OF FERROUS METALS AS A FUNCTION OF TEMPERATURE

severe service without deformation over long periods, provided the following maximum allowable stresses are not exceeded: 26,000 pounds per square inch at 600°F.; 18,000 pounds per square inch at 850°F.; and 6,000 pounds per square inch at 1100°F.   For ordinary cast carbon steel he recommends the use of only about 60 per cent of these maximum allowable stresses.

The thermal expansion of a manganese steel, containing 0.49 per cent carbon, 1.21 per cent manganese, and 0.12 per cent silicon, as determined by Souder and Hidnert (297), is given in Fig. 80, along with the thermal expansion of cast-iron, which has already been discussed.   As a matter of fact, there is very little difference between the thermal expansion of steels of different composition.   The effect of alloys is noted mostly during contraction, particularly in the temperature region at which the anomalous changes occur and in the permanent shrinkage observed on cooling.   Slightly above 1200°F. nearly all ferrous alloys undergo a slight shrinkage during further increase of temperature over a region extending 50°F. to 200°F. Thereafter, uniform expansion with temperature increase is observed, but the rate of increase in expansion is always greater after, than before, the period of contraction.   Upon cooling the steel, the reverse phenomenon takes place, but usually the sample never completely regains its length and a permanent contraction results.   During the period of anomalous expansion all the physical properties of the material are affected, including its thermal, as well as its elastic, characteristics.

Like cast-iron, very little is known regarding the thermal properties of steel at high temperatures.   The mean specific heat for a sample of steel containing 0.30 per cent carbon, after Fahrenwald (314), is plotted in Fig. 75 up to 500°C.   According to these data, the mean specific heat of steel is slightly higher than that of pure iron and has a somewhat greater rate of increase.   The mean specific heat depends a great deal upon the composition and heat-treatment of the sample, as does the mean thermal conductivity.   Thus, the mean specific heat from 0°C. to 100°C. has been reported (15) as 0.123 to 0.113 for carbon steels, 0.129 to 0.115 for chromium steels, and 0.124 for a nickel steel.   In general, the lower figures apply to quenched samples and the higher figures to annealed samples.   The same source gives the mean thermal conductivity from 0°C. to 100°C. as 0.143 to 0.044 for carbon steels, 0.098 to 0.031 for chromium steels, and 0.060 to 0.039 for chrome-nickel steels.   Some data by Jaeger and Diesselhorst (291) give the thermal conductivity of one per cent carbon steel as 0.108 at 18°C. and 0.107 at 100°C., with a decrease of 0.0001 for every degree Centigrade rise in temperature.   Few measurements likewise have been made on the specific gravity of steels at high temperatures.   At ordinary temperatures, this constant ranges from

7.60 to 7.80. With such meagre data on the thermal properties of steel, it is not surprising to find a dearth of information on its diffusivity. Ingersoll and Zobel (296) give the thermal diffusivity of mild steel as 0.173 and of one per cent carbon steel as 0.121.

Heating of Retorts. The setting for cast-iron retorts should be as simple as possible. No great heat control is needed below 650°C. and the simpler flues give equally as good results as the more expensive constructions. There are but two criteria to be observed; first, that the air is best admitted separately from the burners to avoid highly localized temperatures, as is often obtained with the Bunsen type of burner, and, second, the burners should be placed in such a way that the metal retort will not be touched directly by the heating flame. By observing these details, the flue will be heated by a long lazy flame and the retort will be heated by a combination of radiation from the setting walls and convection from the combusted gases, thus giving the retort a uniform temperature, which tends to minimize warping of the casting. The Fuel Research Board carefully observed these two principles in both their horizontal and vertical ovens and therein lies a large part of the secret of their success with metal retorts.

When intense local heating of flat metallic surfaces occurs repeatedly, buckling or cracking is certain to take place. Fahrenwald (314) attributes this to cumulative plastic deformations of the material, caused by excessive alternating temperature stresses. This phenomenon is quite distinct from bulging or sagging, with which it is often confused. The latter arise from the failure of physical strength at elevated temperatures. The plastic deformations, which result in buckling, are due to thermal expansion stresses which exceed the elastic limit of the material and which arise from non-uniform heating. More failures in metallic retorts may be attributed to unequal temperature distribution than to all other design influences, while the necessary cooling down of the retort periodically is the operating factor which limits its servicable life more than any other cause, aside from overheating.

Except for certain heat losses, which occur in the retort setting, practically all the heat imparted to the coal goes to raise the charge to the desired temperature of carbonization and is later discharged from the retort as sensible heat of the coke, as sensible heat of the volatile products, and as latent heat of the condensible vapors.

While there are periods of endothermic reactions, there are also periods of exothermic reactions, and the two tend to counteract each other. So, from a thermal standpoint, the reactions occurring in low temperature carbonization can, in the aggregate, be considered as slightly exothermic. The major proportion of the heat which is imparted goes to raise the temperature of the charge to a point where the desired transformations are effected and, barring heat losses, it is an irreducible quantity, but the other, or minor part, which raises the temperature of the exit vapors, varies with the efficiency of the retort design.

From the standpoint of thermal economy, the use of an insulating material to prevent heat losses is highly important, for, by reducing the surface losses by radiation and convection as much as possible, the amount of heating gas required to effect carbonization can be reduced accordingly. Cole (259) recommends diatomaceous earth and brick with a porous non-conductive nature as the best materials to be used for this purpose. With a furnace temperature of 1800°F., the heat loss through a wall, consisting of 9 inches of firebrick and 8.5 inches of red brick, is of the order of 520 B.t.u. per square foot per hour, with an outer surface temperature of 370°F., whereas a wall of the same total thickness, consisting of 9 inches of firebrick, 4 inches of red brick, and 4.5 inches of insulation, has a heat loss of about 190 B.t.u. per square foot per hour, with a surface temperature of roughly 190°F.

After the heat has been transmitted by conduction through the retort wall it must be transmitted into the interior of the charge. The problem is a simple one, as far as the first layers of the charge are concerned, but thereafter, when the coal has been converted to porous semi-coke, the problem is of quite a complicated nature. Practically no data are available on the thermal conductivity and diffusivity of coke at the temperature at which the process takes place. Even if these data were at hand, the difficulty of treating the subject of heat conduction in the charge has not been overcome, because the hot vapors rising through the porous coke and through the voids of the coal on each side of the plastic layer carry with them much of the heat to the upper levels of the charge and entirely remove a large proportion as sensible and latent heat of a non-recoverable nature.

The rapidity with which the heat can be transmitted through the the retort wall is not the limiting factor of heat transfer, even in refractory retorts, much less than in metallic retorts, for, in either case, the rate at which heat can be transferred through the walls is considerably greater than it can be transmitted into the charge. Hence, the speed at which heat is passed from the retort wall into the charge determines the rate at which heat can be imparted to the retort wall from the flue. In the very early stages of carbonization, the conductivity of the retort wall may be of importance, but it becomes relatively less and less of a factor as the plastic layer progresses inwardly, leaving an ever increasing envelope of non-conducting semi-coke behind, through which heat passes with the utmost difficulty. If heat be imparted to the retort wall from the flue faster than the charge can transmit it inwardly, the retort wall will rise in temperature gradually until, in the case of metallic retorts, the casting will be seriously injured.

Within the retort, heat transfer takes place principally by conduction which argues for a full retort. However, since the evolved gas must pass out, a certain percentage of voids must be permitted to remain. We have already seen that the passage of hot gases through the voids may be an important source of heating by means of convection and, indeed, this expediency has been adopted entirely in certain internally heated retorts. It follows, therefore, that for maximum rate of heat penetration there should be an optimum size of the coal lump. This has been established by Guegnen, as quoted by Fulweiler (258), as being 2.5 inches when the period of carbonization is 4 hours.

A high velocity of flue gas is desirable, for not only does it increase the rate of heat transfer, but it promotes uniform heating of the setting. The generation of heat occurs, of course, at the point where the heating gas is combusted and this is largely at the entrance of the gas to the flue. A high velocity permits the heat to be carried rapidly away and uniformly distributed over the retort and setting. This is of particular importance, where low temperature gas is being used to heat the retort, because of its high thermal value. As a matter of fact, it is not good practice to use the low temperature gas, even in part, for heating purposes. Lower calorific producer gas should be used instead, as it heats the retort more uniformly, and because the more valuable gas of higher thermal content should be reserved for sale where there is a market for its disposition.

The purpose of checker-brick in regenerators is to absorb as much heat as possible from the flue gases before they are vented to the atmosphere, to store the absorbed heat for a short period of time, and, finally, to yield that heat to a cooler gas entering the combustion chamber.   The transfer of heat from and to the gases in the regenerators takes place principally by convection and conduction, although radiation has been observed to play an unimportant part.   As we shall see later, under the subject of convection heat transfer, a thin film of stationary gas surrounds the checkers, its thickness depending upon the velocity of the gas.   Heat transfer takes place from the moving gas through this film to the surface of the brick by conduction, so that, since the film thickness is a function of the gas velocity, heat transfer in the regenerator depends greatly upon the gas velocity.

For use in the regenerator checkerwork, bricks with a high heat-absorbing capacity are, of course, most desirable.   As many bricks as possible should be used in the regenerator, so far as it is compatible with a large exposed surface.   Because of the continual reversal from hot gas to cold air and *vice versa*, regenerator bricks are subject to spalling, so that particular attention must be paid to this property of the refractory.   In addition to these properties, other characteristics of the material must be considered in selecting refractories for checkerwork in regenerators, such as their crushing strength, and resistance to abrasion and corrosion.   The design of the regenerator usually follows the practice established by long experience and the use of standard shapes and high mechanical strength should largely be considered in its construction.   Heat is transmitted to the surface of the brick mainly by convection and is transferred to the interior by conduction at a rate which depends upon the thermal diffusivity of the material.   Consequently, the rate at which heat is stored or delivered by the regenerator depends upon the thermal conductivity, density, and specific heat of the refractory, while the quantity of heat stored depends primarily on the specific heat capacity and the temperature to which the brick is raised.

Ingersoll and Zobel (296) developed a mathematical expression for the amount of heat absorbed by a brick heated from two sides, where the temperature of the two surfaces is held constant, *viz:*

$$H = \frac{-4\,k\,\theta_0\,p}{h^2\,\pi^2} \left\{ \left(\epsilon^{\frac{-h^2\,\pi^2\,t}{p^2}} - 1 \right) + \frac{1}{9} \left(\epsilon^{\frac{9\,h^2\,\pi^2\,t}{p^2}} - 1 \right) \right.$$

$$\left. + \frac{1}{25} \left(\epsilon^{\frac{-h^2\,\pi^2\,t}{p^2}} - 1 \right) + \ldots\ldots \right\} \qquad [30]$$

where H is the heat flow in gram calories through one square centimeter of surface area in t seconds of time; p is the thickness of the brick in cubic millimeters; $h^2 = \dfrac{k}{c\,\rho}$ is the diffusivity, where k is the thermal conductivity in gram calories per centimeter cube per second per degree Centigrade; ρ is the apparent density; c is the specific heat; and, finally, where $\theta_o = \theta_s - \theta_b$, in which θ_s is the temperature of the brick surface and θ_b is the average initial temperature of the brick. For a period greater than 5 minutes only the first three exponential terms need be considered, but the fractional coefficient must be retained, the summation of the fractional series being 1.232.

This equation holds only for the particular case of parallel walls heated from two sides, which approximates the condition in some regenerators. Hougen and Edwards (324) have shown that, when the bricks are placed as checkers in the regenerator, a shape factor amounting to 0.97 must be introduced into the above equation, when the average temperature of the refractory is 750°C. and when the free cross-sectional area of the regenerator passage is equal to the cross-sectional area of the brick.

Hougen and Edwards (324) calculated the time required for bricks of different thickness and made of different refractory materials to reach 95 per cent thermal saturation. Their results are shown in Table 118. The time required for a brick of given thickness to attain a given proportion of its maximum heat absorption varies as the square of the thickness. From the standpoint of thermal properties, it will be seen from the table, that for checker-brick, magnesia is the most desirable and carborundum next in order, but the former is eliminated by its tendency to spall and the latter, in ordinary commercial practice, by its cost.

According to Brown (325), good high duty firebrick for use in checkerwork should contain less than 70 per cent silica and should not soften below 1680°C., while siliceous brick should contain more than 70 per cent silica and should not soften below 1630°C. Searle (263) states that chemical action and dust erosion are the chief causes of low durability in refractories which are used in regenerators and recuperators and their refractoriness is of relatively minor importance. Although costly, basic bricks are preferable to fireclay and grog materials, because the basic nature of the gases causes rapid chemical action on siliceous bricks. On this point, as well as others, magnesia is again the most desirable material, but is ruled out of consideration because of its cost and spalling tendency. The latter fault is also found with silica brick, although in some cases they may be used in the parts of the regenerator, where the temperature does not fall below the critical spalling temperature. When silica can be so used,

TABLE 118

Heat stored by refractories as a function of thickness and time

REFRACTORY	THICKNESS	GRAM CALORIES STORED PER °C. PER SQUARE CENTIMETER	MINUTES TO REACH 95 PER CENT HEAT ABSORPTION
	inches	*gram calories*	*minutes*
Magnesia....................	2.5	1.59	6.9
	5.0	3.18	27.5
	7.5	4.77	61.9
	10.0	6.36	110.0
Carborundum.....................	2.5	1.16	3.0
	5.0	2.35	12.0
	7.5	3.53	27.0
	10.0	4.70	47.0
Silica..............................	2.5	0.934	14.5
	5.0	1.87	58.0
	7.5	2.81	131.0
	10.0	3.73	233.0
Fireclay...........................	2.5	1.15	21.0
	5.0	2.31	64.0
	7.5	3.45	188.0
	10.0	4.62	336.0
Silocel............................	2.5	0.298	75.0
	5.0	0.578	296.0
	7.5	0.867	671.0
	10.0	1.156	1,190.0

its desirable thermal properties are highly advantageous. Phelps, as quoted by Booze (265), has apparently established beyond question that, contrary to the opinion of many operating men, there is a distinct advantage in using machine-pressed brick for the regenerators. He established that the heat-absorbing capacity of brick had a distinct relation to its specific gravity. The difference in this respect may be as much as 6 per cent in favor of the machine-pressed sample.

Convection and Radiation. Heretofore, we have dealt only with the transmission of heat through the retort wall and through the charge. We have seen that this takes place principally by conduction. It remains now to treat the problem of heat transfer from the heating flue to the retort wall. This is accomplished in two ways, by convection and by radiation, the latter being effected both by gaseous and by solid radiation.

The transfer of heat by convection is a function of gas velocity, size of passage, and temperature difference, but it is almost entirely independent of the gas composition. Reynolds investigated heat transfer by convection as early as 1874, giving special attention to the matter of fluid turbulence above the critical velocity, which marks the transition from streamline or non-vortical flow. Above the critical velocity, turbulence becomes an important factor and, hence, heat transfer becomes a function of the fluid velocity. Reynolds attributed this phenomenon to increased molecular bombardment, but it is at present well established that the increase in heat transfer is due to a thin stationary fluid film, whose thickness varies with the fluid velocity.

When gas flows past a stationary surface there is a frictional drag, which causes the gaseous layers next to the surface to lag, to such an extent that the layer immediately in contact with the surface is at rest and is known as the stationary film. The transfer of heat through this film from the moving gas to the stationary surface takes place by pure conduction and, hence, follows the law established in Equation [28], where the film coefficient, h, replaces the coefficient of thermal conductivity divided by the thickness. The film coefficient depends largely upon the unknown thickness of the film, which is a function of the gas velocity and its physical properties, as we shall see presently.

Reynolds (326) (327) deduced a formula for turbulent flow convection heat transfer of the following form:

$$h = a + b\,\rho\,V = a + \frac{b\,W}{A} \qquad [31]$$

where a and b are constants, ρ is the density, V is the velocity of the fluid, and h is the film coefficient of heat transfer. The equation can also be written in the form which involves the mass flow, W, and the cross-sectional area, A, of the flue passage. Although his theory of molecular bombardment has now been displaced by the theory of a stationary film, Reynolds' equation still finds favor. The constant, a, is small, so that the heat transfer is roughly proportional to the velocity. Stanton (328), in verifying Reynolds' equation experimentally, came to the conclusion that the heat transfer varied as a power of the velocity somewhat less than unity.

Among the mathematical investigations of forced convection, the work of Boussinesq (329) (330) deserves particular consideration, but this work is based upon the premises of streamline flow with inviscid and incompressible fluids. Rayleigh (331) continued the study and demonstrated, from the principle of similitude, that the kinematical viscosity of the fluid must be considered. The fully developed Boussinesq equation for heat transfer by forced convection with turbulence can be written as,

$$\frac{h\,D}{k} = K \left(\frac{D\,V\,\rho}{\mu}\right)^{\alpha} \left(\frac{\mu\,C_p}{k}\right)^{\beta} \qquad [32]$$

where h is the film coefficient in British thermal units per square foot per hour per degree Fahrenheit; D is the inside diameter of the flue; k is the thermal conductivity of the gas in British thermal units per hour per foot cubed per degree Fahrenheit; V is the velocity of the gas in feet per second; ρ is the specific gravity referred to water; μ is the kinematical viscosity in poises; C_p is the specific heat of the gas at constant pressure; and, K, α, and β are constants to be determined experimentally.

Many other equations have been proposed for heat transfer from gases in turbulent motion during forced convection. Those derived by Nusselt (332) (333) and by Rice (334) are particularly noteworthy, but both of them have been shown by Cox (335) to be only special cases of the more general Equation [32] derived by Boussinesq and extended by Rayleigh. Thus, Rice (334) found that $K = 53.5$, $\alpha = \frac{5}{6}$, and $\beta = \frac{1}{3}$; and Nusselt (332) for simplicity placed, $\alpha = \beta$, thus eliminating μ, and found that $\alpha = 0.786$, combining the α-powers of D, k, and C_p, with the constant, K, to give a new constant. According to Royds (336), the Nusselt formula can be put in the form,

$$h = e\,(V\,\rho)^{0.786} = e\left(\frac{W}{A}\right)^{0.786} \qquad [33]$$

where e is a constant and the other symbols are the same as used before. When the film coefficient of heat transfer, h, is expressed in British thermal units per square foot per hour per degree Fahrenheit, then $e = 4.10$ for air, $e = 3.39$ for carbon dioxide, $e = 11.01$ for coal gas, and $e = 7.67$ for superheated steam. Later, Nusselt (333) extended his formula in the following manner,

$$h = \frac{12\ k}{D}\left(\frac{D}{L}\right)^{0.054}\left(\frac{V\ \rho\ D\ C_p}{k}\right)^{0.786} \qquad [34]$$

for the heat transfer from a flowing gas inside of a tube of length, L. It will be recognized that, since $W = V\rho$, there is no essential difference in form between Equation [33] and Equation [34]. Nusselt's formula has its limitations and is not applicable to temperatures much above 1000°F., because of gaseous radiation, nor for velocities below the critical, which, according to Nusselt, is located at about 3.3 feet per second, but which, according to Lent (337), is, in the light of recent investigations, more nearly located at 13 feet to 16 feet per second.

Royds (336) feels that the experiments of Nusselt are confirmatory of Reynolds' Equation [31] and, in fact, it will be noted that Equation [33] differs from the former only in dropping the constant, a, which is small, and in raising the second term to a fractional power, as previously established by Stanton (328). The experiments of Jordan (338) on air in pipes may also be taken as confirmatory of the work of Reynolds. Jordan's data evaluated the constants in Equation [31] as $a = 0.0015$, and b varies from 0.00055 to 0.00090, depending upon the hydraulic radius, that is, upon the ratio of the area of flow to the perimeter of the passage, and upon the temperature of the stationary film. The smaller the value of the hydraulic radius and the greater the film temperature, the greater is the numerical value of b and hence the rate of heat transmission. The constant, a, in Reynolds' equation is supposed to represent the heat transferred by conduction and hence should increase with the temperature difference, but Jordan's data, which shows no increase, is inconclusive on this point.

As far as the present author is aware, while there have been limited investigations on forced convection for gases flowing outside of conduits, they have been confined entirely to transverse flow, and no data whatever are published on forced convection for gases in external longitudinal flow, which is the case found in a coke oven flue.   The research of Carrier (339) is applicable only to air flowing transversely across small wrought iron pipes and does not hold when the gas flows longitudinally to a plane surface or either longitudinally or transversely to a large cylinder.   The experiments of Nusselt (332), as well as of Bell (340) (341), and of Jordan (338), are all applicable only to the case of forced convection of gases inside of pipes.   In the latter case, the measurements have been correlated by Weber, as quoted by Walker, Lewis, and McAdams (342), into the following formula, which holds for pipes with diameters up to 2 inches, gas temperatures up to 2000°F., mass flows up to 20 pounds of gas per second per square foot of free area, and for gases with molecular weights varying from 17, as in the case of illuminating gas, to 44, as in the case of carbon dioxide:

$$h = \frac{0.88 \ W^{0.8} \ T^{0.5} \ S^{0.2} \ C_p}{M^{0.3}} \qquad [35]$$

where h is the film coefficient expressed in British thermal units per hour per square foot per degree Fahrenheit; W is the mass velocity in pounds of gas per second per square foot of free area; T is the absolute arithmetic mean gas temperature in degrees Fahrenheit; S is the surface factor, that is, the heat transfer area in feet divided by the volume of the open gas passage; and M is the average molecular weight of the gas.   The mass velocity is equal to the average linear velocity multiplied by the density of the gas.

According to the laws of radiation established by Stefan and Boltzman (343), the total radiant emission of a solid body is proportional to the fourth power of the absolute temperature.   This is exact for an absolute black body, that is, for a prefect radiator, but is sufficiently accurate for other materials to be used in ordinary calculations.   As it is usually the net heat transferred by radiation that is of interest, the Stefan-Boltzman law becomes for the case of two infinite planes:

$$Q = \frac{C \ A \ t \ \theta \left(\dfrac{T_1}{100}\right)^4 - \left(\dfrac{T_2}{100}\right)^4}{\dfrac{1}{p_1} + \dfrac{1}{p_2} - 1} \qquad [36]$$

where Q is the net heat transferred, A is the area, t is the time, T_1 and T_2 are the absolute temperatures of the hot and cold bodies, respectively, and p_1 and p_2 are the relative emissivities of the respective surfaces referred to the black body. The most probable value of the total radiation constant, C is the mean of the corrected observations of many authorities as reported by Coblentz (344), who gives $C = 1.37 \times 10^{-12}$ gram calories per second per square centimeter per degree Centigrade raised to the fourth power. In practice the receiving and emitting radiant surfaces are always peculiarly related, in regard to their shape and relative positions, so that it is necessary to introduce a proportionality shape factor, θ, to provide the necessary correction from the special case of infinite parallel planes.

In most every case for metals, the total relative emissivity increases slightly with rise in temperature up to about 1500°C., after which the increase is rapid. The manner in which the relative emissivities of oxidized cast-iron and steel vary with the temperature is illustrated in Table 119, from the measurements of Randolph and Overholzer

TABLE 119

Variation of total relative emissivities with temperature

MATERIAL	TEMPERATURE		
	200°C.	400°C.	600°C.
Oxidized cast-iron....................	0.643	0.710	0.777
Oxidized steel........................	0.790	0.788	0.787

(345). The relative emissivity of a body is the measure of its radiant energy absorbing power and represents the percentage of the incident radiation which enters the body and is manifest as heat, the remaining energy which impinges being reflected into surrounding space by opaque bodies and being transmitted by translucent bodies. A good radiator is also a good absorber. Although the radiating power of a body varies with the wavelength of the radiation, as established by Kirschoff (346), an average value for the emissivity can be used in engineering calculations with sufficient accuracy to make consideration of the spectral selectivity unnecessary. There is hardly any published data on the emissivity of refractory surfaces at high temperatures, but Green (347) has reported an average value of 0.72 for a firebrick surface heated from 200°C. to 500°C.

Flames are luminous or non-luminous, the luminosity depending upon the amount of solid material held in suspension and heated to incandescence.   Helmholtz in 1890 was the first to investigate radiation from flames and to observe that the radiation from luminous flames was more extensive than that from non-luminous flames. His student, Julius, found that the radiation from combustion products could be attributed almost entirely to carbon dioxide and water vapor and he established that the radiation was highly selective, occurring in sharp bands.   Callendar (348) continued the investigation and found that non-luminous flames radiate about 10 per cent of their heat of combustion, as compared to as much as twice that for luminous flames.   The radiation from each individual incandescent particle in a luminous flame undoubtedly follows the Stefan-Boltzman law and hence the radiation varies as the fourth power of the absolute temperature.   Consequently, as gaseous radiation varies with temperature at a power somewhat less than the fourth, it follows that the more incandescent particles there are suspended in the flame, and, hence, the greater its luminosity, the more nearly it approaches the true Stefan-Boltzman relation.   Haslam and Boyer (349) have conducted experiments which lead them to conclude that the radiation from luminous flames of methane, ethylene, and acetylene is 25 per cent to 30 per cent of the combustion heat and that this radiation is perhaps four fold that from a non-luminous flame.

As distinguished from convection heat transfer, gaseous radiation is a function primarily of temperature, the gas composition, and the shape of the flue.   It is independent of gas velocity, except in so far as the presence of fresh gas maintains the temperature.   From a consideration of the intimate nature of radiation, it can be demonstrated theoretically and verified by experiment that a body is capable of absorbing its own radiations.   Consequently, it is only from near the surface of a flame that radiation is emitted, since radiation from the interior is absorbed by the surrounding gas and does not penetrate great depths of the flame.   However, the greater the mass of the gas, the more easily it can preserve its radiating temperature.

Not all gases have ability to absorb radiation easily and it so happens that the products dealt with in combustion are particularly endowed with this ability, both carbon monoxide and dioxide, as as well as water vapor and hydrocarbons, all being unusually efficient radiators, while oxygen and nitrogen lack the property almost entirely.   Consequently, the radiating efficiency of a given gas mixture falls off as its content of oxygen and nitrogen increases, due to reduction in the concentration of the active gases. The luminosity of the flame, of itself, has nothing whatever to do with its power to radiate but the luminosity of a flame due to suspended particles greatly increases the heat radiated. This, however, is solid radiation, as distinguished from gaseous radiation, an entirely distinct phenomenon. According to its content of suspended particles, such as soot, slag, *etc.*, a flame can pass through all the stages from pure gaseous to solid radiation. Indeed, Lent and Thomas, as quoted by Schack (350), noted that the addition of a little benzol to blast furnace gas, to render it strongly illuminating by particles of

TABLE 120

Gaseous radiation from carbon dioxide and water vapor

GASEOUS LAYER	KILOGRAM CALORIES PER SQUARE METER PER HOUR				
	Temperature				
	600°C.	800°C.	1000°C.	1200°C.	1400°C.
6 per cent water vapor:					
20-in. layer....................	2,000	3,500	6,000	8,500	12,000
60-in. layer....................	3,000	6,000	10,000	16,000	22,500
15 per cent carbon dioxide:					
20-in. layer....................	2,500	4,500	7,500	12,000	17,000
60-in. layer....................	2,700	5,500	10,000	15,000	22,500

soot without increasing its temperature, increased its radiation four fold.

Until the thickness becomes sufficient, the gas radiates energy at a power of the temperature somewhat below the fourth. Table 120, after Schack (350), gives the radiation from water vapor and carbon dioxide as a function of temperature and thickness. The radiating and absorption power of a gas is highly selective for energy of particular wavelengths and is confined entirely to the regions indicated in its absorption spectra. Thus, the radiation and absorption of energy by gases takes place in spectral bands, and the capacity for radiation in each band may be decidedly different. Carbon dioxide radiates from three bands and available measurements indicate that a 12.5 per cent concentration of that gas radiates from the second band, in wavelengths from 4.1 microns to 4.5 microns, practically as a black body when the thickness is only about 3.2 inches, whereas the gaseous layer must be a score or more times that thickness before the radiation from the first band, with wavelengths of 2.6 microns to 2.8 microns, approaches black body conditions. It will be readily appreciated that the effect of gaseous radiation from the carbon dioxide second band may be appreciable even in thin layers. The thickness required of the gas to approach black body conditions in the third band, extending from 13.0 microns to 17.0 microns, is intermediate of the other two. Radiation from water vapor also takes place in three bands of wavelengths, the first extending from 2.6 microns to 2.9 microns, the second from 5.6 microns to 7.6 microns, and the third from 12.0 microns to 25.0 microns.

Haslam, Lovell, and Hunneman (351) investigated the radiation from non-luminous flames and found that it amounted to 14.9 per cent of the total heat of combustion for methane, 13.8 per cent for illuminating gas, and 10.4 per cent for carbon dioxide, when they were burned with the theoretical amount of air, the radiation decreasing with excess air, as established by Helmholtz and by Callendar. They also confirmed the results of Helmholtz that the radiation from a given thickness of flame decreases with the preheat temperature of the primary air. For small thicknesses, of less than 30 cm., the radiation varies almost linearly with the flame thickness in non-luminous flames, but beyond a thickness of 100 cm. it becomes practically constant.

Lent and Thomas (337) measured the heat radiated from a cylindrical gas column 48 in. in diameter, containing 21 per cent carbon dioxide and 2.4 per cent water vapor. They found 2,500 kilogram calories per square meter of flame area per hour radiated at 300°C.; 6,000 kilogram calories per square meter at 500°C.; and 18,000 kilogram calories per square meter at 800°C. A method of calculating heat transfer by gaseous radiation has been proposed by Schack (352) and has been applied by Broido (353) and by Wohlenberg and Lindseth (354) to the problem of heat transfer in boiler furnaces. For a more detailed discussion of the method, reference should be made to the original articles quoted.

An exact calculation of gaseous radiation can be carried out from Planck's law, and Hottel (355) (356) has used this method to compute charts by which the radiation from carbon dioxide and water vapor can be determined easily for flues of various types, for which he has computed the necessary shape factors. His calculations show that, for a heat absorbing body, whose surface is maintained at 800°F. the heat transfer by gaseous radiation is of the same order as that transferred by convection in a 6 inch square flue with an average gas temperature of 1358°F. and with the gas containing 20 per cent carbon dioxide. Since these are temperatures somewhat similar to those obtaining in low temperature carbonization practice, it appears that gaseous radiation plays an important part in heat transfer. It is the order of 965 B.t.u. per square foot per hour.

Goebel, as quoted by Schack, (350), observed that, due to the different radiating power of the gases, the coefficient of heat transfer between regenerative checkerwork and flue gas was higher than between air and the checkerwork during reversal. In designing a heating flue, it is necessary to consider the transfer of heat by both radiation and convection, so that the maximum benefit can be gained from the predominating influence at the zone in question. Thus, at points where the temperature of the gases is extremely high, the gas velocity may be retarded, as radiation is independent of that variable, but where convection heat transfer is dominating, the passages should be narrow and a high gas velocity maintained. The present author is of the opinion that in low temperature carbonization, where the flue temperatures may reach 760°C. heat transfer by gaseous radiation may amount to from 10 per cent to 20 per cent of the total heat transferred, depending upon the design of the particular setting.

CHAPTER VIII

ECONOMICS AND CONCLUSION

Yields. There are such variations between individual processes and particularly between individual coals that it is difficult to make generalized statements on yields from low temperature carbonization. It is well to remember that no processing can increase the heat yield per ton of coal. Aside from a slightly better heat balance in the low temperature process, it must be remembered that individual processes differ only in the distribution of heat units between gas, tar, and coke. Low temperature processes obtain more tar at the expense of less gas than the high temperature processes. Likewise, the lower temperature of the former yields less ammonia and, through absence of cracking, a higher thermal value gas which naturally yields much light oil upon scrubbing.

To present some general idea of the economics of operating a low temperature carbonization plant, assuming the use of a medium grade high volatile bituminous coal as the raw fuel, some representative yields of various types of plants may be set down as a basis of comparison. For convenience of study, we may classify low temperature carbonization processes into three types as follows: Type 1, the average externally heated low temperature retort; Type 2, the average internally heated low temperature retort; and Type 3, the average low temperature process combined with complete gasification of the coke. Type 4, as hereafter given for comparison, represents average high temperature practice. The yields per net ton, given in Table 121, are based upon the various processes that have been proposed.

The data in Table 121, for low temperature processes, have been tabulated from the results reported by about fifteen full-scale plants, as collected by the author, and as gathered by Sinnatt (357). The yields from high temperature operation are those reported by Tryon and Bennit (358) as the average results from by-product coke oven operation in the United States. The reasonability of the results given in Table 121 have been checked by the heat balance given hereafter in Table 122. The fact that the data for Type 1, externally

314

heated process, as given in Table 121, are not the same as those reported in Table 12 of Chapter I is not conflicting, for the former is an average result, while the latter is an individual case. This apparent difference illustrates what departures specific processes may make from the average yield. In this classification, it is assumed that the Type 2 plant obtains its heating medium by the introduction of air at the bottom of the retort to partially gasify enough of the fuel to

TABLE 121

Average yields from various types of carbonization processes

PRODUCT	YIELD PER NET TON COAL			
	Type 1	Type 2	Type 3	Type 4
Pounds coke.................................	1,450	1,050	0	1,515
Cubic feet total gas	4,200	34,100	112,000	11,100
Cubic feet surplus gas................	2,400	34,100	112,000	6,300
B.t.u. per cubic foot................	835	240	175	530
Gallons light oil from gas............	2.4	0	0	2.8
Gallons crude tar.....................	25.1	24.6	30.0	8.3
Pounds ammonium sulphate..........	12.0	37.0	55.0	21.7

TABLE 122

Average heat balance for carbonization processes

PRODUCT	TYPE 1	TYPE 2	TYPE 3	TYPE 4
	per cent	per cent	per cent	per cent
Coke....................................	71.67	51.70		71.40
Gas.....................................	7.71	31.47	75.40	12.84
Light oil...............................	1.36			1.47
Tar.....................................	13.48	13.36	16.28	4.53
Carbonization loss...................	5.78	3.47	8.32	9.76
Heat in coal......................	100.00	100.00	100.00	100.00

distill the charge by the sensible heat of the producer gas thus generated, so that the 34,100 cubic feet of gas produced consist of a mixture of about 4,200 cubic feet of low temperature coal gas and about 29,900 cubic feet of producer gas. It is further assumed, that in the Type 3 plant the low temperature and producer gas are mixed in the proportion of 4,200 cubic feet of the former to 107,800 cubic feet of the latter.

On the assumption of a 13,000 B.t.u. per pound raw coal, the average calorific value of the semi-coke, in the case of Type 1, is about 12,850 B.t.u. per pound, while the solid residuum in Type 2 has a higher ash content, due to partial gasification, and, hence, a lower calorific value of about 12,350 B.t.u. per pound. These figures check with the results of a number of full-scale experiments. The average calorific value of low temperature tar ranges from 15,000 B.t.u. to 16,500 B.t.u. per pound. From these figures it is possible to construct a heat balance of the various types of carbonization processes, as given in Table 122. There is very little doubt but that Type 2 has the greatest thermal efficiency, compared with the others. This arises from the fact that the heat is generated where it is used, thus increasing the efficiency of heat transfer and reducing radiation losses. The externally heated low temperature process, or Type 1, is next the most efficient, because, in comparison to high temperature processes, the thermal gradient is lower with corresponding reduction in heat losses. Furthermore, less sensible heat is carried away by the solid and volatile products.

Revenue from Operation. From the yields reported in Table 121 and known market prices for the products of Type 4, it is possible to construct a financial account for the other types of processes, which, barring prejudice, will represent a fair financial statement in the average case. But it must be borne in mind always that the average represents only a probable condition and a specific situation bears no relation to the average, whatever, but depends upon local market conditions and upon binding contracts for the delivery of large quantities of certain of the carbonization products. Take, for example, the Type 4 process of Table 121, which represents the average high temperature by-product coke oven. As reported by Tryon and Bennit (358), the average price received in the United States during 1926 for by-product coke was $6.95 per net ton, while the same coke, when sold wholesale for domestic fuel, brought an average price of $7.40 per net ton. The coke breeze, of which the total coke yield amounts to about 6.5 per cent, was disposed of at an average price of $3.50 per net ton. The average price in the United States of by-product coke oven tar was $0.051 per gallon and 93.3 per cent of it was used for fuel in boilers and in open hearth, or other metallurgical furnaces. The average price of coke oven gas was $0.163 per thousand cubic feet, but this average was composed of a wide variation of sale prices. Of the entire by-product oven gas yielded in the United States during 1926, 25.5 per cent was sold for city gas at $0.335 per thousand cubic feet, 8.2 per cent was sold as industrial fuel at $0.163 per thousand cubic feet, 62.5 per cent was sold to steel mills at $0.112 per thousand cubic feet, and the remaining 6.6 per cent was used as boiler fuel at $0.55 per thousand cubic feet. Gentry (359) has also pointed out a specific case of this variation in price for a single by-product coke plant.

On the basis of the average prices quoted above and of the average yields reported in Table 121, the author has estimated in Table 123 the average revenue to be expected in the United States for Type 4 process. Type 4a is based upon the average known sale prices,

TABLE 123

Average revenue from operation of carbonization processes

PRODUCT	REVENUE PER NET TON OF COAL CARBONIZED				
	Type 1	Type 2	Type 3	Type 4a	Type 4b
Coke............................	$5.62	$3.89		$5.16	$5.60
Surplus gas......................	1.30	2.56	$6.16	1.03	2.11
Tar oils.........................	2.18	1.60	1.95	1.06	1.06
Ammonium sulphate.............	.25	.78	1.16	.46	.46
Total receipts.................	$9.35	$8.83	$9.27	$7.71	$9.23
Coal..........................	3.25	3.10	3.10	3.88	3.88
Gross revenue.................	$6.10	$5.73	$6.17	$3.83	$5.35

while Type 4b is based upon the assumption that all the coke was sold at the average known price received for domestic coke and that all the surplus gas was sold at the known average price obtained for wholesale city supply. The average cost of raw gas coal at the ovens in the United States during 1926 was $3.88 per net ton, according to Tryon and Bennit (358). It is possible to use, in low temperature carbonization processes, classes of high grade, high volatile, but yet cheaper coals, which are not suitable for use in high temperature ovens. It is reasonable, therefore, to value the raw coal for a Type 1 process at $3.25 per net ton and that for Type 2 and Type 3 processes, which can satisfactorily use a lower grade of fuel, at $3.10 per net ton. Figured conservatively, on a straight heat content basis from the average price of $0.335 per thousand cubic feet received for coke oven gas sold for city use, the Type 1 process gas is worth $0.540 per thousand cubic feet. On a straight thermal basis, Type 2 gas is worth $0.075 per thousand cubic feet and Type 3 gas should bring $0.055 per thousand cubic feet when calculated from the average price of $0.163 obtained for coke oven gas in the United States. This more conservative evaluation of the lower calorific gas is adopted because of the greater difficulty associated with its disposition. The price of $0.065 per gallon, assigned to low temperature tar, is half a cent higher than that given by Porter (360), is equal to a contract price reported by Runge (361), and is considerably below the value assigned to it by many other authorities. The light oil

TABLE 124

Revenue from full-scale low temperature carbonization processes

PRODUCT	REVENUE PER TON OF COAL CARBONIZED					
	Maclaurin (248)	Coalite (362)	Tozer (363)	Nielsen (251)	K. S. G. (361)	Sutcliffe-Evans (357)
Coke......................	$5.76	$5.37	$1.44	$3.75	$6.58	$4.90
Surplus gas...............	2.64	2.88		5.01	1.47	1.00
Tar oils...................	1.56	1.99	4.56	1.25	1.97	2.25
Ammonium sulphate......	.27	.21	.48	.37		.41
Total receipts...........	$10.23	$10.45	$6.48	$10.38	$10.02	$8.56
Coal....................	7.37	7.50	3.50	4.87	5.00	6.25
Gross revenue...........	$2.86	$2.95	$2.98	$5.51	$5.02	$2.31

Note: These data are not strictly comparable. Consult authorities for details.

has been figured at $0.228, which was the average price obtained for benzol in the United States during 1926. In all cases, the average ammonium sulphate sale price of $0.021 per pound during the same year has been used. The value of Type 2 coke for domestic fuel is deemed equal to that of Type 4b, while, all things being considered, that of Type 1 coke should be sold easily at the slightly enhanced price of $7.75 per net ton. This figure is considerably lower than that given by Runge (361) and that known to the present author for individual sales.

Since the market conditions in Europe are different from those in the United States, and in particular since the operating costs, due largely to cheaper labor, are lower, one may expect a lower gross revenue from a carbonization plant in operation abroad than from one in the United States. The data in Table 124 are largely from full-scale plants existing in Great Britain. The figures for the Maclaurin plant are after Tupholme (248), those for Coalite are by Everard-Davies (362), those for the Tozer process were announced by the management (363), Tupholme (251) reported the data on the Nielsen process, Runge (361) those for the K. S. G. retort, and Sinnatt (357) secured the figures for the Pure Coal Briquet or Sutcliffe-Evans process from the management. The average gross revenue for these six plants is $3.60 per ton, which is somewhat greater than the $2.16 per ton computed by Pope (364), using very conservative yields, slightly greater than $3.14 given by Brooks (365), and considerably less than the $4.32 figured by Runge (366).

Capital and Operating Costs. The capital expenditure required to erect a complete low temperature carbonization plant is difficult to ascertain; first, because there is such a variation between the many processes that have been devised and between the numerous coals treated, second, because there is a wide divergence in the cost of labor and material in various localities, and, third, because little has been made public, or few records kept, of those large-scale plants which have been built. Even if such records were available, these plants were more or less experimental in nature and many expensive alterations, which would not be necessary in another installation, were made. The by-product plant, however, is more or less standard, so that for these items in the capital cost, a fairly accurate estimate can be made. As far as the by-product condensing, the light oil scrubbing, and the ammonium sulphate plants are concerned, a very careful estimate, on a comparative basis, has been made from standard practice. Including everything except land, power plant, and gas-holders, the cost estimates for the various types of plants previously discussed are given in Table 125 on the basis of the investment required per net ton of daily coal throughput. Type 1a refers to an average externally heated low temperature process which involves a large number of static units, while Type 1b refers to an average externally heated low temperature process which involves a large dynamic unit, such as a rotary retort. It is assumed that the plant capacity will be at least 1000 tons of coal per day.

The only point that can really be questioned in Table 125 is the item representing the cost of the various retorts and settings. In justification of these estimates, it may be said that many have been quoted at a higher and many at a lower figure and, in the absence of a more complete knowledge of costs, those estimated in the table are considered as close an approximation as one may expect. As a matter of fact, the present author has record of eleven independent estimates of the total cost of six specific low temerature carbonization plants complete, including by-product equipment, the average of which is $1,495 per ton of daily throughput. This is considered an excellent check on the figures of Table 125, when it is noted that the average of the four types of processes is $1,540 per ton of daily throughput. Four independent estimates of two Type 2 processes, known to the author, averaged $1,265 and compare favorably with $1,290

TABLE 125

Estimated capital cost of low temperature carbonization plants

ITEM	INVESTMENT PER NET TON OF DAILY COAL THROUGHPUT			
	Type 1a	Type 1b	Type 2	Type 3
Retorts, settings, etc..................	$1,200	$750	$825	$900
By-product condensing plant, etc.....	120	120	275	510
Light oil scrubbing plant, etc.........	185	185		
Ammonium sulphate plant, etc.......	85	85	190	730
Total cost........................	$1,590	$1,140	$1,290	$2,140

given in the table. Likewise, three independent estimates of two Type 1a processes, known to the author, averaged $1,635, which is in fair agreement with the figure tabulated. In special cases, it is not doubted that the investment given in Table 125 can be considerably reduced, even to the figure of $800 per ton of daily throughput, quoted by Brooks (365) as being conservative, but hardly to $600, as given by some other writers, unless, of course, radical omissions or departures are made from standard by-product equipment.

Turning attention now to operating expenses and fixed charges, the essential items of cost, as distributed among various accounts, are estimated in Table 126, on the basis of cost per net ton of coal processed, assuming 90 per cent capacity factor for the plant. The supplies include, among other minor items, the sulphuric acid necessary in the manufacture of ammonium sulphate, the steam includes that admitted to the retort and that used in the by-product plant, while the power includes all the requirements for driving the retort mechanism, coal handling devices, conveyors, pumps, *etc.* In justification of these figures, it may be said that the average of five independent estimates and the records of total operating expenses for different low temperature plants, known to the author, was $1.39 per ton of coal treated, with a range extending from $1.58 to $1.20. This is considered in good agreement with the figures given in Table 126. The average cost of labor and supervision combined, as reported in thirteen independent estimates, known to the author, on

TABLE 126

Estimated operating cost and fixed charges of low temperature carbonization plants

ITEM	EXPENSE PER NET TON OF COAL			
	Type 1a	Type 1b	Type 2	Type 3
Labor................................	$0.80	$0.50	$0.40	$0.30
Supervision, clerical, etc..............	0.12	0.12	0.12	0.12
Maintenance, repairs, etc.............	0.45	0.35	0.35	0.30
Supplies, etc.........................	0.10	0.10	0.12	0.25
Power, steam, etc....................	0.18	0.22	0.28	0.85
Total operating expense............	$1.65	$1.29	$1.27	$1.82
Depreciation 10 per cent...........	0.44	0.31	0.35	0.59
Interest 8 per cent.................	0.35	0.25	0.28	0.47
Taxes and insurance 3 per cent.....	0.13	0.09	0.11	0.18
Total operating and fixed charges..	$2.57	$1.94	$2.01	$3.06

six specific processes was $0.61 per ton of coal. Eight estimates of maintainance and repairs on five specific processes averaged $0.36 per ton of coal, while five estimates of power and steam for three specific processes gave a mean figure of $0.22 per ton of coal. Consequently, the figures of Table 126 are taken to agree with the consensus of expert opinion, both individually and as a whole, although they are somewhat higher than the $1.10 per ton given by Brooks (365), and are considerably higher than the $0.94 per ton given by Pope (364) for the total average operating expense in low temperature installations. It should be noted that no charge for heating the retorts or for the raw coal has been made in Table 126, as these expenses have already been charged off of gross receipts in Table 123, the former, by computing the revenue only on surplus gas. It now remains to write off fixed charges, at the rate of 10 per cent for depreciation, 8 per cent for interest on the investment, and 3 per cent for taxes and insurance, to give the total operating and fixed charges per ton of coal treated. Subtraction of the total operating and fixed charges per ton of coal in Table 126 from the gross revenue per ton of coal in Table 123 gives the net revenue available for amortization of the investment, reserve funds, and dividends.

Of all the items making up the cost of processing coal by carbonization at low temperatures, the fixed charges are the greatest, cost of labor is second, and maintenance and repairs are third. This indicates that economical primary carbonization requires, first, that the investment per unit of throughput must be reduced to a minimum, second, that labor requirements must be kept as low as possible, by simplicity of operations and by the installation of labor-saving machinery, and, third, that rugged construction and continuous operation with mass throughput should be encouraged, to gain the benefit of low repair and maintenance charges. Supervision and supplies are practically irreducible quantities.

Economics. So far as the economics of low temperature carbonization are concerned, the production of primary products is the only part of the problem which needs consideration, for upon these, alone, the industry must justify itself. The fractionation of low temperature tar into its many derivatives is another industry, that of tar refining, and it is not anticipated that the economics of primary oil distillation will be greatly different from those already obtaining in the petroleum and tar refining industries, notwithstanding certain plant changes as will be necessary to facilitate treatment of a different crude oil stock.

The sale of low temperature tar and gas is a wholly new problem from that of the disposition of gas and tar from by-product coke ovens or from gas retorts, for they are distinctly different from the analogous products of high temperature distillation. The same may be said of low temperature coke. Nevertheless, there is bound to be a certain amount of indirect competition between them, to the extent that the price fluctuations of the products of the two different methods of coal processing can never be wholly unrelated.

Table 127, illustrating the products of low temperature carboniza-

TABLE 127

Principal products of low temperature carbonization and their uses

Coal			
Hydrocarbon gases	Fuel gas	Domestic / Industrial	
	Alcohols	Ethyl / Isopropyl / Secondary butyl / Secondary amyl / Secondary hexyl	Solvents for lacquers / Automobile paints / Artificial leather, etc.
	Liquefied gases	Metal cutting / Illumination	
	Light oil (benzine)	Motor fuel / Solvents / Dyers and cleaners / Benzine	
Ammoniacal liquor	Sulphate of ammonia	Fertilizer	
Crude oil	Light oil (benzine)	(as above)	
	Carbolic acid / Phenols	Plastics-bakelite, explosives / Dyes, medical compounds	
	Cresols	Disinfectants, antiseptics	
	Creosote oil	Wood preservative	
	Lubricating oil	General purposes	
	Gas oil	Enriching water gas / Cracking to benzine	
	Diesel engine oil	Internal combustion engines	
	Fuel oil	Boiler fuel / Gas manufacture	
	Paraffin wax	General purposes	
	Heavy tar / Pitch	Roofing material / Paving material / Briquets	
Semi-coke	Boiler fuel	Hand fired / Stokers / Pulverized fuel	
	Fuel for producer gas and water gas	Industrial gas / Domestic fuel gas	
	Briquets / Smokeless fuel	Locomotive fuel / Domestic fuel / Marine fuel	

tion and their uses, as slightly modified by the author, was compiled by Ditto (367) and given later by Blauvelt (368). It shows very strikingly a few of the more important derivatives to be obtained from the primary products of coal and the manner in which they are absorbed by industry. It will be readily appreciated that this table resembles in part a similar tabulation of the products and uses of high temperature by-product coking, of gas manufacture, and of petroleum distillation. A few of the products which occur in each of these industries are missing and other products take their place. As a whole, however, the final uses are practically the same, a situation which demonstrates an ultimate relationship in the market fluctuations of high and low temperature carbonization products. The difference in the price levels of the two distinct classes of products must, therefore, be justified by their special values and the price movements of each will reflect, not only the conditions of supply and demand for products of its own class, but also for products of the other class. For this reason, no discussion of the economics of low temperature carbonization can avoid a study of the markets for high temperature products. A very excellent and comprehensive study of the problem of marketing the by-products from coal carbonization has been made by McBride (369).

Practically all of the products of coal carbonization compete industrially with other materials. Thus tar, as a fuel, must compete with both anthracite and bituminous coal, as well as with petroleum, and coke must compete with anthracite both as a domestic fuel and as a fuel for the generation of water gas. Coal gas and water gas compete for their place as domestic and industrial fuels. Light oil is used mostly as a motor fuel, and, as such, its price is determined by the market for petroleum and its refined products. Ammonia, used largely as a fertilizer, has its price determined by the availability and supply of other forms of fixed nitrogen.

Aside from the prices for carbonization products determined by competitive markets, the rulings of public regulatory bodies further complicate the sale of by-products, particularly in the case of gas, which finds its most logical market in the city gas supply. In ordinary industrial enterprises, the margin of profit is determined by competition, but under the system of public utility regulation, the profits are limited by a public authority endowed with the power of establishing rates. Under such a system of regulation, the consumer of one or more of the products must bear the loss of income from other products. Consequently, a situation arises, by virtue of this close relationship, whereby the price of one product can be almost entirely determined by the market conditions for another.

While there are assuredly markets for coke, gas, and oils, they are not, at the present time, markets in which any special advantages of low temperature products are recognized. There is a difference in the quoted prices of foundry and of furnace coke by virtue of their special properties, but there can be no reflection of special value in the price of low temperature coke over coal as a domestic fuel until this special value is generally recognized by the consumers. In the case of low temperature gas, the recognition is not hard to secure, but appreciation of the desirable nature of primary oils will be somewhat more difficult to obtain. It is an illogical proposition to expect an industry to pay the cost of treatment without being entitled to some financial return over the cost of preparing products which are more desirable for particular purposes. As long as the fundamentals of such an industry are sound, the special value of the products will ultimately be reflected in their price.

A good deal has been said at one time or another about the calorific value of semi-coke, relative to the raw coal from which it was made. As this is the characteristic of most importance in determining the value of low temperature coke, it is worthwhile to examine this point. Runge (366) has determined the thermal value of many semi-cokes produced from coals of the United States and elsewhere, as compared with the calorific value of the raw coal before primary distillation. He found, as a general rule, for high volatile low oxygen coals, that the thermal value of the coke was from 700 B.t.u. per pound to 1000 B.t.u. per pound less than that of the coal. With high volatile coals, the thermal values of the coal and coke were about the same, or the latter was slightly higher. This was particularly true of lignite, where, because of the high moisture content it was not unusual to find that the char had an increased calorific value of as much as 2,000 B.t.u. per pound over the raw material.

Another point of view, in assessing the value of a fuel, is the consideration of what is known as form value or heat availability. A consumer will obviously pay more for a heat unit in the form of gas or of oil than in the form of coal or of coke, by reason of the adaptability of these fuels to special purposes, where the heat of coal would not be available. The object of all coal processing is to increase its form value and all processing is accompanied by losses of material, incidental to handling, and of heat units, incidental to the production of power and heat for processing. Consequently, the output of heat units after processing will be materially less than before, but their form or availability will be increased. To be economically sound, the conversion of the heat units from one form to another, must be such as to increase the value of the units sufficiently to make up for the conversion losses, pay the cost of processing, and yield a fair return on the capital investment. Doubtlessly, low temperature carbonization raises the form factor of the fuel and increases the availability of heat.

The value of the carbonization products, other than the solid fuel, as seen from Table 123, represents approximately 40 per cent of the total receipts for Type 1, externally heated processes; about 56 per cent for Type 2, internally heated processes; and 100 per cent for Type 3, complete gasification processes. It is quite obvious from this, that, unless the cost of the raw material be unusually cheap, as in the case of shales and coal refuse, low temperature carbonization can never be commercially successful in externally heated processes for the sake of by-products alone, unless there is a great advance in the market price of these materials, relative to the raw coal. It is absolutely essential to the success of externally heated processes that the semi-coke be adequately disposed of and almost correspondingly essential, in the case of internally heated processes by partial gasification, that the by-products be well marketed. Low grade slack coal is particularly adapted to low temperature carbonization processes. There are many mines in the United States and abroad, which are now closed, but which are capable of producing large quantities of this material. The reopening of such workings to fulfill the demands of a new industry would not only be of mutual benefit, but of a national economic importance.

In considering the economics of carbonization, McBride (370) has pointed out that the counter-effect of fluctuations in the price of one by-product on the value of another by-product, or of a principle product, must not be overlooked. In the gas manufacturing industry, for example, it is well known that the price of gas is roughly the difference between the gross expenditure and the income derived from by-products. Consequently, the lowering of ammonium sulphate as much as one cent a pound may mean a difference of as much as five cents per thousand cubic feet of gas. The gas and coke from any coal carbonization industry have to fluctuate inversely with the price of ammonium sulphate to bear the increased cost of production.

Porter (360) has attempted to summarize the three phases of development that will give a great impetus to the progress of low temperature carbonization. From the viewpoint of producing a smokeless fuel, these possibilities are: (1) to lower the cost of processing below $1.00 per ton; (2) to establish a sufficiently enhanced value for the semi-coke to enable it to bring a price equal to the coal from which it was made; and (3) to discover new uses for the primary tar and gases, such as will enhance their value above the by-product tar and gas of present commerce. Noteworthy advance in any of these fields will firmly establish the economics of low temperature carbonization, but all three phases will likely be solved in some measure of success. It is merely a question of raising the form value of the products and of lowering costs of conversion.

The only economic justification for low temperature carbonization, or any other carbonization system for that matter, is its ability to show a satisfactory yield on the capital invested, through recovery and sale of by-products. In the case of low temperature carbonization integrated with another industry, such as the manufacture of city gas or the generation of electricity, the financial return need be only such as will show a reduction in the cost per unit of the final product, but in the case of manufacture of a solid fuel, to be merchandized to domestic and industrial consumers, the financial return must be such as to carry the additional costs of distribution.

Unlike many European countries, low temperature carbonization cannot be justified in the United States, at the present time, on the grounds of national defense. From a defense standpoint, the only products of importance are the oils and the fixed nitrogen. For oils, the United States is now happily independent of other countries; for explosives, sufficient toluene and picric acid can be recovered in existing gasworks and by-product plants; and for nitrogen products, enough can be recovered from gasworks and coke plants, augmented by synthetic fixed nitrogen, to meet all emergency requirements.

The Coke Market. In order to avoid confusion, Gentry (371) has noted that it is necessary to distinguish between the production of three types of solid fuel: boiler char, smokeless fuel, and anthracite substitute. These three cases are rather clearly defined and the price which the semi-coke can command depends greatly upon which of the three forms of fuel is produced. The manufacture of an artificial anthracite by low temperature carbonization certainly requires the application of pressure at some stage during carbonization. In some processes, we have seen that this takes the form of briquetting, before, after, or between stages of distillation; in others, the necessary compression is obtained by the weight of the superincumbent charge or by intumescence of the coal. A number of attempts have been made to effect the same result by introduction of pistons, or other mechanical devices, within the retort. Although it may be said, that the application of pressure to the semi-coke, either by briquetting or otherwise, increases greatly the cost of processing, the resultant artificial anthracite will command a higher price because of its strength and density. Anthracite substitutes can be sold considerably below the market price for anthracite with a substantial profit, but a smokeless fuel cannot sell much below the raw coal and realize sufficient return on the investment. After all is said and done, in a new industry, where the advantages of a new fuel are not tremendously self-evident, the new fuel cannot command a price greater than that of the established competitive fuel.

Of the several varieties of coke on the market, that is, beehive, by-product, gas coke, and semi-coke, the price and availability of any one has its effect on the price of all the others, even though these classes of coke are not strictly competitive, since they are not always directly interchangeable. The first is used almost wholly for metallurgical purposes, the second is used for the manufacture of water gas and as a domestic fuel, as well as metallurgically, while the third is used almost exclusively for water gas manufacture, domestic fuel, and industrial heating. In no case is gas coke suitable for metallurgical purposes. As may be expected from this state of affairs, metallurgical coke plants often place their surplus coke on the market during slack seasons, thereby bringing about considerable price fluctuation and readjustments in the entire industry by a break in spot prices and a sag in the contract market.

Aside from the manufactured gas industry and the metallurgical coke industry, as sources of coke for domestic fuel, there has come into existence the merchant by-product coke ovens. Since these plants are related to neither of the foregoing industries, their existence is justified by their ability to undertake or arrange for the complicated marketing of their coke and by-products. For them, the favorable support of the local fuel merchants is a very necessary factor for their success.

Practically all by-product coke ovens use the breeze as a fuel, so that approximately 80 per cent of it is used in this way. In both high temperature and low temperature practice, the breeze amounts, on the average, to about 10 per cent of the total coke yield. It makes a fairly satisfactory boiler fuel, generally being combusted on chain-grate stokers, since high temperature breeze is too abrasive to pulverize economically. The friability of semi-coke, however, makes it somewhat more desirable as a pulverized fuel and, while there is great variation from process to process in its abrasiveness, generally, it is no more abrasive and requires no more power to grind than bituminous coal, and, in fact, some experiments report even less. About the only other outlet for coke breeze is to briquet it for a domestic fuel, but the cost of the additional processing, together with the fact that the breeze is always high in ash, makes this procedure undesirable if the product can be directly consumed.

Coke has been offered to the domestic market in sizes corresponding roughly to those familiar in the anthracite trade, that is, egg, stove, nut, pea, and breeze. It must, however, be as carefully sized as anthracite, for, while stove or nut sizes can be used satisfactorily alone, if mixed indiscriminately with the other sizes, the tendency is for the fuel bed to pack, so that a satisfactory fire cannot be maintained. Since these sizes are smaller than the metallurgical sizes, the metallurgical coke industry stands as a potential producer of domestic fuel, but they can never hope to compete seriously with a more satisfactory fuel, such as semi-coke, unless they are willing to undercut the latter considerably in price and are prepared to change their merchandizing policy, to the extent of assuring the domestic fuel market an adequate supply at all times. As McBride (369) points out, there are many who believe the fluctuating demands of the metallurgical industry and the steady market for domestic fuel are too wholly incompatible phenomena and that it is utterly impossible to serve both ends at the same time.

The establishment of coke as a permanent domestic fuel, be it low temperature coke, gas coke, or by-product coke, will require a long educational program to overcome the inertia of the public, which is

loath to change from established practice. The principal induce-
ment to its use is a price differential in its favor, but often its introduction must be accompanied by an assurance of instruction in the
proper method of using it.

Although coke is the best available substitute for anthracite, and
is a potential substitute for bituminous coal, it has incurred great
disfavor as a domestic fuel for two reasons; first, because of the uncertainty of the supply, due to the irregularity with which it is placed
upon the domestic fuel market by the producers and, second, because
of the inferior quality of the product diverted from metallurgical
uses. Thus, much of the coke which has been placed in the domestic
market, while suitable for metallurgical purposes, is wholly unsatis-
factory for household use. Occasionally, cokes containing excessive
sulphur have been dumped on the domestic market by the manu-
facturers to the end that, while the ordinary domestic purchaser is
little concerned with the chemical composition, the odor and corrosive
fumes from such a high sulphur product are very objectionable and
have, in consequence, injured the reputation of coke. For these
reasons, any attempt to introduce low temperature coke extensively
in some localities must be associated with an educational program
which will eliminate the bad reputation that such indiscretions have
aroused.

Much of the difficulty that has been experienced by domestic
consumers with the use of coke has been its incombustibility, a feature which semi-coke does not share with the high temperature by-
product or gas coke. The low temperature coke contains two or
three times more volatile matter than the others and, structurally, it
is of a far more combustible form. In the past, much coke with a
low fusion point ash has been put upon the market, with the result
that the average householder has been annoyed with clinker formation.

Due to its greater bulk, weight for weight, coke requires more
storage space than either anthracite or bituminous coal. Likewise,
a greater furnace volume is necessary for the same frequency of firing.
Some of the difficulties that have arisen from the use of coke may be
attributed to the fact that too large sizes have been used in a furnace
accustomed to anthracite, with the result that the fire burns out
quickly and can be banked only with difficulty on account of the
fuel's greater bulk.

The value of semi-coke, as a domestic fuel, depends entirely upon its physical condition when delivered from the retort. There is no doubt that, for domestic use, the semi-coke will have to be in lumps or in briquets. In this form it possesses all the desirable properties of anthracite, except possibly its density. On the other hand, it will, for the most part, contain less ash than the grades of anthracite now found on the market. Runge (366) feels that, as a competitor of anthracite, semi-coke could be marketed as a household fuel at $1.00 per ton less than the former. Since anthracite sells at $8.50 to $9.00 per ton f.o.b. mines and retails for $13 to $15 a ton within a radius of 100 miles of the mines, allowing $2.00 for delivery charges, the semi-coke should be sold at the plant, located near the center of consumption, at $10 to $12 per ton, from which must be deducted a further $2.00 per ton for merchandizing costs. It is not generally desirable for the carbonization plant to undertake merchandizing its coke, but it is more logical to arrange with local fuel merchants to take care of its distribution to the consumer. From the standpoint of the dealer, this involves new problems, for coke requires greater storage space in his yards, larger delivery trucks, and must be handled with greater care than anthracite, because it is more fragile than coal. These considerations, together with the inherent hesitation of people to enter new fields, makes it necessary to offer the merchant a liberal profit, sometimes as much as $3.00 per ton, to induce him to handle the product. Gas coke is often merchandized directly by the producer, however, first, because of the narrow margin of profit, and, second, because the strength of the product is such that it will not stand the extra handling and haulage of the middle-man.

Porter (360) has noted, in the matter of smoke abatement, that there is a great deal of human psychology involved. Despite the great economic loss to each individual in the form of expenditures for painting, laundry, *etc.*, the consumer, when confronted with additional outlay to secure a smokeless fuel to reduce this atmospheric pollution, hesitates because the returns are intangible. Among the larger consumers, such as the railroads, utilities, and industrial manufacturing establishments, this hesitancy can be overcome by force of public opinion. To those, such as the domestic consumer and small manufacturer, who have to take close account of each outlay, the appeal to use smokeless fuels in place of cheaper competitive fuels is useless.

Legislation to force smoke abatement upon the masses is as undesirable, as enforcement would be impracticable, so that the only rational solution is to provide a fuel that is smokeless at a price equal to or only slightly in advance of the raw fuels now available.

Large quantities of coke are used in competition with anthracite for the generation of water gas. Although minor changes in the operation of the water gas plant are necessary to change from one to another of these fuels and although each has certain individual advantages, the chief consideration, that determines which is used, is solely one of price, as reflected in the cost of manufacture of a unit of gas.

Another outlet for low temperature coke has been under experimentation both in the United States and in Japan. It consists of associating low temperature carbonization with high temperature coke ovens to precarbonize part of the high temperature charge in order to furnish a low volatile material for blending with the remainder of the coal, thereby obtaining the strength and porosity required in the final metallurgical high temperature coke.

The Gas and Light Oil Markets. McBride (369) has pointed out that the low average price for coke oven gas in the United States arises partly from the fact that some of the largest producers in the country are affiliated with blast furnace or steel plants and the gas is carried on the books and reported to the government at a purely nominal value, which in no respect portrays its true worth, for it represents no real sale of the product in the open market. For this reason, great care must be exercised in applying average statistical values to specific cases.

The serious problem in the disposition of gas is two fold; in the first place, it is bulky and the storage cost is great, so that it cannot be stored more than a few hours, at best not more than one day, and, second, the cost of transportation requires a market within the immediate vicinity of the plant or such as can be reached by pipelines or gas mains. In this manner the gas differs from the other products of carbonization, which can be stored for long periods and shipped indefinite distances. The quantity of gas that can be sold at a reasonable profit often determines the size of carbonization plant to be erected and the location of this market often determines the plant location also.

The sale of gas by a carbonization plant to a public utility becomes a matter of negotiation between the parties concerned. Such contracts, however, must usually be approved by the public authority charged with the regulation of public service corporations, so that, in a measure, the price which is received for the gas is determined by an independent group. As a rule, such a supervision offers little trouble, because the carbonization plant can usually offer the by-product gas profitably at a cost slightly below that at which it can be generated as a principal product, with the result that the regulating body will approve the contract as in the best interests of the public. Sometimes, however, even an attractive price for the gas will not induce a coke operator to enter into contract to supply a public utility with gas for any extended period, preferring to sell his gas industrially at a much lower rate. The reason for this is quite apparent, for such a contract may require him to run his ovens at full capacity to meet the gas contract at a time when the market for his coke and other by-products is depressed, an eventuality which might cause him a good deal of embarrassment.

The light oil is commonly refined at the coke plant, motor benzol being the chief product. Most of this refined motor fuel, and some of the crude benzol, is sold directly to petroleum refiners for blending with gasoline. The sale is usually by contract, so that the producer will not have to provide storage facilities and so that the petroleum refiner will be assured of a continuous supply of benzol. On the whole, spot benzol is distinctly lower than contract benzol and both follow rather closely the trend in gasoline prices, except that the fluctuations are not as great.

The market can absorb readily all light oil that is obtained from coal carbonization, and even all that could be produced, if the entire annual production of bituminous coal were carbonized. According to McBride (369), even in such a contingency, the production of light oil would hardly exceed one-sixth of the requirements for motor fuel. Practically no light oil is produced by gasworks, as it is used to enrich the gas, but quantities of this product are marketed from by-product coke ovens. As pointed out, however, the potential demand is so unlimited that competition from low temperature light oil is unimportant.

The chemical industries can use only limited quantities of light oil for commercial solvents, consequently by far the major proportion goes into blended motor fuel, which, because of its various advantages, can command a slightly higher price than ordinary gasoline. Since one gallon of light oil can be used to enrich several gallons of gasoline, to make a blended motor fuel, it is seen that the market price of light oil is determined by the gasoline market at a few cents per gallon above the gasoline price.

The Tar Market.   Weiss (372) states that there is more variation in quality among low temperature than among high temperature tars.   Secondary tar is so cracked by the temperatures employed that all tars are more or less reduced to the same grade, but the absence of cracking makes the quality of primary tar more closely related to the coal from which it was extracted.   Low temperature tars have been known to vary among processes from a content of 7 per cent tar acids to 50 per cent tar acids, as has already been noted in Chapter III, under the discussion of tar acids, and from 40 per cent by volume distilled upon fractionation to a temperature of 300°F. to 80 per cent distilled to the same pitch.   Consequently, in evaluating any low temperature tar, a careful assay is of the utmost importance.   And likewise, because of this vast difference in tars, it is dangerous to make generalizations.

While enormous quantities of raw tar are being burned as a fuel, a great deal of creosote oil and other derivatives of tar are being imported into the United States.   The tar is thus debased solely because the producer receives greater immediate benefit from it when so used.   This leads to a study of the economics of coal tar distillation. Any attempt to refine tar, for the purpose of providing creosote to take the place of importations, involves the simultaneous production of other tar derivatives.   Besides creosote, the tar refiner must produce light oil and a carbonaceous residuum, which can take any of three forms: soft pitch, hard pitch, or still coke.   Which of the latter is the most desirable to produce depends upon market conditions.   The production of creosote is at a maximum when still coke is left as the residuum and it is at a minimum when soft pitch is produced.   In the past, there was no market, whatever, for still coke and, in recent years, it has been somewhat limited.   Since both the creosote oil and a good road tar contain some of the same constituents, it is obvious that the two cannot be manufactured at the same time.

The reason so much tar is burned as a fuel at large coke ovens which are affiliated with metallurgical plants, according to McBride

(369), is one of business and economics, rather than of technical consideration. The only cause for the existence of such coke ovens is to insure continuity of coke supply to the metallurgical department and the policy of most companies is not to encourage expansion into fields of chemical industry other than the smelting of iron and the manufacture of steel. If the tar were not burned, other fuel would have to be purchased for the open hearths, so that it is considered less of an annoyance to burn the tar in the open hearth furnaces or under boilers than to undertake the uncertainties of tar sales. Only a bookkeeping price need be assigned to the tar, in such instances, as a matter of record only, and this is a contributory cause of the low average value assigned to tar for the United States as a whole. The net heating value of 166 gallons of tar is approximately equal to that of a short ton of 12,500 B.t.u. per pound coal, which is to say, that when coal is worth $5.00 per net ton delivered, on a strictly calorific basis, tar is worth $0.03 per gallon. On the other hand, tar has many practical advantages over coal that tend towards greater economy, so that a safe criterion is that the value of the tar as a fuel in cents per gallon is numerically equal to the price of coal in dollars per ton.

Those plants, which do not wish to burn their tar as a fuel, endeavor to dispose of it with a minimum of effort on their part, with the result that most of the sales are made through a tar broker on a commission basis, or else are delivered directly to the tar distiller under contract. Practically all of the tar placed upon the market is thus sold under long term agreements, so that there is really no such thing as a spot price for this by-product.

Competitive bidding is entirely too inactive to advance the price of tar for refining. The situation is very similar to that of any commodity, where the supply very greatly exceeds the demand. The refiners do not have to offer the producers a price very far exceeding its worth as a fuel to get all the good quality tar that they can handle. Furthermore, tar is of such low value that it cannot economically stand transportation for very great distances. In certain districts, there are very few tar distillers and the producers in such localities are faced with accepting what is offered or with the consequence of having it left on their hands, as a result of their inability to reach other consumers.

The complex specifications for tar products that are used in various trades, coupled with the difficult problem of merchandising, have made it desirable, from the viewpoint of most coke oven and gas retort operators, to confine this business to a separate industry of tar distillation, but there are a few small operators who undertake their own tar refining.   However, should consideration be given to the financial possibilities of refining low temperature tar, it would be found that about 60 per cent would be yielded as oil and 40 per cent as pitch, with a 300°F. melting point.   Runge (366) has discussed the economics of this procedure and concludes that the only assured outlet for the pitch, in large quantities, is that of a fuel, for which purpose it should bring $0.25 per ton of coal carbonized.   Assuming a yield of 25 gallons of low temperature tar per ton of coal, there would remain about 15 gallons of low temperature oil which could be used principally in three ways: as a wood preservative, as a disinfectant, and as a flotation oil, without any regard for its possibilities as a Diesel engine fuel, as crude stock for gasoline cracking, for the manufacture of artificial resins and other condensation products, or for many special uses.   With creosote oil for wood preservation selling at about $0.17 per gallon wholesale and flotation oils at about $0.22 per gallon, an average value of $0.16 per gallon would seem to be conservative for the distilled low temperature oil.   At this value, it would bring a revenue of $2.40, plus the return from the pitch, or a total return of $2.65 per ton of coal carbonized.   This is equivalent to over $0.08 per gallon for the raw tar, after deduction of $0.02 per gallon for distilling cost.

The extent to which tar distillation can be carried out successfully essentially is based upon a well balanced demand for all of the products.   Tar cannot be refined economically unless all of its derivatives can be sold within a reasonable time after production and at a price which represents a fair margin of profit above their allocated costs of crude stock and of refining.   The unbalanced condition in the market of tar products is responsible for the fluctuation in prices and it depends more upon the relation between supply and demand of specific products than upon any consideration of value or cost of production.   As far as the light oil fraction is concerned, there is no limitation to its market, hence, the quantity of tar which is distilled depends entirely upon the outlets for the other products.   While there are various uses in the chemical industries for tar derivatives, the requirements are small compared to the potential supply and, moreover, many of the desired compounds can be manufactured synthetically, a method which has an economic advantage over tar distillation, in that it has only one final product to be sold.

During distillation of the tar, the first volatile constituents to be removed are the light oils up to 170°C. or 200°C., which contain a very small proportion of nitrogen bases and phenolic derivatives. When only the light oils and water are distilled from the crude stock, the heavy tar remaining is used in surfacing roads, painting of pipe, and for saturating roof felt and other porous materials. Removal of more of the volatile matter leaves a soft pitch suitable for the impregnation of paving blocks, for a road binder, for the manufacture of built-up roofing, and for other waterproofing requirements. If the distillation be carried to a point where all the volatile is removed, pitch or still coke remains. The pitch coke can be used for certain metallurgical requirements, where a fuel of low ash and sulphur is desirable. Its strength, however, is such as to prohibit its use in furnaces where the fuel is required to carry a heavy burden. Most of the still coke is used as a fuel, but it does not burn very readily on grates. The two important characteristics of pitch, which determine its availability for various uses, are its hardness and its brittleness at ordinary temperatures. As a roofing material, it is obvious that a pitch which softens and becomes sticky during summer temperatures is quite as undesirable as one which cracks under foot during the winter, because of its brittleness.

The acids are removed from crude tar through forming a water-soluble compound by treatment with caustic soda, after which the tar acids are recovered with sulphuric acid and are finally washed and redistilled. These tar acids, in the form of either crude or refined phenols and cresols, are used in the preparation of synthetic resins and other condensation products, as well as in the manufacture of insecticides and of disinfectants. Although formaldehyde condensation products, of the bakelite type, have been prepared from the creosote fractions of low temperature tars, Soule (373) has some doubt regarding the ability of this market to absorb any large quantities of low temperature tar products, but their extreme cheapness may stimulate their use in a variety of related ways.

According to Soule (374), the tar distiller receives his largest financial return from creosote oil which is used as a wood preservative. Coffin (375) ascribes the superiority of low temperature tars for wood preservation, first, upon their high acid content and, second, upon the oxygenation of the low temperature oil.   This oxygenation converts the hydrocarbons from liquids to solids, in the surface layers of the impregnated material, and forms a permanent filler for the cell walls.   Consequently, it is felt that low temperature oils are particularly adapted to what is known as the empty cell method of creosoting, regardless of its superiority from a toxic standpoint. While large amounts of tar are refined to produce creosote oil for the preservation of timbers, which are placed in the ground or other damp places, it is by no means without competition in this field. Zinc chloride is also extensively used for impregnating mine timbers, posts, railroad ties, *etc*.   The insolubility of creosote oil is distinctly an advantage in its favor.   As far as resistance to decay is concerned, there is no doubt that creosote is superior to zinc chloride, but in many cases the timbers have to be removed because of mechanical wear long before they have decayed.   In treating railroad ties for main lines, where the traffic is heavy, this consideration is of particular importance and results in selecting the cheaper preservative.

The specifications for creosoting oils are now based principally upon the physical characteristics of the oil, such as the boiling point, viscosity, and specific gravity, instead of upon an analysis of the creosote content.   The name of creosote oil is applied to this fraction of the tar because of the phenolic derivatives that are present and which prevent the growth of fungi by their toxic action.   According to Weiss (372), with a few exceptions, the primary oils are too low in specific gravity to meet the present standards of wood preservation, but this does not mean that they will not make good preservatives. The situation is somewhat analogous to water gas tar, which was pushed for over ten years before it became acceptable for this purpose, and low temperature tars must face and overcome the same situation by demonstrating their usefulness and by requiring a change in obsolete standards.   A number of railroad ties have been in service eight years, after being treated with low temperature creosote oil, and they are in substantially the same condition as those treated with creosote oil which met the specifications for wood preservation.

There has been a good deal of discussion regarding the manufacture of lubricating oils from low temperature tar.   It has been thought likely that the ready oxidation of the phenolic constituents would cause trouble.   Practical tests, however, have shown that this difficulty is not great for lubrication in accessible places where the parts can be cleaned. A high grade lubricant can be produced, nevertheless, by removing the phenolic derivatives, but that somewhat increases the cost of production. Soule (373) states that the low temperature hydrocarbons below 326°C. apparently have only slight value as lubricants, but the readiness with which these compounds polymerize suggest the possibility of treating them further with aluminum chloride, as a polymerizing agent according to the method of Heusler (376), to convert them into lubricating oils. The value of unsaturated hydrocarbons in lubricants has often been brought out and it has been shown that the frictional resistance between rubbing surfaces bears a relationship to the amount of unsaturates present. Consequently, it is anticipated that low temperature oils above 300°C. possess considerable lubricating value.

This latter view has been substantiated by Nielsen and Baker (377) (378) in tests by the British National Physical Laboratory on the lubricating properties of a refined low temperature oil from the Nielsen process. As compared with a well known English brand of mineral lubricating oil, both the density and viscosity of the low temperature oil was greater. There was very little difference in the journal friction between the two samples, but the low temperature specimen apparently had a less abrupt siezing temperature and was a more satisfactory lubricant than the mineral oil at high loads. Nielsen and Baker reconcile the difference of opinion, expressed by many authorities, regarding the suitablity of low temperature oil for lubrication, by the fact that these oils depend so much upon the process of production for their quality. Thus, redistillation and cracking of the oils in poorly designed externally or internally heated retorts greatly injures the value of the low temperature oil as a lubricant.

For use as a paint, the thickening of low temperature tar in air, due to the oxidation of the phenols, is of practical value. Used alone, the tar gives a soft brown color, but this, of course, may be modified by the addition of pigments. In one test of low temperature tar as a coating for woodwork and ironwork, after two years of exposure, both the paint and the coated material are said to have been in good condition.

Despite statements to the contrary, Runge (366) has pointed out that very little work has been done in ascertaining the nature of low temperature tar derivatives as applied to their use in the preparation of dyestuffs and pharmaceuticals and comparatively few of the tar derivatives, as now known, can be used for these purposes.

The special properties of low temperature tars adapt them to certain applications where they should command a good price, provided they are not produced in excessive quantities, in which case they can find immediate consumption only as a fuel oil. Undoubtedly important industrial uses will be developed for the special constituents of low temperature tar, but it is inconceivable that any such markets could be of a scale comparable to a national use of semi-coke as a domestic and power fuel. These special uses may be sufficient to command a premium for low temperature tar as a raw material during the initial stages of development in the industry, but when the manufacture of low temperature coke assumes a tremendous scale, the only assured price for primary tar is that of its use as raw stock for the manufacture of motor spirit, lubricants, and fuel oils, a price set largely by the petroleum industry at the present time.

The Fixed Nitrogen Market. As far as ammonium sulphate is concerned, this by-product can be neglected in most cases, when studying the economics of low temperature carbonization, because of the relatively small quantities that are recovered, in processes of the externally heated type, and because of the great cost of recovery apparatus of large capacity, in processes of the internally heated type. The uncertainties of the nitrogen market and present price levels, with little hope for future betterment, strengthen the argument, so that about the best that can be said, in general, for the nitrogen products of low temperature carbonization is that they constitute a potential supply, should the nature of the process and market conditions warrant recovery. However, because of the controversial nature of this point, the author included the revenue from ammonium sulphate in Table 123 and estimated the capital cost of the ammonium sulphate plant in Table 125, together with its operating costs and overhead in Table 126. To better clarify the reasons for this situation, it is necessary to study the fixed nitrogen market.

Although the bulk of the fertilizer demands for nitrogen is met by saltpeter and ammonium sulphate, they must compete in a minor way with other plant foods which contain fixed nitrogen, such as tankage, cotton-seed meal, *etc.* For most agricultural purposes, the two principal nitrogen fertilizers are interchangeable, but both have special advantages under particular conditions. As a consequence, the trend of ammonium sulphate prices follows very closely that of Chilean nitrate. The price of the latter is fixed annually for each country in the world by the association of Chilean producers, after consideration of the available supplies of fixed nitrogen throughout the world and the prospects for competition. This price having been fixed, the price of ammonium sulphate is adjusted accordingly and thereafter, throughout the year, the fluctuations of spot sulphate are determined wholly by the demand and available supply in each locality.

By-product coke plants usually recover the ammonia as ammonium sulphate, while gasworks usually recover it as ammoniacal liquor. There is very little difference in the market price of these two nitrogen products per unit of ammonia. Since the liquor is much easier to make than the sulphate, even a very slight advance in price of liquor, relative to sulphate, will stimulate the manufacture of the former to such an extent that there will be a recession in price. According to McBride (369), in 1920 only about 25 per cent of the gasworks of the United States recovered ammonia from their coal gas retorts, even though the ammonia had to be scrubbed from the gas by a surplus of water to purify it, simply because the local market value was insufficient to pay the cost of its concentration. The marketing of ammoniacal liquor from the few very large plants which dispose of it is a very simple task, for long term contracts are usually made with ammonia companies to take the entire liquor output. The ammonia company then customarily arranges for a local concentrating plant, so that the liquor can be concentrated to a strength which will make shipment economical. The problem of its ultimate disposition is thus left in the hands of an independent company.

The market for liquid ammonia, including the demand of chemical industries and the refrigeration trade, is decidedly limited and is greatly exceeded by the potential production. In the past, these markets have been controlled by a few ammonia companies, which obtained their ammoniacal liquor from gasworks, but the advent of synthetic ammonia has brought about serious competition in this field. The same may be said of the explosive industry where, in the past, ammoniacal liquor concentrated to 25 per cent ammonia content, has been used in the manufacture of gunpowder. This requires the concentration of gasworks ammonia to a strength many times exceeding that at which it is produced, an operation far less convenient than dilution of anhydrous synthetic ammonia. The outcome of the entire situation is that, like all other ammonia products, the liquid ammonia price follows very closely the price of fertilizer.

There is a general consensus of opinion that cheap fixed nitrogen is more likely to come from development of the direct synthetic processes than from any other source. According to Curtis (379), a number of estimates indicate that it can be produced at a price ranging near $0.07 per pound of fixed nitrogen, or about $0.05 per pound of ammonia, and present indications are that the market for anhydrous and aqua ammonia in the United States will be saturated from this source. This is about one-half the price of ammonia in ammoniacal liquor and one-third the price of nitrogen in Chilean nitrate. It does not follow that, given cheap ammonia, there will be cheap fertilizer, for it must be combined with sulphuric acid, phosphoric acid, or otherwise, before it is available for this use.

However, Curtis (380) says that the cost of producing synthetic ammonium sulphate by any process now available is considerably in excess of the cost of producing ammonium sulphate in a by-product coke oven. Furthermore, before the gas can be used for most domestic and industrial uses, it must be purified and the ammonia removed either as the sulphate or otherwise, regardless of the market price of fixed nitrogen. Consequently, by-product ammonia is absorbed in the market before the synthetic stocks are drawn upon By-product ammonium sulphate has never enjoyed a selling price determined by its cost of production. Before the advent of synthetic nitrogen products, the imports of Chilean nitrate set the market price. But even Chilean nitrate was not sold on a basis of production cost, but enjoyed a suspension of the usual laws of economics, in that it formed practically a world monopoly. Apparently, however, the cost of producing synthetic ammonia is now much below the selling price of Chilean nitrate in the past, so that, for the first time, that source of supply is facing serious competition. It is unlikely, that the Chilean guana fields will ever again hold this dominating position over the world market for fixed nitrogen. Consequently, the outlook for the future is lower prices for fixed nitrogen and, hence, for by-product ammonium sulphate. Despite this forecast of reduced prices, however, the production of by-product ammonium sulphate will continue to increase for reasons already set forth. But even so, the relative place of coal as a source of nitrogenous fertilizer will become of less and less importance. Curtis (380) notes that a score of years ago Chilean saltpeter was the principle source of supply for fertilizer, a decade ago by-product nitrogen was foremost, but today synthetic fixed nitrogen supplies more than all the rest combined. The relative importance of these three major sources as they now stand will probably never again change.

Synthetic ammonia made by the fixation of atmospheric nitrogen has become an active competitor of gasworks in the ammonia market, with the result that the larger gas plants have found it expedient to curtail their production of ammoniacal liquor and produce ammonium sulphate instead. But even in the fertilizer field, where ammonium sulphate competes with Chilean nitrate, synthetic ammonia plants stand as a potential source of these materials.

Among other ammonia salts, ammonium chloride has a large potential market and present demands are largely met by importation. The price differential, however, is such that, whether or not a producer would undertake its production, depends entirely upon its market price relative to ammonium sulphate. If cheap phosphoric acid were made available, ammonium phosphate could be easily manufactured and would find a receptive fertilizer market. Such a compound would be an ideal fertilizer, as it contains two essential foods for plant life.

Chilean nitrate and synthetic fixed nitrogen products can be sold at a market price fixed only by supply and demand and the cost of production, but ammonium sulphate from gasworks or by-product ovens is only one of several related products and there is no relation between its market price and its cost, such as must prevail in the case of the former materials.

McBride (369) points out that approximately 90 per cent of the ammonium sulphate produced in the United States is marketed on a commission basis and practically all of the business is done under contract by a single selling agency, which maintains an elaborate organization in this country and abroad to keep in touch with market conditions. Very little of the exported ammonium sulphate is handled independently. The increased production of this chemical by foreign plants, however, has made serious inroads on this foreign trade, to such an extent that the export price is usually below the domestic price, which, in turn, is so low as to practically prohibit imports.

Nevertheless, the domestic fertilizer business is the greatest potential field for the permanent disposition of ammonium sulphate, but for any great development in this line an educational campaign will be necessary for the benefit of the companies who manufacture fertilizers, as well as for the farmers who consume them. As a matter of national economics, as well as of national independence, it is desirable that much of the Chilean saltpeter that is annually imported for fertilizer in the United States be replaced by domestically produced ammonium sulphate. In nitrogen equivalent, the ammonium sulphate that is exported from the United States annually amounts to 35 per cent or 50 per cent of the nitrogen equivalent of imported nitrate from Chile. In further consequence of such a development, would be a strengthening of the national defense, by rendering the country independent of regular nitrate importations for the manufacture of munitions of war.

Curtis (379) notes that there has always been great parity in the United States between the prices of Chilean nitrate and those of ammonium sulphate, compared on the basis of nitrogen content. Until 1916, Chilean nitrate was always slightly below the price of ammonium sulphate, but, after that date, the ammonium sulphate has remained correspondingly cheaper. About 1895, Chile supplied approximately 75 per cent of the world's nitrogen requirements, but today that country supplies somewhat less than 40 per cent of the world's demand, although both consumption and production have greatly increased. It would appear, therefore, that, at present, Chilean nitrate would no longer control the nitrogen market, but such is not the case. By its very nature, nitrogen from by-product plants will be sold always at a price which will insure its sale, the balance of the market being taken by the Chilean nitrate.

Bain (381) has estimated that Chilean nitrate can be profitably marketed in the United States until the price of $35 per short ton is reached. Below that price, even the most improved methods of production, of transportation, and of marketing, can not maintain the full imports and the importations will fall off in proportion as the price falls below that figure. At approximately $28 per short ton, it is estimated that there would be practically no offerings. These figures for nitrate correspond roughly to $46 per ton and $37 per ton, respectively, for ammonium sulphate, when computed on the nitrogen equivalent, and they may be taken as indications of the minimum prices that ammonium sulphate will attain, unless synthetic fixed nitrogen can be produced in quantities more cheaply than this.   As long as the above prices are maintained, it is assured that ammonium sulphate will continue to be produced by all by-product coke ovens, except the smaller less economical plants, whose shutdown would not materially affect the supply.   The production of ammonium sulphate will depend, therefore, more upon the production of coke and gas than upon the market price of sulphate.

Potential Markets. It has heretofore been noted, that essential to the economic success of any process for the treatment of high or medium grade fuels by low temperature carbonization is an adequate disposition of the solid residuum.   A study of the consumption of solid fuel by industries will give, therefore, some indication of the markets in which semi-coke can compete and also some idea of the extent to which low temperature carbonization can be carried out when proper outlets develop for the by-products which would arise from future expansion.

The last statistics for the consumption of coal by industries in the United States were compiled for 1923 by the Department of Commerce (382), but, while there have been changes in the total fuel consumption, there is reason to believe that there was no essential change in the percentage consumption by each industry up to 1927. The figures are tabulated in Table 128.   It will be observed from the table that the railroads are by far the largest consumers of coal in the United States, accounting for 26.5 per cent of the entire consumption.   Next, in order of importance, comes the domestic and general industrial trades, each of which use approximately 19.5 per cent of the entire amount.   The various methods of coal carbonization that are already in existence, that is, gasworks, beehive ovens, and by-product ovens, all together account for approximately 14.0 per cent of the total consumption. Deducting that already carbonized, together with that consumed for miscellaneous purposes, we note that about 80 per cent of the entire coal consumption of the United States can be substituted by processed solid fuel.

While it is quite true that the future will see increased use of gas by the domestic and industrial markets, such a substitution merely means a shifting of coal consumption from one industry to another and there is no basic reason why such an increase in the use of gas should not be met by carbonization at low temperatures.   There is also a tendency towards electrification of railroads, mines, and other industries, a development which, in the future, will doubtlessly shift the coal consumption to large central electric stations.   Such impending changes in coal utilization will increase the efficiency with which the fuel is consumed, thereby conserving the national fuel

TABLE 128

Consumption of coal by industries in the United States during 1923

INDUSTRY	NET TONS			
	Anthracite	Bituminous	Total	Per cent
Mines and quarries..........	8,018,000	12,955,000	20,973,000	3.46
Railroads...................	4,578,000	155,795,000	160,373,000	26.47
Gasworks...................	1,010,000	5,150,000	6,251,000	1.03
Electric utilities and railways......................	2,273,000	36,800,000	39,073,000	6.43
Beehive coke................		30,085,000	30,085,000	4.96
By-product coke.............		54,280,000	54,280,000	8.96
Domestic and foreign bunkers...................		8,035,000	8,035,000	1.33
Iron and steel works........		30,220,000	30,220,000	4.99
General industrial use.......		119,280,000	119,280,000	19.68
Domestic...................	52,344,000	66,400,000	118,734,000	19.60
Miscellaneous...............	18,600,000		18,600,000	3.07
Total....................	86,914,000	519,000,000	605,914,000	100.00

resources.   On the other hand, the centralization of fuel utilization will make its processing an altogether more profitable enterprise.

Of the estimated world's production of 117,000,000 net tons of coke in 1925, the United States produced 44 per cent, according to statistics gathered by Tryon and Bennit (383).   The production of by-product coke has increased tremendously from 3,462,000 net tons in 1905 to 43,921,000 net tons in 1927, the production of beehive coke declining from 28,768,000 net tons in 1905 to 7,004,000 net tons in 1927.   The coke imports to the United States amount to less than 0.5 per cent, while the exports account for approximately 2 per cent of that produced.   During the decade from 1917 to 1926, inclusive, the total value of the products from by-product ovens in the United States ranged from $8.86 to $13.55 per net ton of coal carbonized, the cost of the raw coal ranged from $3.88 to $7.73 per net ton, while the excess value of the carbonization products over the coal ranged from $2.38 to $5.82 per net ton of coal.

From 77 per cent to 83 per cent of the coke produced in the United States is consumed by blast furnaces, which, together with other metallurgical uses, leaves less than 5 per cent for consumption in the domestic market and we have seen that this supply is very irregular, depending, as it does, upon depressions in the steel industry. As interesting as these statistics may be, they do not have as much bearing upon the marketing of low temperature coke as do statistics gathered from the manufactured gas industry. McBride (369) investigated this subject and reported that in 1918 the manufactured gas industry of the United States sold 1,813,000 net tons of coke, representing roughly 60 per cent of that produced, at an average price of $7.70 per net ton. In 1920, the sales amounted to 1,378,000 net tons, or roughly 40 per cent of that produced, and were disposed of at an average price of $8.44 per net ton. The reason for this decrease was attributed to the coal strike, which made it desirable to use the coke at the plant in water gas manufacture. In general, the price received for coke is governed by local conditions and it usually retails at $1.00 to $2.00 per ton less than anthracite. In 1918, the sale price ranged from $2.75 to $19.13 per ton, while, in 1920, it ranged from $1.00 to $15.17. These figures are all wholesale prices for domestic fuel, or to other companies for use in manufacturing water gas. According to Tryon and Bennit (383), 1,125,000 net tons of by-product coke, valued at $7.92 per net ton, were produced in the manufacture of city gas during 1925. These authorities report a variation in average value of the coke produced by the by-product ovens of the manufactured gas industry from $7.32 per net ton to $11.42 per net ton over the period 1918 to 1925, inclusive.

The receptiveness of the trade to a processed fuel is indicated by the fact that the production of fuel briquets in the United States increased from 581,000 net tons in 1924 to 971,000 net tons in 1927 and the briquetting industry seems to have held its place after an abundance of anthracite was placed upon the market, following the end of the coal stoppage. The possibilities of increase in this industry are recognized, when it is noted that Germany alone produced approximately 5,500,000 net tons of coal briquets and 40,100,000 net tons of brown coal briquets during 1927.

In 1918 there were produced 263,300,000 gallons of coke oven tar in the United States, of which 200,200,000 gallons, or 76.0 per cent, were sold. The production increased to 529,500,000 gallons in 1926, while the sales increased to 277,300,000 gallons, or only 52.3 per cent. This great decrease in the percentage of tar that was sold illustrates the extent to which the market has become saturated and shows the increasing extent to which coke oven tar has found consumption as a fuel. Out of a total of 416,979,000 gallons of tar, of all varieties, that were produced during 1918 in the United States, the manufactured gas industry contributed 52,694,000 gallons of coal gas tar and 100,985,000 gallons of water and oil gas tar, the remainder being derived from coke ovens, as above. While the total tar production had increased to 549,775,000 gallons in 1923, the increase occurred mainly in coke oven tar, which accounted for 440,907,000 gallons, coal gas tar from the manufactured gas industry increasing only slightly to 58,877,000 gallons, and water and oil gas tar decreasing tremendously to 49,991,000 gallons. McBride (369) reported that during 1920 about 51,000,000 gallons of tar were produced by the manufactured gas industry, of which appoximately 90 per cent was sold and 6 per cent was burned. The average price received in that year for coal gas tar by 316 plants in the United States was $0.043 per gallon, although 72 plants received over $0.06 per gallon and 21 plants obtained $0.10 per gallon, or more.

In 1920, the total amount of crude light oil produced by all sources in the United States was 123,333,000 gallons, of which 106,564,000 gallons were refined on the premises and the remainder sold as crude stock. Of this total, 109,710,000 gallons were recovered by coke ovens, 2,906,000 gallons by water gas plants, and 10,717,000 gallons came from manufactured coal gas plants. In 1926, the total production had increased to 164,060,000 gallons, of which 159,590,000 gallons were refined on the premises, yielding benzol as the principal product. The total production of benzol in the United States, including both the crude and refined, as well as motor benzol, was 83,371,000 gallons in 1920, of which 72,995,000 gallons were sold at an average price of $0.239 per gallon. The total production increased to 112,489,000 gallons in 1926, of which 111,489,000 gallons were sold at an average price of $0.191 per gallon.

The total production of motor fuel in the United States during 1918 amounted to 3,901,000,000 gallons, of which 3,570,000,000 gallons came from refining petroleum, 283,000,000 gallons were extracted from natural gas, 45,000,000 gallons came from coke ovens, and 3,000,000 gallons were distilled at tar refineries. The total production had increased to 12,135,000,000 gallons in 1925, of which 10,903,000,000 gallons came from petroleum, 1,128,000,000 gallons came from natural gas, 104,000,000 gallons came from coke ovens, and only 742,000 gallons came from tar refineries. Regarding the other products of petroleum, gas and fuel oil production amounted to 9,660,000,000 gallons in 1921, increasing to 15,340,000,000 gallons in 1926, while lubricating oils were produced to the extent of 876,000,000 gallons in 1921 and 1,355,000,000 gallons in 1926.

The shale oil distillation industry of the United States (384), while not large, is making progress. In 1923, approximately 10,300 net tons of shale were carbonized to yield 392,000 gallons of oil and in 1924 about 23,400 net tons of oil shale were distilled to recover 600,000 gallons of oil. Some of this oil was sold for fuel, while a large part was refined for its by-products.

Coffin (375) states that from 6 pounds to 12 pounds of creosote oil per cubic feet of timber are used in wood preservation, depending upon whether the vacuum or the pressure process of treating is employed. In other words, from 2.5 gallons to 5.0 gallons of oil are consumed in creosoting each railroad tie that is so treated. In addition to the treatment of railroad ties, there is a vast outlet for creosote oil in treating poles, posts, piles, mine props, shingles, and other forms of lumber. The domestic production of creosote oil increased from 59,100,000 gallons in 1919 to 90,300,000 gallons in 1926, while imports to the United States, mainly from England and Germany, increased from 6,500,000 gallons to 95,400,000 gallons in the same years. There is no real difficulty, therefore, in disposing of the creosote fractions of either low temperature or high temperature tar, as far as the market is concerned. Incidentally, it might be mentioned, that a good deal of low temperature oil from the Maclaurin process has actually been imported to the United States, where it has been sold as creosote oil and is said to have been of better quality than that ordinarily found in the local market.

The real difficulty in the tar distilling industry has been the burden of pitch disposal. The use of the residual tar and petroleum distillates has grown tremendously in the past decade, until today the demand for road material constitutes one of the largest single fields for tar products. In 1925, there were consumed in the United States about 100,000,000 gallons of road bitumen, of all types, and this figure is increasing at the rate of about 8 per cent per annum. Soule (385) states that, while the market for creosote oil in increasing, the market for pitch is rapidly decreasing, due to competition from petroleum asphalt, as a roofing material, and from both petroleum asphalt and concrete, as a paving material. The tendency, therefore, is for the tar refiners to distill more and more of the tar to a hard pitch. Consequently, the outlook for the pitch is only its value as a fuel, in which field it can command about $0.03 per gallon. For this reason, the tar, which contains the greatest amount of creosote oil and the least amount of pitch, as does primary tar, is worth the most to the distiller and, hence, will doubtlessly command a higher price in the future than high temperature tar.

Another outlet for low temperature oil is that of gas oil for carburetting water gas, a use for which tests have demonstrated its suitability. Since 743,000,000 gallons, of gas oil were used in 1920, according to McBride (386), it is estimated that upwards of one billion gallons were consumed in the United States during 1927.

In the past, disposal of pitch has been a difficult problem, as it has faced a highly competitive market from bitumen from other sources, such as the petroleum industry. At times, it could not even be sold at any price and the accumulated surplus itself became a burden. Ultimately, it was found that this pitch could be coked in abandoned beehive ovens to yield a material useful for special purposes. Beehive pitch coke is very hard and, because of its freedom from ash and sulphur, it has been found to be particularly suitable for certain phases of the metallurgical industry, to the extent that its price is considerably greater than that of by-product coke. The pitch coke market is not yet saturated and Weiss (372) states that some 300,000 net tons have been disposed of in the United States from 1921 to 1926.

It is generally conceded that the trend is for lower manufactured gas prices in the future, especially if any great expansion takes place, through increased consumption for domestic heating, and increased production, through a general adoption of low temperature carbonization, either for the preparation of a domestic fuel or a boiler fuel.

On the other hand, depletion of the natural gas supply is likely to increase the price of this fuel to a point more compatible with the value per thermal unit that has been enjoyed by other gaseous fuels. While coke oven gas has been gradually replacing natural gas for a number of years, the general trend is yet too indefinite to determine the extent of this substitution. The replacement of natural gas by coke oven gas for city distribution is the normal outcome of depletion of the natural gas fields. There are also additional factors which affect the situation, among them the relative prices of anthracite and gas oil, both of which are used in the production of manufactured gas.

According to Tryon and Bennit (383), the total gas sales of the United States increased from 895,000,000,000 cubic feet in 1915 to 1,834,000,000,000 cubic feet in 1925. Of the total in 1915, surplus coke oven gas represented 9.4 per cent, or 34,000,000,000 cubic feet; manufactured coal and water gas, 20.3 per cent, or 182,000,000,000 cubic feet; and natural gas 70.3 per cent, or 629,000,000,000 cubic feet. Of the total in 1925, surplus coke oven gas represented 19.7 per cent, or 362,000,000,000 cubic feet; manufactured coal and water gas, 15.4 per cent, or 283,000,000,000 cubic feet; and natural gas, 64.9 per cent, or 1,189,000,000,000 cubic feet. The production of natural gas in the United States has been irregular in trend (387), increasing from 582,000,000,000 cubic feet in 1913 to 795,000,000,000 cubic feet in 1917, after which it decreased, through exhaustion of the known fields, to 662,000,000,000 cubic feet in 1921, rising again to 1,164,000,000,000 cubic feet in 1925, with the discovery of new supplies.

Statistics, gathered by Curtis (379), show a regularly increasing trend of sodium nitrate importations from Chile, rising from 656,000 net tons in 1910 to a maximum of 2,199,000 net tons in 1919. Thereafter the importations have had erratic fluctuations, rising to 1,383,000 net tons in 1920, falling to only 121,000 net tons in 1921, and again climbing to 1,266,000 net tons in 1925.

The ammonium sulphate produced in by-product coke ovens of the United States, according to Curtis (379), increased from 35,000 net tons in 1915 to 348,000 net tons in 1922 and the total ammonium sulphate equivalent, including what might have been manufactured from the ammoniacal liquor which was recovered, increased from 81,000 net tons to 449,000 net tons over the same period. The amount of nitrogen that was recovered from the manufactured gas industry was far less and the trend of production indicated a decrease of recovery. The total ammonium sulphate equivalent, obtained from coal gas plants in the United States, decreased from 54,000 net tons in 1912 to 30,000 tons in 1922.

An analysis of the nitrogen supply of the United States, made by McBride (369), shows an increase from 76,000 net tons of nitrogen in 1919 to 117,000 net tons in 1924, exclusive of Chilean nitrate, but including all other nitrogenous forms. Of the 1924 supply, 91.5 per cent was recovered from coke ovens, 4.7 per cent came from gasworks, 3.0 per cent was produced from atmospheric fixation, and 0.8 per cent was imported as ammonium sulphate. The production of synthetic ammonia has increased substantially since these statistics were gathered. Of these supplies, 38.5 per cent was consumed in mixed fertilizer, 23.1 per cent was exported, 15.9 per cent was sold as aqua ammonia, and 11.5 per cent as anhydrous ammonia, the remainder being used in the manufacture of chemicals and explosives or consumed directly as an unmixed fertilizer.

Orrok (388) has noted that the entire fixed inorganic nitrogen supply of the United States in 1926 amounted to 282,000 net tons of nitrogen content, of which roughly 38 per cent was represented by ammonium sulphate, obtained from the distillation of coal; 56 per cent was imported from Chile as saltpeter; 2 per cent consisted of other nitrogenous imports; while the remaining 4 per cent was furnished by the synthetic fixed nitrogen industry. This supply was consumed to the extent of 36 per cent as domestic fertilizer; 24 per cent for export; 28 per cent was used as ammonia, principally as a refrigerant; and 12 per cent found its way into the chemical and explosive industries.

Central Station By-Product Recovery. One of the greatest fields for low temperature carbonization is in the preparation of a boiler fuel with simultaneous by-product recovery. In this instance, the smokeless characteristic of semi-coke loses its significance, where large power stations, equipped with modern high efficiency combustion equipment, are concerned. The application of low temperature carbonization to such plants, therefore, must be largely justified by the economies which it effects in the cost of power, through the recovery and sale of by-products, rather than upon consideration of the civic interests of the community. Economically, the most favorable situation for the integration of low temperature carbonization with central electric stations is obviously where the electric power company is affiliated with a city gas company. In such cases, the natural growth of gas load can be met by gas from the carbonization plants, built to provide a processed fuel for new steam generating capacity, installed to meet the growth in the electric load. Furthermore, such an affiliation provides an assured and adequate outlet for the most difficult of all by-products of carbonization to market.

Brownlie (389), in discussing the application of low temperature carbonization to by-product recovery in central electric stations, classifies the processes into three general methods: first, those in which the coal is carbonized in the slack or crushed condition and is fed to the furnace on stokers; second, those in which the coal is distilled while in the powdered form, in which case the semi-coke is fired to the furnace as a pulverized fuel; and, third, those in which the solid fuel is completely gasified and the gas is burned under boilers or is used as a fuel for internal combustion engines. He further divides the first class into two types: those which are primarily intended to be used in conjunction with a boiler furnace, and those which are segregated from and may be operated entirely independently of a boiler furnace. In the last category, practically all low temperature processes may be included.

Some full-scale experimental work has been carried on in England (390) on the use of low temperature gas from an internally heated partial gasification process as a fuel for internal combustion engines. The scheme has been quite successful, when using a low grade refuse fuel as the raw material. In the United States, however, the use of gas fuel in internal combustion engines has never made great headway and it is unlikely that the advent of low temperature carbonization will materially change the situation in America, except possibly for small local power supplies which are remote from markets for the gas. Notwithstanding the successful development of the gas turbine, any extensive expansion of low temperature carbonization, as applied to power generation, is more likely to develop along the lines of preparing a boiler fuel for use in the generation of steam to supply high efficiency, high capacity turbines.

A number of different low temperature processes have been tried experimentally in the preparation of boiler fuel. Among these the

McEwen-Runge process for pulverized coal, installed at the Lakeside station in Milwaukee, and the Piron-Caracristi lead bath process, formerly installed at the River Rouge, Michigan, and at the Walkerville, Ontario, plants of the Ford Motor Co., have already been described fully in Chapter VI and need not be further discussed here. A short description of some of the other installations, not heretofore described, are pertinent at this point, however.

The Pintsch process (391) involves the use of a short vertical retort, located immediately above the front end of the chain-grate stoker of a boiler furnace. The raw coal, being fed to the boiler, is thus carbonized by internal heating with a portion of the hot products of combustion withdrawn from the furnace. The semi-coke is delivered from the bottom of the retort directly upon the chain-grate stoker and fed hot to the combustion chamber. The gases, after removal of the volatile products, are returned to the boiler and burned. Approximately 35,000 cubic feet to 45,000 cubic feet of the combustion gas at 1200°F. is withdrawn from the furnace for carbonization purposes and subsequently leaves the retort at about 250°F. This process is used in Germany for non-coking and brown coals. The first installation was at the Municipal Electricity Station of Lichtenberg, near Berlin, in 1919, but more than twelve plants are said to have been installed in Germany and Sweden since that date.

Practically all of the processes invented by Merz and McLellan (392) involve the use of internal carbonization by superheated steam. The various systems also employ a vertical retort, but their chief novelty lies in the scheme for steam extraction and return of heat to heat-exchangers. These processes have been used experimentally at the Dunstan station, Newcastle-on-Tyne, England. Steam is bled from the turbine at a pressure of about one pound per square inch, and is superheated to about 950°F. in a separate superheater. This superheated steam is then admitted to the bottom of the retort and, as it rises, it distills the descending charge. The mixture of steam and volatile products then passes to a heat-exchanger, wherein the heat is extracted and returned as low pressure steam to the lower stages of the turbine.

The Wisner (393) process, otherwise known as the Carbocite process, is a two-stage method carried out in rotary retorts. It has been under experimental investigation for the preparation of boiler fuel at the Philo, Ohio, station. The coal is treated in the first or upper retort by partial oxidation to destroy its agglutinating properties. Thereafter, the coal descends at a temperature of about 600°F. to the second stage, consisting of two parallel retorts, located immediately below. The carbonizing cylinders are heated externally.

The Hanl process (391), used at the Bismark mine in Upper Silesia, Germany, consists of a vertical cast-iron retort, which contains an agitator provided for the purpose of stirring the charge vigorously during its descent. The retort is heated internally by the introduction of a regulated amount of air to effect partial gasification. The heating medium, generated by a small amount of partial gasification, is augmented by the withdrawal of a portion of the combusted gas from the furnace. The hot semi-coke discharges directly upon a mechanical stoker.

The Salerni process (394), otherwise known as the Salermo process, has been established experimentally at the Langerbrugge station at Ghent, Belgium. This is an externally heated process provided with a number of long narrow semi-cylindrical cast-iron troughs, each fitted with a paddle agitator. The crushed charge flows along progressively from one trough to another during carbonization.

In recent years, central electric stations have shown a tendency to adopt pulverized fuel, in which certain advantages have been seen. If the present trend continues, consideration must be given to the production of semi-coke suitable for firing as a pulverized fuel. There are three possible cases; pulverization of the fuel after low temperature carbonization, pulverization between primary and secondary carbonization, and pulverization before carbonization. Practically all processes can more or less lay claim to the first method.

Soule (385) has suggested that between two powdered materials as a pulverized fuel at the same cost per thermal unit, the cost of generating steam will be the least in that (1) which burns faster, (2) which liberates more of its heat in an available form, and (3) which is adapted the more readily to automatic control. The faster a fuel burns, the smaller the furnace volume required to combust a given amount of fuel and also the higher the furnace temperature and the greater is the steam generating capacity for a given area of heating surface. The heat losses in the combustion of bituminous coal are distributed among several items, of which about 4.2 per cent is in the latent heat of water vapor, formed from the combustion of hydrogen in the raw coal; 4.0 per cent is lost as sensible heat in the flue gas;

one per cent as radiation; 0.5 per cent as unburned combustible in the ash; and 0.3 per cent is lost in the evaporation of free moisture in the coal. The first and last of these offer the greatest promise of reduction. Hence, the less hydrogen and free moisture present in the fuel, the more efficiently it can be combusted. Concerning the third point, it is quite obvious that the fuel which involves the lowest firing cost is the one which can be fed to the furnace with the least difficulty under automatic control.

As compared with pulverized coal, powdered semi-coke has no tendency to fuse and agglomerate upon admittance to the furnace, which together with its greater reactivity makes it considerably more combustible. In the second place, removal of practically all the moisture and nearly all the hydrogen during carbonization increases the fuel efficiency of semi-coke 4 per cent to 5 per cent, as compared with the raw coal. Finally, as compared with pulverized coal, the flowing qualities of powdered semi-coke are said to be vastly superior, thereby resulting in greater ease of transport and permitting more success in automatic control. On the other hand, semi-coke will have a greater ash content than the coal from which it was made, and its calorific value per pound may be more or less than the raw coal, depending upon the type of fuel originally carbonized. Taking all these matters into consideration, but without regard to other advantages, such as smokelessness, high combustion rate, etc., Soule (385) concluded that as a pulverized boiler fuel, semi-coke was worth on the whole, pound for pound, as much as the pulverized coal from which it was made, a conclusion reached independently from similar considerations by the present author, under the discussion of power char in Chapter IV.

Some actual tests of a pulverized fuel boiler of the Woodeson type, using semi-coke from the Nielsen process, have been reported (395). The particular boiler had 5,200 square feet of heating surface and 2,400 square feet of economizer surface. It was rated at a capacity of 40,000 pounds to 50,000 pounds of steam evaporated per hour at a pressure of 250 pounds per square inch. The test was highly successful. The calorific value of the fuel was 10,670 B.t.u. per pound and the combusted gas contained 16.5 per cent carbon dioxide with a flue temperature of 390°F. The feed-water temperature was 112°F. and the average steam pressure 218 pounds per square inch, superheated to 537°F. The equivalent evaporation was 69,300 pounds of steam per hour from and at 212°F., which amounted to an evaporation of 9.2 pounds of steam from and at 212°F. per pound of semi-coke. Each gross ton of the raw coal yielded, aside from the production of 72.5 per cent of its weight as semi-coke, 23.5 gallons of crude oil, of which 25 per cent was a good lubricant, and 7,000 cubic feet of gas with a thermal value of 485 B.t.u. per cubic feet.

The direct burning of fuel in the generation of electric power with modern large turbo-generators, efficient boilers, and improved methods of firing, requires the minimum capital expenditure, and consumes less fuel in the production of a kilowatt-hour of electricity than does any other method. It does not follow, however, since that procedure does not recover the by-products of the fuel, that it is the cheapest means of electrical generation. The degree, to which this is so, is contingent upon the cost, capital and operating, of extracting the by-products and upon the condition of the markets for their disposition. As far as conservation of national resources is concerned, while, indeed, the burning of raw coal constitutes a waste of by-products, the extraction of by-products involves the consumption of more coal. From that standpoint, it is merely a question of which is the more important nationally, conservation of by-products or conservation of coal.

All by-product recovery schemes in central electric stations, as compared with direct coal firing, require a larger outlay of capital, increased cost of operation, and a larger fuel consumption, to provide for a given power demand and to generate a given quantity of electricity. An essential factor in the financial stability of a by-product recovery scheme, in conjunction with a power plant, is a sustained market for the by-products, fluctuations in the market value of which would be reflected in the cost of power generation. Thus, not only would the cost of a unit of electricity depend upon the cost of coal, but also upon the selling price of the tar, gas, light oil, and ammonium sulphate, if it be recovered. From the standpoint of power plant operation, there are many drawbacks to incorporation of a carbonizing plant, such as the increased transportation charges through handling a greater amount of coal, larger employment of labor, and a generally greater complexity in plant operation and coördination. If the production of a boiler fuel be coupled with the manufacture and sale of a certain amount of the coke as a domestic fuel, then the financial aspects of carbonization, as an adjunct to central stations, changes completely, for a portion of the solid fuel is thereby treated as a by-product.   It is anticipated, however, that central power stations would be loathe to complicate their business by expansion into the domestic fuel processing field.

Porter (260) feels that an integration of coal carbonization and power generation does not offer great promise of financial success, at the present time, because he believes that the over-all efficiency from raw coal to steam by direct burning is too great in modern furnaces with modern combustion equipment to be counter-balanced by the recovery and sale of by-products, through introduction of a less thermally efficient system from coal to steam.   From this argument, he concludes that the possibilities of such an integration rest solely on increased efficiency of the carbonization process, or on the development of some system, such as low temperature carbonization, wherein the by-products are of a character which will yield sufficient returns to reduce the net cost of available heat in the solid fuel.

Wellington and Cooper (89) studied the economics of low temperature carbonization, as applied to English central electric stations, in a number of different forms, including direct firing of the semi-coke, complete gasification of the residual fuel, and various other combinations.   They concluded that the method of complete gasification cannot receive serious consideration, as compared with direct coal firing of the boilers, but that the best solution of low temperature carbonization applied to a boiler plant is that in which the semi-coke is directly fired to the furnace, along with the surplus gas.   In this case, they concluded that the cost of generating a kilowatt-hour of electricity was below that of direct coal firing, but they pointed out that there were certain fluctuations in the market value of the residuals, which would be reflected as a fluctuation in the cost of generating power.   It is obviously non-essential that the gas be combusted in the boiler, if it can be profitably disposed of otherwise.

As a matter of record, in connection with the economics of the preparation of boiler fuel by low temperature carbonization, Savage (396) has called attention to a case in the Western United States where 65,000 net tons of raw coal, costing $3.05 per net ton delivered, are annually burned as fuel for a large power station.   The peculiar market conditions in the vicinity of that plant were such, that it was estimated that the entire fuel requirements of the station could be met by carbonizing 93,000 net tons of coal annually, at a net revenue of $1.47 per net ton of raw coal, over and above the cost of the fuel, when the carbonized fuel was charged to the boilers at a price equivalent to the raw coal, weight for weight.

Soule (385) has studied the economics of pulverized coal carbonization in power plants. According to this authority, the investment in such a carbonization plant is less than $1,000 per net ton of raw coal daily throughput, including cost of the by-product plant. He figured the fixed charges, at 80 per cent capacity factor, to be $0.50 per ton and the operating expense to be $0.70 per ton, giving a total carbonizing cost of $1.20 per net ton of coal. With the sale of tar at $0.055 per gallon, motor fuel at $0.15 per gallon, and gas at $0.30 per thousand cubic feet, he calculated the revenue from by-products at $3.60 per net ton of coal, which cost $4.50 delivered. On a yield of 73.8 per cent semi-coke, this places the net cost of one net ton of power char at $2.85, as compared with $4.50 per net ton of raw coal.

Orrok (388) (397), quoting Junkersfeld (398), has demonstrated rather convincingly how rapidly a new turbine, or central electric station, is superseded by more efficient equipment, which, in its turn, assumes the burden of carrying the base load of a particular electric supply system and he concluded, with Klingenberg (399), that the economical 100 per cent capacity operation of a coal processing plant is difficult to reconcile with the variable output and 50 per cent, or lower, capacity operation of a central electric station. The validity of such an argument, however, loses force when it is recognized as non-essential that the sensible heat of the coke be utilized. In reality, the heat lost on this item amounts to comparatively little and a large part of this can be recovered by rational cooling or dry quenching. Consequently, there is no good reason why the carbonization plant cannot be operated at full load, storing processed fuel for use on the peak demands of the system. And in five years, when obsolescence shall have reduced the station load factor from 50 per cent to 35 per cent, the carbonization plant will yet be operating at 70 per cent capacity factor.

Plant Location. It is customary for a carbonization plant, located near the market, to carry from one to two months' coal supply in storage, thus assuring the plant against any coal stoppages of short duration, either because of mine shut down or because of transportation curtailments. Furthermore, the location of coke plants at large transportation centers permits them to draw upon a number of different sources for their fuel supply or to route their raw material by a number of different transportation lines. For this reason, a carbonization plant located near the point of consumption is more independent of conditions beyond its control than one located at the mines and dependent upon a single source for its raw fuel and a single carrier for its transportation facilities. Location of the carbonization plant adjacent to the mine has the distinct advantage of permitting the use of low grade fuels, which cannot be economically transported very great distances, because of their large proportion of incombustible material. Mine-mouth carbonization plants, however, suffer the disadvantage of necessitating transportation of the distillation products, of which the gas becomes particularly burdensome, unless high pressure transmission can be effected or unless there is a nearby market.

Lander (400) is convinced that the proper location for low temperature carbonization is at the mine pit, as far as the use of waste and other low grade fuels is concerned, and he is equally convinced that, for other materials, the gasworks is the proper place for primary carbonization, for there, only, can the full value be secured for the gas. The value of the gas at the gasworks is roughly five times that of the gas for heating purposes at the mine mouth. Lander (400) has also pointed out that it makes little difference where the coke is made, for the freight rate over a given distance is approximately the same for the coke produced from a ton of coal as it is for the ton of raw coal itself. While the weight of coke that must be transported is roughly 70 per cent of the weight of coal, the volume of the coke produced is approximately the same as that of the raw coal.

Christie (401) has noted, that, while in general the low temperature carbonization plant is best located near the market for its products, there are exceptions to this rule. The impending exhaustion of natural gas from districts where coal deposits exist make low temperature carbonization a possibility in such cases, for then the existing natural gas pipelines can be used for its transportation.

In addition to the question of proper location of the carbonization plant, consideration must be given to the best location for the tar refinery, if the two industries are to be integrated under one organization. While, in the past, there may have been some justification for shipping tar from the producer to a distant point for distillation, because of insufficient quantities to warrant an individual refinery, this is no longer the case when tar is produced in large quantities. Soule (385) says that, by distilling the tar at the point of production, from $0.02 to $0.03 per gallon can be saved in freight and only the high value oil need be shipped. The still coke can then be mixed with the coal and coked to a solid fuel.

Examination of the freight tariffs on bituminous coal for approximately a hundred different sets of origins and destinations shows a great diversity (402) (403). While there is much variation from the mean, the average rate increases from about $1.80 per net ton, for a 100-mile haul, to about $3.80 per net ton, for a 500-mile haul. Individual tariffs may vary above or below these figures by as much as 25 per cent.

The freight rates on solid fuels depend quite as much on their volume as upon their weight, so that the specific weights of the different materials give some idea of the relative costs of transportation. The freight tariff, for a given distance and a given weight, varies approximately inversely as the weight of the material per cubic feet. The specific weight of anthracite varies from 53 pounds per cubic feet to 60 pounds per cubic feet, with an average of about 55 pounds per cubic feet, depending upon its source and size. The specific weight of bituminous coal varies from 43 pounds per cubic feet to 67 pounds per cubic feet, with an average of 49 pounds per cubic feet. The specific weight of by-product coke varies from 32 pounds per cubic feet to 29 pounds per cubic feet, with an average of 30 pounds per cubic feet.

Although the coke weighs approximately 70 per cent less than the coal from which is was made, weight for weight, it is bulkier. Consequently, the coke produced from a ton of coal occupies approximately the same volume as the original coal. This means that approximately as many freight cars are required to haul the coke as to transport the raw coal. For this reason, added to the greater value of the coke per ton, freight rates on coke are distinctly higher than on coal. Mc Bride (369) states that formerly freight rates were based on beehive coke, which was manufactured near the mines and had to be transported to the markets, but with the present tendency to locate by-product ovens at the point of consumption, together with the impending competition of coke with anthracite as a domestic fuel, there are indications of freight readjustments, but, for the present, the freight tariff on coke is very complicated. There is also a complicated relationship between coke tariffs and those on bituminous coal. If the rate on coke is relatively the higher, the situation favors location of the plant at the point of consumption and, if it is relatively low, the tendency is to locate near the mines. Finally, the establishment of railroad tariffs is in the hands of a public authority, which may have many consequences to consider in rate fixation.

The freight rate on coke varies from about $2.50 per net ton, for a distance of 100 miles, to about $4.50 per net ton, for a 400-mile haul. Chatfield (404) reported the tariff, established by the Interstate Commerce Commission on fuel oil and gas oil in tank cars, as increasing from about $0.19 per 100 pounds, for a 200-mile haul, to about $0.36 per 100 pounds, for a 700-mile haul. The tariff for gasoline was fixed at about 25 per cent higher than the rate for fuel oil and gas oil. Individual tariffs may vary from these figures by as much as 15 per cent. Coke oven tar takes essentially the same freight rate as fuel oil. The tariff on ammonium sulphate increases from about $0.20 per 100 pounds, for a distance of 100 miles, to about $0.30 per 100 pounds, for a distance of 400 miles.

According to Wagner (405), natural gas gasoline has been successfully transmitted through a 3-inch pipe for a distance of approximately 15 miles at the rate of 50,000 gallons per day. In this case, however, the terrain was almost flat with a gentle down-grade slope, so that this success sets no precedence for transmission over an irregular topography, where gas accumulation at the apex of high points in the pipeline may be a serious difficulty.

If low temperature tar could be transported by pipeline and if the quantities were sufficient to warrant laying the pipe, quite a saving could be effected over the cost of its transportation by rail in tank cars. While the viscosity of most low temperature tars is high, there is no reason why they could not be treated in much the same way as the heavy crude petroleums of the Western United States are handled, that is, by warming the fluid between pumping stations to increase its fluidity and by the use of rifled pipe.

The main petroleum trunk lines of the United States are 8-inch pipe, but a few 6-inch and 10-inch pipes are in existence. Diesel engines are usually employed to drive the pressure pumps, which are used for forcing the oil through the pipes. These pumping stations are located at intervals of from 10 miles to 35 miles, depending upon

the topography of the country, the viscosity of the oil, and the prevailing temperatures in the region.   When a very viscous oil is transported, it is often necessary to heat it at the pumping stations to
increase its fluidity.   Up to 1920, the longest petroleum pipeline was
1,610 miles.   According to Rathburn (406) (407), roughly 95 per
cent of the crude petroleum in the United States is moved by pipeline at a cost estimated to be approximately 65 per cent of the cost
of transportation by rail.

The feasibility of transmitting large quantities of gas by pipeline
to the consumption centers depends primarily upon the utilization of
this gas for the base load, the peaks of the distribution system being
taken by gas which is generated locally.   Experience with the transmission of natural gas and coke oven gas by pipeline indicates that
the technical aspects of handling low temperature gas in this manner
are not serious and that the problem is wholly one of economics.

There are two pipelines over 300 miles long for the transmission
of natural gas from West Virginia to Ohio.   These lines are composed
of 20-inch and 16-inch welded steel pipe.   A similar line 450 miles
long, operating at 450 pounds per square inch initial pressure, maintained at intervals by seven compressor stations, driven by gas engines supplied with fuel from the line, has been contemplated.   In
the Ruhr district of Germany, coke oven gas is transmitted 63 miles
by pipeline and consideration has been given to the high pressure
distribution of coke oven gas from this district over a maximum distance of 450 miles.   In the United States coke oven gas is transmitted
by pipeline from South Bethlehem, Pa., to the Philadelphia district
and similar projects, involving transmission of coke oven gas over
distances up to 40 miles, have been under consideration.

A low temperature plant, treating 1000 tons of coal per day and
selling all the high calorific value low temperature gas, using producer gas for heating the retorts, would generate about 200,000 cubic
feet of gas per hour by the externally heated method.   According to
a study made by Crowell (408), a 12-inch pipeline, operating at an
initial pressure of 90 pounds per square inch, would deliver this gas
at a terminal pressure of 20 pounds per square inch at a distance of
100 miles.   He figures the total cost of delivery, including all carrying and operating charges at $0.28 per 1000 cubic feet of gas, when
gas engine compressors are used.   The present author, however,
believes that, by raising the initial pressure to 400 pounds per square

inch and using a correspondingly smaller welded pipe, the cost of delivering the gas 100 miles could be reduced to $0.12 per 1000 cubic feet, or less.   In any event, these figures illustrate how essential it is to transmit the gas at as high a pressure and for as short a distance as is feasible to reach the market.

Fuel Resources.   Redmayne (409) has estimated the coal reserves of the world in 1924 at approximately 8,300,000,000,000 net tons, of which the United States had about half.   A tabulation of the reserves by countries is given in Table 129.   The reserve given by

TABLE 129
World's coal reserve in 1924

COUNTRY	MILLIONS OF NET TONS			
	Anthracite	Bituminous	Sub-bituminous	Total
United States....................	21,600	2,154,000	2,050,000	4,225,600
Canada.........................	2,400	312,000	1,043,000	1,357,400
China...........................	426,000	668,000	700	1,094,700
Germany........................		452,000	14,700	466,700
Great Britain...................	12,500	196,000		208,500
Australia.......................	700	145,700	36,000	182,400
India...........................		84,000	2,900	86,900
Russia..........................	40,300	23,000	1,800	65,100
Africa..........................	12,800	49,600	1,200	63,600
South America..................	800	34,500		35,300
France.........................	3,600	14,000	1,800	19,400
Other countries................	24,600	164,500	146,000	335,100
Total........................	545,300	4,297,300	3,298,100	8,140,700

Redmayne for the United States is somewhat larger than the 3,419,300,000,000 tons reported by Cambell (410), as of the end of 1925, but in this latter estimate the resources of Alaska and certain deep deposits are apparently not included.   Only about two-thirds of this is recoverable, however, for the mining losses amount to about 35 per cent, by the present methods of mining.

The sub-bituminous coals and lignites of the Western United States constitute about half of this country's supply and a large proportion of these reserves are of low heating value and contain a large amount of moisture.   As the Eastern fuel reserves become exhausted and the cost of power for manufacturing becomes correspondingly greater, the migration of the center of industry westward will draw upon the fuel reserves nearest the market and there will arise a need for processing these low grade fuels, to appreciate their market value and to increase the efficiency of their utilization. Even now, if the Dakota lignites could be treated by low temperature carbonization, or otherwise, to raise their form value sufficiently to meet the local fuel needs, an enormous expenditure for freight on hauling bituminous coal from the Eastern fields would be saved annually.

TABLE 130

World's coal production

COUNTRY	THOUSANDS OF NET TONS				
	1922	1923	1924	1925	1926
United States..........	476,000	655,000	570,000	580,000	656,000
Germany...............	306,000	209,000	282,000	302,000	328,000
Great Britain...........	279,000	308,000	298,000	272,000	141,000
France.................	35,100	42,400	49,500	52,800	57,600
Japan..................	32,100	33,800	35,200	36,800	37,000
Czechoslovakia.........	31,700	31,400	39,200	34,700	36,600
Belgium................	23,300	25,200	25,600	25,400	27,500
India..................	21,300	21,900	23,600	23,400	22,400
Canada.................	15,100	17,000	13,600	13,100	18,600
Australia...............	13,800	14,100	15,500	16,200	15,900
Africa.................	9,700	13,300	14,100	14,700	15,700
Other countries........	103,900	122,900	123,700	138,900	143,700
Total.................	1,347,000	1,494,000	1,490,000	1,510,000	1,500,000

Statistics gathered by the United States Bureau of Mines and shown in Table 130 give the world's production of coal by countries for various years. The United States is by far the largest producer, having supplied from 38 per cent to 46 per cent of the entire world's supply for the fifteen years preceding 1926. Next in order of importance comes Germany, Great Britain, and France. The figures given in Table 130 include anthracite, semi-anthracite, bituminous, semi-bituminous, lignite, and brown coals. About half of the German production and about 13 per cent of the entire world output consists of sub-bituminous coals.

White (411) estimated the proved world's petroleum resources, as of 1928, at 43,100,000,000 barrels, which are recoverable by present methods. This estimate was increased to 60,000,000,000 barrels as the world's total resources, proved and prospective. Outside of the United States, the most important petroleum deposits are believed to be in Mexico, Venezuela, Columbia, Bolivia, Argentine, Russia, Mesopotamia, Persia, Assyria, Arabia, East Indies, China, Siberia. Japan, India, and probably Northern Africa.

A careful examination of the oil resources of the United States, both developed and prospective, was made in 1922 by a joint committee of the United States Geological Survey and the American Association of Petroleum Geologists, in collaboration with many consulting specialists who were familiar with the stratigraphy and geologic structure of given localities. According to White (411), they concluded that the oil reserve of the United States at that time was 9,150,000,000 barrels, recoverable by present methods, about half of which belongs to the heavy grade of fuel oil petroleum. As approximately 5,500,000,000 barrels had been produced in the United States at the end of 1922, the original oil reserve must have been about 15,000,000,000 barrels, of which 7,750,000,000 barrels, or roughly half, had been removed from the ground at the end of 1926. The reserve thus left is less than 15 years supply for the United States at the present rate of consumption and by present means of recovery. However, all the oil deposits cannot be located in that period of time, so that in all probability the wells will keep producing a constantly decreasing amount of petroleum for perhaps 75 years to come.

The world's production of crude petroleum by countries, according to statistics by the United States Bureau of Mines (382), is given in Table 131. It will be observed that the United States is by far the world's largest producer, accounting for 65 per cent of the entire amount in 1922 and 71 per cent in 1926, and, even then, it was necessary to import large quantities of petroleum to meet the national requirements.

Oil shales are found in Scotland, England, Wales, Ireland, Canada, Australia, New Zealand, Africa, France, Jugoslavia, Sweden, Bulgaria, Germany, Italy, Switzerland, Esthonia, Brazil, Argentine, Chile, Uraguay, China, Arabia, Syria, and Russia. Vast deposits of oil shale are found in the United States, notably in Colorado, Nevada, Utah, Wyoming, Montana, Illinois, Missouri, Indiana,

New York, Kentucky, Ohio, Pennsylvania, Tennessee, California, and West Virginia. There has been practically no increase in the world's production of oil shale from 3,435,000 net tons in 1920 to 3,540,000 net tons in 1924 and about 93 per cent of the entire output came from Scotland alone. The only country which has shown any appreciable growth is Esthonia, which increased from 1.5 per cent of the world's production in 1920 to 7.4 per cent in 1924. Even though the present development of oil shale distillation throughout

TABLE 131

World's production of crude petroleum

COUNTRY	THOUSANDS OF BARRELS (1 BBL. = 42 GAL.)				
	1922	1923	1924	1925	1926
United States.......	558,000	732,000	714,000	764,000	773,000
Mexico..............	182,000	150,000	140,000	116,000	90,000
Russia	35,500	39,000	45,500	52,500	61,000
Venezuela...........	2,000	4,000	9,000	19,500	37,000
Persia...............	22,000	28,500	32,500	35,000	35,500
Rumania............	10,000	11,000	13,500	16,500	23,000
Dutch East Indies...	17,000	20,000	20,500	21,500	22,000
Peru................	5,500	5,500	8,000	9,000	10,500
India................	8,500	8,500	8,500	8,000	8,500
Argentine...........	3,000	3,500	4,500	5,500	6,500
Columbia...........	500	500	500	600	6,500
Poland..............	5,000	5,500	5,500	6,000	5,500
Trinidad............	2,500	3,000	4,000	4,500	5,000
Other countries.....	7,500	8,000	8,000	9,400	12,000
Total..............	859,000	1,019,000	1,014,000	1,068,000	1,096,000

the world appears to be practically at a standstill, the vastness of the world deposits remains as a potential source of motor fuel and of lubricants.

Conclusion. As the products of carbonization pass from crude to more highly refined and specialized materials, they pass from industry to industry, each step adding an increment to their economic worth. Unfortunately, the demand for the highly refined products is, at present, limited and, consequently, much of the by-product material is used to an inferior economic advantage. Thus, McBride

(369) notes that about half of the total tar produced in the United States, at the present time, is burned as a fuel, instead of being separated into its more valuable constituents. The industrial absorption of all the possible tar derivatives will require many years of study to ascertain their full possibilities, but the time will doubtlessly arrive when no coal will be burned in its raw condition. Such an enlightened epoch may yet remain distantly in the future, but reasonable advances may be expected year by year. However, the practical attainment of this larger vision must rely upon the joint efforts of the various branches of the carbonization industry, of which primary distillation is one, and must rest for its realization upon such sound technical, economic, and business principles, as the present author has endeavored to outline.

In regard to the national problem of coal carbonization, be it either by high or low temperature methods, Porter (260) concludes that it should and will be carbonized only to the extent that the economic demand, for the special products thus derived, creates a price which will justify their extraction. Furthermore, there is neither economy nor conservation in the transformation of energy from the form of coal to those of coke, tar, and gas, if in those forms it is generally less useful, as indicated by the market values of these products relative to the raw coal.

There is a certain rivalry between high temperature and low temperature carbonization systems, inasmuch as the former is based upon years of experimentation and practice and has behind it a wealth of data and experience. The high temperature carbonization advocates are apt to judge low temperature carbonization in the light of this specialized experience, with its criteria and dogmata and without a true appreciation of the methods underlying the art, its *raison d'être*, or the characteristics of its products. Each system fills a distinct field with regard to its adaptability in treating different fuels and somewhat in regard to the markets for its principal products. Runge (412) points out that there is really no grounds for fear of serious competition between high temperature and low temperature carbonization, because the solid residuums do not fall in the same sphere of usefulness, due to their difference in physical and chemical properties; the tars are entirely distinct in composition and should find different markets; the low temperature gas should be supplemental to, rather than competitive with, high temperature gas; and, finally, the only really common field for the two is found in the use of light oil as a motor fuel.

According to the same authority, low temperature carbonization has suffered because of adverse criticism, arising from three sources: failure of a number of full-scale processes, exploitation of untried processes that have been based upon ridiculous assertions, and the unfortunately prolific writing of those not familiar with the art. This unfavorable atmosphere, while discouraging, has not prevented progress by those who recognize its possibilities.

Coming now to a conclusion of this presentation of the technology of low temperature carbonization, the author has endeavored to fulfil the task which he undertook at the outset, namely to coördinate the experimental researches of many workers and the expert opinion of many authorities, in such a way, as to establish the art upon firm technical foundations and thereby overcome the empiricism which heretofore has hindered its progress. An earnest effort has been made to present all phases of the subject in an unbiased manner, giving the *pro et contra* of all controversial subjects. Finally, in *dénouement*, the author can do no better than to quote Slosson (413) in the words with which he addressed the representatives of thirteen nations assembled in convention to discuss the world's problems of fuel and of fuel processing: "There is no world organization that can exercise the right of eminent domain over natural resources and compel a country to stop wasting its coal and oil, or to employ its unused land and water power. But all the same, and all the more, we should rejoice when anyone discovers how to make a profit out of a waste product or how to make a process more efficient. When a way is found to convert a low grade lignite into a high class motor fuel, ... or to clean the air of our industrial towns, or to raise the efficiency of a fuel by low temperature carbonization, he has thereby benefited the human race, living and to come. . . . . ."

BIBLIOGRAPHY

1. Shirley, Philosophical Transactions, June, 1667.
2. Clayton, Philosophical Transactions, 1739.
3. Richards, "A Practical Treatise on the Manufacture and Distillation of Coal Gas," 1877.
4. Lowther, Philosophical Transactions, 1733.
5. Molinari, "General and Industrial Chemistry," 1913, p. 36.
6. Clegg, "A Practical Treatise on the Manufacture and Distribution of Coal Gas," 1866, p. 4.
7. Thorpe, "Dictionary of Applied Chemistry," v. 2, p. 103.
8. Wagner, "Coal and Coke," 1916.
9. Mansfield, Jour. Chem. Soc., v. 1, 1849, p. 244.
10. Runge, Poggendorff's Annalen, v. 31, 1834, pp. 65–78, pp. 513–524; v. 32, 1834, pp. 308–328.
11. Perkin, Jour. Chem. Soc., 1896, pp. 596–637.
12. Perkin, British Patent, No. 1984, August 26, 1856.
13. Rambush, "Modern Gas Producers," 1923, p. 3.
14. Heinrich and Ries, "Economic Geology," p. 11.
15. "International Critical Tables," v. 2, 1927.
16. Lessing, Proc. Int. Conf. on Bit. Coal, Pittsburgh, 1926, p. 187.
17. Lewes, "The Carbonization of Coal," 1912.
18. Dundoroff, "Grundzuge und Ziele der Steinkohlenchemie," 1881.
19. Burgess and Wheeler, Trans. Chem. Soc., v. 97, 1910, p. 1917; v. 99, 1911, p. 649.
20. Clark and Wheeler, Proc. Chem. Soc., v. 103, 1913, pp. 1704–1715.
21. Parr and Layng, Ind. Eng. Chem., v. 13, No. 1, January, 1921, p. 14.
22. Bone, Gas. Jour., v. 155, July 6, 1921, p. 31.
23. Gluud, "Die Tieftemperaturverkokung der Steinkohle," 2nd ed., 1921.
24. Gentry, Proc. Int. Conf. on Bit. Coal, Pittsburgh, 1926, p. 190.
25. Perkins, British Patent, No. 307, 1853.
26. Sparr, British Patent, No. 430, 1854.
27. Scott-Moncrief, Nature, 1880, No. 23, p. 150.
28. Parker, British Patent, No. 67, 1890.
29. Parker, British Patents, Nos. 14365 and 17347, 1906.
30. Parr and Francis, "Modification of Illinois Coal by Low Temperature Distillation," Bulletin No. 24, Univ. of Illinois, 1908.
31. Parr and Olin, "The Coking of Coal at Low Temperatures," Bulletin, No. 60, University of Illinois, 1912.
32. Automotive Industries, August 30, 1923, p. 432.
33. Audibert and Raineau, Fuel in Science and Practice, July, 1925, pp. 307–310 *et seq.*
34. Schültz and Buschmann, Iron and Coal Trades Review, August 7, 1925, p. 212.

35. Schültz and Buschmann, Stahl und Eisen, No. 29, 1925.
36. Fieldner, N. E. L. A. Prime Movers Report, Distillation Products of Coal, 1927, p. 10.
37. Parr and Olin, Bull. 79, Eng. Exp. Sta. Univ. of Illinois, 1915.
38. Schültz, Buschmann, and Wissebach, Ber., v. 56, 1923, pp. 869–874, pp. 1967–1975.
39. Fischer and Gluud, Ber., v. 52, 1919, p. 1053.
40. Fromm and Eckard, Ber., v. 56, 1923, p. 948.
41. Gluud, Ges. Abhandlungen zur Kenntnis der Kohle, v. 2, 1917, p. 302.
42. Jones and Wheeler, Trans. Chem. Soc., v. 105, 1914, pp. 140–151.
43. Schültz, Brennstoffchemie, v. 4, 1923, p. 84.
44. Burgess and Wheeler, Trans. Chem. Soc., v. 107, 1915, p. 1916.
45. Morgan and Soule, Ind. Eng. Chem., v. 15, 1923, pp. 587–591, pp. 693–697.
46. Weissberger and Moehrle, Brennstoffchemie, v. 4, 1923, p. 81.
47. Fischer, Schroeder, and Zerbe, Ber., v. 55, 1922, p. 57.
48. Morgan and Soule, Chem. and Met. Eng., v. 26, 1922, pp. 923–928, pp. 977–981.
49. Fischer, Brennstoffchemie, v. 1, 1920, pp. 31, 47.
50. Gluud and Breuer, Ges. Abhandlungen zur Kenntnis der Kohle, v. 2, 1917, pp. 236–256.
51. Pictet and Bouvier, Compt. Rend., v. 157, 1913, p. 779.
52. Pictet, Kaiser, and Labouchère, Compt. Rend., v. 165, 1917, p. 113.
53. Broche, Ber., v. 56, 1923, pp. 1787–1791.
54. Gollmer, Brennstoffchemie, v. 4, 1923, p. 19.
55. Schültz and Buschmann, Stahl und Eisen, No. 29, 1925.
56. Schroeder and Zerbe, Brennstoffchemie, v. 3, 1922, p. 372.
57. Burgess and Wheeler, Jour. Chem. Soc., v. 97, 1910, pp. 1917–1935; and v. 98, 1911, p. 649.
58. Lessing, Jour. Soc. Chem. Ind., 1912, pp. 465, 671.
59. Gray and King, Fuel Research Board Tech. Paper No. 1, 1921.
60. Fischer and Gluud, Ges. Abhandlungen zur Kenntnis der Kohle, v. 1, 1915, p. 143.
61. Nielsen, Proc. Int. Conf. on Bit. Coal, Pittsburgh, 1926, p. 670.
62. Layng and Hawthorne, Ind. Eng. Chem., v. 17, 1925, p. 2.
63. Foxwell, Jour. Soc. Chem. Ind., v. 40, 1921, p. 193T.
64. Mahler, Compt. Rend., v. 113, 1891, p. 862.
65. Euchène, Jour. Gas Lighting, v. 76, 1900, p. 1080.
66. Constam and Kolbe, Jour. Gas Lighting, v. 107, 1909, p. 696.
67. Hollings and Cobb, Gas Jour., v. 126, 1914, p. 917.
68. Hollings and Cobb, Trans. Chem. Soc., v. 107, 1915, p. 1106.
69. Strache and Fromm, Brennstoffchemie, v. 3, 1922, p. 340.
70. Parr, Proc. Int. Conf. on Bit. Coal, Pittsburgh, 1926, p. 635.
71. Gentry, Proc. Int. Conf. on Bit. Coal, Pittsburgh, 1926, p. 436.
72. Davis and Place, Ind. Eng. Chem., v. 16, June, 1924, p. 589.
73. Davis and Place, Fuel in Science and Practice, December, 1924, p. 434.
74. Klason, Zeit. angew. Chem., v. 22, 1909, p. 1205.

75. Davis, Place, and Edeburn, Fuel in Science and Practice, July, 1925, p. 286.
76. Davis, Fuel in Science and Practice, January, 1925, p. 38.
77. Hulett and Capps, Ind. Eng. Chem., v. 9, 1917, p. 927.
78. Thompson, "Thermochemistry," 1920.
79. Euchène, Trans. Int. Gas. Congress, Paris, 1900.
80. Rambush, Fuel in Science and Practice, January, 1926, p. 12.
81. Lessing, Jour. Gas Lighting, v. 127, 1914, p. 570.
82. Lessing, Proc. Int. Conf. on Bit. Coal, Pittsburgh, 1926, p. 180.
83. Marson and Cobb, Gas Jour., v. 171, 1925, p. 39.
84. Evans, Proc. Am. Gas Inst., v. 8, 1913, pp. 668–709.
85. Fischer, Ges. Abhandlungen zur Kenntnis der Kohle, v. 3, 1918, p. 109.
86. Layng and Hawthorne, Ind. Eng. Chem., February, 1925, p. 165.
87. Parr, Ind. Eng. Chem., v. 18, June, 1926, pp. 640–648.
88. Ryan, Fuel in Science and Practice, v. 5, No. 4, p. 150.
89. Wellington and Cooper, "Low Temperature Carbonization," 1924.
90. McBride and Selvig, "Coking of Illinois Coal in Koppers Oven," U. S. Bureau of Standards Bull. No. 137, 1919.
91. Nielsen, Engineering, March 24, 1922, p. 347.
92. Fuel Research Board, Technical Paper No. 7.
93. Roberts, Trans. Inst. of Mining Eng., v. 62, 1921, pp. 9–32.
94. Brownlie et al., Iron and Coal Trades Review, April 28, 1922, pp. 606–608.
95. Börnstein, Zeit. für Gasbeleuchtung, v. 49, 1906, pp. 627–630, pp. 648–652, pp. 667–671.
96. Porter and Ovitz, "The Volatile Matter of Coal," U. S. Bureau of Mines, Bull. No. 1, 1912.
97. Davis and Parry, "Low Temperature Carb. of Penna. Coals; the Pittsburgh and Upper Kittaning Beds," Carnegie Inst. of Tech. Bull. No. 8, 1923.
98. Taylor and Porter, "The Primary Volatile Products of the Carb. of Coal," U. S. Bureau of Mines, Tech. Paper No. 140, 1916.
99. Giles and Vilbrandt, Ind. Eng. Chem., v. 16, August, 1924, p. 779.
100. Monett, Chem. and Met. Eng., v. 23, December 29, 1920, pp. 1246–1249.
101. Report of Investigations, U. S. Bureau of Mines, Ser. No. 2278, 1921.
102. Burgess and Wheeler, Trans. Chem. Soc., v. 105, 1914, pp. 131–140.
103. Burgess and Wheeler, Fuel in Science and Practice, May, 1925, p. 208.
104. Burgess and Wheeler, Fuel in Science and Practice, v. 5, No. 2, p. 65.
105. Proc. South Wales Inst. of Eng., April 20, 1922.
106. Fuel Research Board Tech. Paper No. 4, 1921.
107. Trenkler, Zeit. V. D. I., v. 69, April 25, 1925, p. 555.
108. Canfield, Gas Jour., June, 29, 1920, p. 838.
109. Redwood, "Mineral Oils and Their By-Products," 1897.
110. Young, British Patent, No. 13292, October 17, 1850.
111. Mills, "Destructive Distillation," 1892, p. 50.
112. Garvin, U. S. Bureau of Mines, Bull. 210, 1922.
113. Finley and Bauer, U. S. Bureau of Mines, Tech. Paper No. 398, 1926, p. 8.

114. Report of Fuel Research Board, 1920–1921, 2nd Section.
115. Report of Fuel Research Board, 1920–1921, 1st Section.
116. Landolt-Börnstein, "Physikalisch-Chemische Tabellen," 4 Auflage, 1912.
117. Parrish, Fuel in Science and Practice, v. 5, No. 10, p. 436.
118. Berry, Univ. of Wisconsin Bull. No. 635, 1914.
119. Fischer, Zeit. angew. Chem., v. 32, 1919, p. 337.
120. Fischer, Brennstoffchemie, v. 4, 1923, p. 51.
121. North and Garbe, "Low Temperature Distillation," 1925.
122. Schneider, Ges. Abhandlungen zur Kenntnis der Kohle, v. 2, 1917, p. 80.
123. Weindel, Brennstoffchemie, v. 4, 1923, p. 321.
124. Edwards, Jour. Soc. Chem. Ind., v. 43, 1924, pp. 143T–148T and pp. 150T–156T.
125. Brittain, Rowe, and Sinnatt, Fuel in Science and Practice, v. 4, June, 1925, p. 263; July, 1925, p. 299; August, 1925, p. 337.
126. Jaeger, Brennstoffchemie, v. 4, 1923, p. 257.
127. Williams, Jour. Chem. Soc., v. 15, 1862, p. 130.
128. Schorlemmer, Jour. Chem. Soc., v. 15, 1862, p. 419.
129. Pictet and Bouvier, Compt. Rend., v. 160, 1915, p. 629.
130. Pictet and Bouvier, Ber., v. 46, 1913, p. 3342.
131. Pictet and Bouvier, Ber., v. 48, 1915, p. 926.
132. Whitaker and Crowell, Ind. Eng. Chem., v. 13, 1921, p. 300.
133. Frank and Arnold, Zeit. angew. Chem., v. 36, 1923, pp. 217–218.
134. Whitaker and Crowell, Ind. Eng. Chem., v. 9, 1917, pp. 261–269.
135. Klein, Brennstoffchemie, v. 7, 1926, p. 3.
136. Kruber, Ber., v. 57, 1924, p. 1008.
137. Kaffer, Ber., v. 57, 1924, p. 1261.
138. Ruhemann, Zeit. angew. Chem., v. 36, 1923, p. 153.
139. Parrish and Rowe, Jour. Soc. Chem. Ind., v. 45, 1926, p. 99T.
140. Schültz, Ber., v. 56, 1923, p. 162.
141. Davis and Galloway, Proc. Am. Gas Assoc., 1925, pp. 887–899.
142. Morgan and Meigham, Ind. Eng. Chem., v. 17, 1925, pp. 626–628.
143. Church and Weiss, Analysist, 1914, v. 6, p. 396.
144. Morgan, Report of Carb. Committee, Am. Gas Assoc., 1926, p. 100.
145. Fischer and Breuer, Ges. Abhandlungen zur Kenntnis der Kohle, v. 3, 1918, p. 89.
146. Gollmer, Brennstoffchemie, v. 4, 1923, pp. 1, 19.
147. Avenarius, Zeit. angew. Chem., v. 36, 1923, p. 165.
148. Gluud, Ges. Abhandlungen zur Kenntnis der Kohle, v. 3, 1918, p. 66.
149. Marcusson and Picard, Zeit. angew. Chem., v. 34, 1921, p. 201; v. 36, 1923, p. 253.
150. Tropsch, Brennstoffchemie, v. 2, 1921, p. 251.
151. Morgan and Soule, Columbia University Bulletin No. 8, 1922.
152. Fischer and Gluud, Ges. Abhandlungen zur Kenntnis der Kohle, v. 2, 1917, pp. 295–342; v. 3, 1918, pp. 39–45.
153. Lessing, British Patent, No. 130362, 1919.
154. Dalton, Phil. Trans. Roy. Soc., v. 99, 1809, p. 446.
155. Bertholet, Compt. Rend., v. 62, 1866, p. 905.

156. Bertholet, Compt. Rend., v. 63, 1866, p. 788.
157. Bertholet, Bull. Soc. Chem., v. 7, 1877, p. 217.
158. Williams-Gardner, Fuel in Science and Practice, October, 1925, p. 430.
159. Anschutz, Ber., v. 11, 1878, p. 1213.
160. Haber, Ber., v. 29, 1896, p. 2691.
161. Thorpe and Young, Proc. Roy. Soc., v. 19, 1871, p. 370.
162. Jones, Jour. Soc. Chem. Ind., v. 36, 1917, p. 3.
163. Curtis and Beekhuis, Chem. and Met. Eng., v. 33, November, 1926, pp. 666–669.
164. Morrell and Egloff, Ind. Eng. Chem., v. 17, No. 5, May, 1925, p. 473.
165. Egloff and Morrell, Proc. Int. Conf. on Bit. Coal, Pittsburgh, 1926, p. 788
166. Morrell and Egloff, Nat. Petroleum News, April 28, 1926.
167. Fischer, Brennstoffchemie, v. 2, November 15, 1921.
168. Fischer and Schroeder, Brennstoffchemie, v. 1, 1920, pp. 4–6.
169. Fischer and Zerbe, Brennstoffchemie, v. 4, 1923, p. 309.
170. Bergius, British Patent, No. 4574, 1914.
171. Bergius, French Patent, No. 470551, 1914.
172. Bergius, German Patent, Nos. 303893 and 304348.
173. Fischer and Lessing, "Conversion of Coal into Oils," 1925.
174. Fischer and Schroeder, Ges. Abhandlungen zur Kenntnis der Kohle, v. 5, 1920, p. 516.
175. Sabatier, "Catalysis in Organic Chemistry," 1922.
176. Fischer, Ges. Abhandlungen zur Kenntnis der Kohle, v. 1, 1916, p. 337.
177. Fischer, Ber., v. 49, 1916, p. 252.
178. Kling, Chaleur et Industrie, suppl., December, 1924, pp. 53–71.
179. Waterman and Perquin, Proc. K. Akad. Wentensch, Amsterdam, v. 26, 1923, p. 226.
180. Skinner and Graham, Fuel in Science and Practice, v. 6, No. 2, p. 74.
181. Fischer and Gluud, Gluckauf, v. 52, pp. 721–729.
182. Engelhardt, Gas Jour., v. 159, p. 421.
183. Runge, Chemical Age, v. 30, 1922, p. 9.
184. Davis and Berger, Carnegie Inst. of Tech. Bull. No. 1, 1922.
185. Gentry, Proc. Int. Conf. on Bit. Coal, Pittsburgh, 1926, p. 130.
186. Lander and McKay, "Low Temperature Carbonization," 1924.
187. Engineering, October 28, 1921, p. 600.
188. Jour. Soc. Chem. Ind., June 30, 1917, p. 620.
189. Black Diamond, October 23, 1920.
190. The Engineer, September 23, 1921, p. 324.
191. Cobb and Greenwood, Jour. Soc. Chem. Ind., March, 1922.
192. Roberts, Proc. North of Eng. Inst. of Min. and Mech. Eng., August 6, 1921.
193. Audibert and Delmas, Fuel in Science and Practice, v. 6, No. 3, pp. 131–140; No. 4, pp. 182–189.
194. Charpy and Godchot, Génie Civil, v. 73, 1917.
195. Bone, "Coal and Its Scientific Uses," 1925.
196. Roberts, Proc. South Wales Inst. of Eng., April 20, 1922.
197. Koppers, Stahl und Eisen, v. 41, 1921, pp. 1173, 1254.

198. Koppers, Stahl und Eisen, v. 42, 1922, p. 569.
199. Bunte, Gas und Wasserfach, March 6, March 13, 1926.
200. Bunte, Gas und Wasserfach, v. 65, 1922, p. 593.
201. Fischer, Breuer, and Broche, Brennstoffchemie, v. 4, 1923, pp. 33.
202. Bahr, Brennstoffchemie, v. 5, 1924, p. 384.
203. Davis and Greene, Report of Am. Gas Assoc., Carbonization Committee, 1926, pp. 66–70.
204. Kreisinger, Ovitz, and Augustine, U. S. Bureau of Mines, Tech. Paper No. 137, 1917.
205. Thau, Chem. and Met. Eng., March 3, 1924, pp. 347–350.
206. Garland and Kratz, Univ. of Illinois Bull. No. 50, 1911.
207. Fishenden, Fuel Research Board, Tech. Paper No. 3, 1921.
208. Gentry, Proc. Int. Conf. on Bit. Coal, Pittsburgh, 1926, p. 764.
209. Elec. World, February 12, 1927.
210. Fieldner, Selvig, and Paul, U. S. Bureau of Mines, Bull. No. 193, 1922.
211. Simmersbach, Stahl und Eisen, v. 34, 1914, pp. 1153, 1209.
212. Armstrong, Chemical Trade Journal, v. 67, 1920, p. 736.
213. Curtis *et al.*, Chem. and Met. Eng., v. 28, 1923, pp. 11–17, pp. 60–62, pp. 118–123, pp. 171–173.
214. Ramsay and Young, Trans. Chem. Soc., v. 88, 1884.
215. Foxwell, Jour. Soc. Chem. Ind., 1922, No. 8, pp. 114T–125T.
216. Foxwell, Gas World, July 1, 1922, pp. 10–13.
217. Mott and Hodsman, Gas Journal, August 15, 1923, pp. 530–531; August 22, 1923, pp. 578–580; September 12, 1923, pp. 737–739.
218. Greenwood and Hodsman, Gas Journal, September 6, 1922, pp. 527–529; September 13, 1922, pp. 595–596.
219. Greenwood and Hodsman, Gas World, October 7, 1922, pp. 16–19.
220. Monkhouse and Cobb, Gas World, October 15, 1921, pp. 337–343.
221. Monkhouse and Cobb, Gas World, June 24, 1922, pp. 542–548.
222. Tervet, Jour. Soc. Chem. Ind., v. 3, 1883, p. 446.
223. Powell and Parr, Univ. of Illinois Eng. Exp. Sta. Bull. No. 111, 1919.
224. Powell, Ind. Eng. Chem., v. 12, November, 1920, pp. 1069–1077.
225. Campbell, Bull. Am. Inst. Min. Eng., 1916, p. 177.
226. Gentry, Proc. Int. Conf. on Bit. Coal, Pittsburgh, 1926, pp. 809–811.
227. Parr, Am. Inst. of Min. Eng., 1919, p. 1807.
228. Fraser and Yancey, Bull. Am. Inst. of Min. Eng., 1919, p. 1817.
229. Powell, Ind. Eng. Chem., v. 11, 1920, pp. 1077–1081,
230. Oteha, Zeit. angew. Chem., 1897, p. 330.
231. Roscoe and Schorlemmer, "Treatise on Chemistry," v. 2, 1907, p. 1208.
232. Brownlie, Engineering, July 8, 1927, pp. 36–38.
233. Fieldner, U. S. Bureau of Mines Tech. Paper No. 396, 1926.
234. McIntire, Proc. Int. Conf. on Bit. Coal, Pittsburgh, 1926, pp. 650–663.
235. Fuel Research Board, "Report of Test on Parker Low Temperature Carbonization Plant at Barugh," 1924.
236. Brownlie, Chem. and Met. Eng., January 4, 1922, pp. 23–27.
237. Tupholme, Chem. and Met. Eng., v. 30, January 14, 1924, pp. 54–55.

238. Fuel Research Board, "Report of Test on Freeman Multiple Retort at Willesden," 1925.
239. Fuel Research Board, Tech. Paper No. 7, 1923.
240. Report of The Fuel Research Board, 1924.
241. Fuel Research Board, Tech. Paper No. 17, 1927.
242. Tupholme, Chem. and Met. Eng., v. 29, October 22, 1923, pp. 752–755.
243. Fuel Research Board, "Report of Test on Fusion Retort at Cledford," 1926.
244. Greene, Proc. Int. Conf. on Bit. Coal, Pittsburgh, 1926, pp. 712–728.
245. Cantieny, Zeit. V. D. I., April 25, 1925, pp. 547–553.
246. Mueller, Proc. Int. Conf. on Bit. Coal, Pittsburgh, 1926, pp. 766–777.
247. Maclaurin, Jour. Soc. Chem. Ind., v. 36, 1917, pp. 620–625.
248. Tupholme, Chem. and Met. Eng., v. 29, 1923, pp. 1138–1140.
249. Runge, Proc. Int. Conf. on Bit. Coal, Pittsburgh, 1926, pp. 697–711.
250. Nielsen, Proc. Int. Conf. on Bit. Coal, Pittsburgh, 1926, pp. 664–690.
251. Tupholme, Chem. and Met. Eng., v. 29, 1923, pp. 1008–1012.
252. Piron, Proc. Int. Conf. on Bit. Coal, Pittsburgh, 1926, pp. 729–746.
253. Caracristi, Power, May 29, 1923, pp. 831–836.
254. Evans, Proc. South Wales Inst. of Eng., v. 38, p. 341.
255. Marshall, Gas Jour., March 4, 1919, pp. 451–454.
256. Caracristi, Jour. Franklin Inst., September, 1926, pp. 323–336.
257. Simpkin, Fuel in Science and Practice, May, 1925, pp. 218–221.
258. Fulweiler, Proc. Am. Gas. Inst., v. 3, 1908, pp. 578–666.
259. Cole, Jour. Am. Ceramic Soc., v. 9, No. 7, July, 1926, pp. 462–473.
260. Porter, "Coal Carbonization," 1924.
261. Gill, Proc. Int. Conf. on Bit. Coal, Pittsburgh, 1926, pp. 245–330.
262. Gardner, Gas Jour., v. 175, 1926, pp. 664–667.
263. Searle, "Refractory Materials," 1924.
264. Harvey and McGee, Jour. Am. Ceramic Soc., v. 7, 1924, p. 895.
265. Booze, Southern Pig Iron and Coke Assoc., Ashland, Ky., 1925.
266. Wologdine, Bul. Soc. Encouragement, v. 3, 1909, p. 879.
267. Dudley, Trans. Am. Electrochemical Soc., v. 27, 1915, p. 285.
268. Dougill, Hodsman, and Cobb, Jour. Soc. Chem. Ind., v. 24, 1915, pp. 465–471.
269. Hersey and Butzler, U. S. Bureau of Mines, Report of Investigations, Ser. No. 2564, 1924.
270. Green, Gas World, v. 76, 1922, pp. 554–559.
271. Green, Gas World, v. 85, 1926, Coking Sec., pp. 112–114.
272. Green, Gas World, v. 85, 1926, Coking Sec., pp. 111–112.
273. Green, Gas, Jour., September 29, 1926, p. 766.
274. Wilson, Holdcroft, and Mellor, Trans. Ceramic Soc., v. 12, Part II, pp. 279–285.
275. Bradshaw and Emery, Trans. Ceramic Soc., v. 19, 1920, p. 84.
276. Ross, U. S. Bureau of Standards, Tech. Paper 116, 1919.
277. Norton, Jour. Am. Ceramic Soc., v. 8, 1925, pp. 799–815.
278. Bogitch, Compt. Rend., v. 173, 1921, pp. 1358–1360.
279. Norton, Jour. Am. Ceramic Soc., v. 8, 1925, pp. 29–39.

280. Mellor, Report of Refractories Committee of the Gas Engineers Institute, 1914.
281. Bodin, Ceramique, v. 23, 1920, pp. 177–184.
282. Le Chatelier, Revue de Metallurgie, June, 1917.
283. Carpenter, Proc. Saffordshire Iron and Steel Inst., v. 32, 1916–1917, pp. 31–63.
284. Carpenter, The Engineer, May 20, 1927, p. 544.
285. Schwartz, Proc. Am. Soc. Testing Materials, v. 19, 1919, Part II, pp. 248–265.
286. Crane Co., Circular 163, 1924.
287. Harper and MacPherran, Iron Age, v. 110, 1922, pp. 793–794.
288. Campion and Donaldson, Proc. Inst. of British Foundrymen, v. 15, 1922, p. 211.
289. Smalley, Proc. Inst. British Foundrymen, v. 15, 1921–1922, p. 688.
290. Kennedy and Oswald, Trans. Am. Foundrymens Assoc., v. 34, 1926, pp. 871–880.
291. "Smithsonian Physical Tables," 1924.
292. Schmitz, Proc. Roy. Soc., v. 72, 1903.
293. Nichol, Phil. Mag., v. 12, 1881.
294. Harker, Proc. Physical Soc., London, v. 19, 1905, p. 703.
295. Kaye and Laby "Table of Physical and Chemical Constants," 1921.
296. Ingersoll and Zobel, "An Introduction to the Mathematical Theory of Heat Conduction," 1913.
297. Souder and Hidnert, U. S. Bureau of Standards, Scientific Paper No. 433, 1922.
298. Rugan and Carpenter, Jour. Iron and Steel Inst., 1909, No. II, Part 2, pp. 29–143.
299. Outerbridge, Jour. Franklin Inst., v. 157, 1904, pp. 121–140.
300. Outerbridge, Trans. Am. Inst. Min. and Met. Eng., v. 35, 1905, pp. 223–244.
301. Schwinning and Flössner, Stahl und Eisen, June 30, 1927, pp. 1075–1079.
302. Carpenter, Jour. Iron and Steel Inst., v. 83, No. 1, 1911, pp. 196–248.
303. Oberhoffer and Piwowarsky, Stahl und Eisen, July 9, 1925, pp. 1173–1178.
304. Honegger, B. B. C. Mitteilungen, October, 1925, pp. 202–209.
305. The Metallurgist, suppl. to The Engineer, July 29, 1927, pp. 99–100.
306. Donaldson, Foundry Trade Jour., February 17 and February 27, 1927.
307. Andrew and Hyman, Jour. Iron and Steel Inst., May, 1924.
308. Dupuy, Engineering, September 9, 1921, pp. 391–394.
309. Malcolm, Trans. Am. Soc. Testing Materials, v. 5, 1924, pp. 256–275.
310. Tapsell and Clenshaw, Engineering, December 30, 1927, p. 837.
311. French and Tucker, Proc. Am. Soc. Testing Materials, v. 24, 1924, Part II, pp. 56–87.
312. French and Tucker, Iron Age, v. 112, 1923, pp. 193–195, pp. 275–278.
313. White and Clark, Trans. Am. Soc. Mech. Eng., v. 48, 1926, pp. 1075–1093.
314. Fahrenwald, Proc. Am. Soc. Testing Materials, v. 24, 1924, Part II, pp. 310–347.

315. Lynch, Mochel and McVetty, Proc. Am. Soc. Testing Materials, v. 25, 1925, Part II, pp. 5–26.
316. French, Trans. Am. Soc. Steel Treating, v. 2, 1927, p. 409.
317. Perrine and Spencer, Columbia School of Mines Quart., v. 35, 1914, p. 194.
318. Dickenson, Jour. Iron and Steel Inst., v. 106, 1922, p. 103.
319. Mellanby and Kerr, Proc. Inst. Mech. Eng., No. 1, 1927, pp. 53–98.
320. MacPherran, Proc. Am. Soc. Testing Materials, v. 21, 1921, p. 852.
321. Bregowsky and Spring, Proc. Int. Assoc. Testing Materials, 6th Congress, N. Y. 1912, v. 2, Part 2.
322. Mochel, Trans. Am. Soc. Steel Treating, 1926.
323. Malcolm, Proc. Am. Soc. Testing Materials, 1925, pp. 43–48.
324. Hougen and Edwards, Chem. and Met. Eng., v. 29, 1923, pp. 800–803.
325. Brown, Gas Age Record, v. 54, 1924, pp. 459–462.
326. Reynolds, Proc. Lit. Phil. Soc., Manchester, v. 14, 1874, p. 8.
327. Reynolds, Trans. Roy. Soc., London, 1883, p. 158.
328. Stanton, Trans. Roy. Soc., London, v. 190A, 1897, p. 67.
329. Boussinesq, Compt. Rend., v. 133, 1901, p. 257.
330. Boussinesq, Compt. Rend., v. 132, 1901, p. 1382.
331. Rayleigh, Nature, v. 95, 1915, p. 66.
332. Nusselt, Zeit. V. D. I., October 23 and October 30, 1909.
333. Nusselt, Zeit. V. D. I., August 18, 1917, pp. 685–689.
334. Rice, Ind. Eng. Chem., v. 16, 1924, pp. 460–467.
335. Cox, Trans. A. S. M. E., Petroleum Sec., 1928.
336. Royds, "Heat Transmission by Radiation, Conduction, and Convection," 1921.
337. Lent, Mechanical Engineering, June, 1926, pp. 610–612.
338. Jordan, Proc. Inst. Mech. Eng., 1909, pp. 1317–1357.
339. Carrier, Trans. A. S. M. E., v. 33, 1911.
340. Bell, International Engineering Congress, San Francisco, Mech. Eng. Sec., 1915.
341. Bell, "Experiments on the Rate of Heat Transfer from a Hot Gas to a Cooler Metallic Surface." Babcock and Wilcox Co., 1916.
342. Walker, Lewis, and McAdams, "Principles of Chemical Engineering," 1923.
343. Boltzman, Wied. Ann. der Phys., v. 22, 1884, pp. 31, 291.
344. Coblentz, U. S. Bureau of Standards, Scientific Paper No. 406, 1920.
345. Randolph and Overholzer, Phys. Rev., v. 2, 1913, p. 144.
346. Kirschoff, Pogg. Ann. der Phys., v. 109, 1860, p. 275.
347. Green, Trans. Ceramic Soc., v. 25, 1925–1926, pp. 361–385.
348. Callendar, Jour. Gas Lighting, v. 111, 1910, p. 644.
349. Haslam and Boyer, Ind. Eng. Chem., v. 19, 1927, pp. 4–6.
350. Schack, Zeit. V. D. I., v. 58, 1924, pp. 1017–1020.
351. Haslam, Lovell, and Hunneman, Ind. Eng. Chem., v. 17, 1925, pp. 272–277.
352. Schack, Mitteilung Nr. 55, der Warmesteele Dusseldorf des Vereins Deutscher Eisenhüttenleute.

353. Broido, Trans. A. S. M. E., v. 47, 1925, pp. 1123–1177.
354. Wohlenberg and Lindseth, Trans. A. S. M. E., v. 48, 1926, pp. 849–937.
355. Hottel, Trans. Am. Inst. Chem. Eng., v. 19, 1927, pp. 173–205.
356. Hottel, Ind. Eng. Chem., v. 19, 1927, p. 888.
357. Sinnatt, Gas Jour., February 14, 1928, pp. 90–111.
358. Tryon and Bennit, U. S. Bureau of Mines, Bull., 1927.
359. Gentry, Proc. Int. Conf. on Bit. Coal, Pittsburgh, 1926, pp. 627–629.
360. Porter, Proc. Int. Conf. on Bit. Coal, Pittsburgh, 1926, pp. 599–604.
361. Runge, Trans. A. S. M. E., Fuel Sec., 1928.
362. Everard-Davies, Chem. and Met. Eng., v. 34, 1927, pp. 480–483.
363. The Engineer, September 23, 1921, pp. 324–325.
364. Pope, Fuel in Science and Practice, v. 5, 1926, pp. 510–511.
365. Brooks, Power, v. 62, 1925, pp. 634–638, pp. 680–684.
366. Runge, Mechanical Engineering, v. 49, 1927, pp. 875–878.
367. Ditto, Yearbook of American Iron and Steel Inst., 1925, p. 225.
368. Blauvelt, Jour. Franklin Inst., September, 1927, pp. 307–321.
369. McBride, "Coke and By-Products in 1924," U. S. Bureau of Mines, 1927.
370. McBride, Proc. Int. Conf. on Bit. Coal, Pittsburgh, 1926, pp. 597–598.
371. Gentry, Proc. Int. Conf. on Bit. Coal, Pittsburgh, 1926, pp. 693–696.
372. Weiss, Proc. Int. Conf. on Bit. Coal, Pittsburgh, 1926, pp. 449–456.
373. Soule, Chemical Age, v. 30, 1922, pp. 251–253.
374. Soule, Power, v. 66, 1927, pp. 222–224.
375. Coffin, Gas Age Record, August 6, 1921, pp. 97–99.
376. Heusler, Zeit. angew Chem., v. 9, 1896, pp. 288, 318.
377. Nielsen and Baker, Mech. Eng. v. 49, 1927, pp. 1109–1110.
378. Nielsen and Baker, Engineering, June 3, 1927, pp. 665–666.
379. Curtis, "Nitrogen Survey," U. S. Dept. of Commerce, Trade Information Bull. No. 226, 1924.
380. Curtis, Proc. Int. Conf. on Bit. Coal, Pittsburgh, 1926, pp. 573–576.
381. Bain, "Nitrogen Survey," U. S. Dept of Commerce, Trade Information Bull. No. 170, 1924.
382. "Commerce Yearbook, 1925," U. S. Dept. of Commerce, 1926.
383. Tryon and Bennit, "Coke and By-Products in 1925," U. S. Bureau of Mines, 1928.
384. "Mineral Resources of the United States, 1924," Part II, U. S. Dept. of Commerce, 1927.
385. Soule, Combustion, v. 18, 1928, pp. 237–243, p. 260.
386. McBride, "Mineral Resources of the United States, 1920," Part II, U. S. Dept. of Interior, 1923.
387. "Statistical Abstract of the United States, 1925," U. S. Dept. of Commerce, 1926.
388. Orrok, Mech. Eng., v. 49, 1927, pp. 1055–1060.
389. Brownlie, World Power, December, 1927, pp. 301–309.
390. The Engineer, February 26, 1926, p. 236.
391. N. E. L. A. Prime Movers Report, Distillation Products of Coal, 1927.
392. Merz and McLellan, British Patent, No. 171290, 1917.
393. Wisner, Proc. Int. Conf. on Bit. Coal, Pittsburgh, 1926, pp. 800–806.

394. Chemical Age, October 9, 1926, pp. 346–347.
395. Engineering, December 10, 1926, p. 720.
396. Savage, Mech. Eng., v. 49, 1927, p. 1059.
397. Orrok, Elec. World, v. 86, 1925, pp. 620–622.
398. Junkersfeld, Trans. A. S. M. E., v. 44, 1922, p. 1157.
399. Klingenberg, "Bau Grösser Elektrizitätswerke," 1924.
400. Lander, Proc. Int. Conf. on Bit. Coal, Pittsburgh, 1926, pp. 618–619.
401. Christie, Mech. Eng., v. 49, 1927, p. 878.
402. Report of Am. Railway Assoc. Conf., Committee with U. S. Coal Commission, 1923.
403. "Saward's Annual," 1928.
404. Chatfield, Nat. Petrol. News, May 4, 1927, p. 54.
405. Wagner, Nat. Petrol. News, December 19, 1923, p. 58.
406. Rathburn, Petrol. Age, April 1, 1924, p. 97.
407. Rathburn, Petrol. Age, March 1, 1925, p. 61.
408. Crowell, Gas Age Record, April 2, 1927, pp. 484–486.
409. Redmayne, Trans. World Power Conf., v. 1, London, 1924, pp. 420–448.
410. Cambell, Proc. Int. Conf. on Bit. Coal, Pittsburgh, 1926, pp. 5–64.
411. White, Mech. Eng., v. 44, 1922, pp. 567–569.
412. Runge, Coal, April 1, 1926, pp. 196–201.
413. Slosson, Proc. Int. Conf. on Bit. Coal, Pittsburgh, 1926, pp. 221–223.

NAME INDEX

American Association of Petroleum
  Geologists, 366.
Andrew, 293, 377.
Anschutz, 113, 374.
Armstrong, 164, 217, 375.
Arnold, 88, 90, 373.
Arrhenius, 169.
Avenarius, 90, 91, 97, 373.
Audibert, 16, 137, 140, 141, 143, 151,
  370, 374.
Augustine, 148, 375.

Bahr, 146, 375.
Bain, 344, 379.
Baker, 339, 379.
Banks, 24, 170.
Bauer, 56, 274, 372.
Becher, 3.
Beehuis, 116, 374.
Bell, 308, 378.
Bennit, 314, 316, 317, 346, 347, 351,
  379.
Benson, 52, 102, 133, 163.
Berger, 125, 126, 164, 374.
Bergius, 81, 121, 122, 123, 374.
Berry, 77, 373.
Bertholet, 16, 18, 113, 373, 374.
Beilby, 223.
Bischof, 4.
Blauvelt, 324, 379.
Bodin, 283, 284, 377.
Bogitch, 280, 376.
Boltzman, 308, 310, 378.
Bone, 12, 13, 142, 370, 374.
Booze, 272, 304, 376.
Börnstein, 37, 71, 90, 372, 373.
Boussinesq, 306, 378.
Bouvier, 86, 87, 371, 373.
Boyer, 310, 378.
Bradshaw, 278, 376.

Bregowsky, 296, 378.
Breuer, 90, 146, 371, 373, 375.
British National Physical Labora-
  tory, 339.
Brittain, 86, 88, 89, 90, 91, 94, 95, 96,
  97, 217, 373.
Broche, 87, 146, 371, 375.
Broido, 312, 379.
Brooks, 319, 320, 321, 379.
Brown, 303, 378.
Brownlie, 38, 206, 218, 353, 372, 375,
  379.
Bunsen, 299.
Bunte, 146, 375.
Burgess, 10, 19, 47, 48, 49, 50, 78, 79,
  163, 164, 370, 371, 372.
Burton, 81.
Buschmann, 16, 17, 87, 90, 91, 95, 97,
  370, 371.
Butzler, 274, 376.

Callendar, 310, 312, 378.
Cambell, 364, 380.
Campbell, 194, 375.
Campion, 287, 377.
Canfield, 52, 102, 133, 163, 372.
Cantieny, 235, 376.
Capps, 23, 372.
Caracristi, 246, 247, 248, 254, 256, 258,
  354, 376.
Carpenter, 285, 289, 291, 292, 293, 377.
Carrier, 308, 378.
Charpy, 141, 374.
Chatfield, 362, 380.
Christie, 360, 380.
Church, 89, 373.
Clark, 11, 295, 370, 377.
Clayton, 1, 370.
Clegg, 2, 3, 270.
Clenshaw, 295, 377.

Sans Tache

Sans Tache

IN THE "elder days of art" each artist or craftsman enjoyed the privilege of independent creation. He carried through a process of manufacture from beginning to end. The scribe of the days before the printing press was such a craftsman. So was the printer in the days before the machine process. He stood or fell, as a craftsman, by the merit or demerit of his finished product.

Modern machine production has added much to the worker's productivity and to his material welfare; but it has deprived him of the old creative distinctiveness. His work is merged in the work of the team, and lost sight of as something representing him and his personality.

Many hands and minds contribute to the manufacture of a book, in this day of specialization. There are seven distinct major processes in the making of a book: The type must first be set; by the monotype method, there are two processes, the "keyboarding" of the MS and the casting of the type from the perforated paper rolls thus produced. Formulas and other intricate work must be hand-set; then the whole brought together ("composed") in its true order, made into pages and forms. The results must be checked by proof reading at each stage. Then comes the "make-ready" and press-run and finally the binding into volumes.

All of these processes, except that of binding into cloth or leather covers, are carried on under our roof.

The motto of the Waverly Press is *Sans Tache*. Our ideal is to manufacture books *"without blemish"*—worthy books, worthily printed, with worthy typography—books to which we shall be proud to attach our imprint, made by craftsmen who are willing to accept open responsibility for their work, and who are entitled to credit for creditable performance.

The printing craftsman of today is quite as much a craftsman as his predecessor. There is quite as much discrimination between poor work and good. We are of the opinion that the individuality of the worker should not be wholly lost. The members of our staff who have contributed their skill of hand and brain to this volume are:

Keyboards: Hannah Scott, Helen Twardowicz, Mary Franck, Mildred Lambert, Louise Hilpert, Vera Taylor, Anna Rustic.

Composing Room: Harry Harmeyer, Arthur Baker, Anthony Wagner, Herbert Leitch, George Moss, Ernest Salgado, James Armiger, Ray Kauffman, Andrew Rassa, James Jackson, Richard King, Henry A. Shea, Harry Susemihl, Edward Rice, Theodore Nilson.

Press Room: Leo Ledlick, August Hildebrand, Fred Lucker, Emory Parsons, Andrew Becker, Henry Shreck, Robert Ginter.

Casters: Kenneth Brown, Charles Aher, Ernest Wann, Martin Griffen, Henry Lee, Mahlon Robinson, George Smith, Charles Fick, George Bullinger.

Proof Room: Sarah Katzin, Mary Reed, Alice Reuter, Ruth Jones, Ethel Strasinger, Dorothy Strasinger, Audrey Tanner, Angeline Eifert, Lucile Bull, Lillian Gilland, Ida Zimmerman.

Cutter: William Armiger.

Folders: Laurence Krug, Shipley Dellinger.